RATES OF EX

and

WHY COME TO SLAKA?

MALCOLM BRADBURY was a well-known novelist, critic and academic. He set up the famous creative writing department at the University of East Anglia, whose students have included Ian McEwan and Kazuo Ishiguro. He was the author of seven novels: *Eating People is Wrong* (1959); *Stepping Westward* (1965); *The History Man* (1975), which won the Royal Society of Literature Heinemann Prize; *Rates of Exchange* (1983), which was shortlisted for the Booker Prize; *Cuts* (1987); *Doctor Criminale* (1992); and *To the Hermitage* (2000). He wrote several works of non-fiction, humour and satire, including *Who Do You Think You Are?* (1976), *All Dressed Up and Nowhere to Go* (1982) and *Why Come to Slaka?* (1983). He was an active journalist and a leading television writer, responsible for the adaptations of *Porterhouse Blue*, *Cold Comfort Farm*, and many TV plays and episodes of *Inspector Morse*, *A Touch of Frost*, *Kavanagh QC* and *Dalziel and Pascoe*. He was awarded a knighthood in 2000 and died the same year.

ALSO BY MALCOLM BRADBURY

Eating People is Wrong
(1959)

Stepping Westward
(1965)

The History Man
(1975)

Who Do You Think You Are?
(1976)

All Dressed Up and Nowhere to Go
(1982)

Cuts
(1987)

Doctor Criminale
(1992)

To the Hermitage
(2000)

Malcolm | Bradbury

Rates of Exchange
and
Why Come to Slaka?

PICADOR

Rates of Exchange first published 1983 by Secker & Warburg Ltd
and published 2000 by Picador
Why Come to Slaka? first published 1986 by Secker & Warburg Ltd
and published 2000 by Picador

This edition published 2003 by Picador
an imprint of Pan Macmillan Ltd
Pan Macmillan, 20 New Wharf Road, London N1 9RR
Basingstoke and Oxford
Associated companies throughout the world
www.panmacmillan.com

ISBN 0 330 41289 2

1 3 5 7 9 8 6 4 2

A CIP catalogue record for this book is available from
the British Library.

Typeset by SetSystems Ltd, Saffron Walden, Essex
Printed and bound in Great Britain by
Mackays of Chatham plc, Chatham, Kent

RATES OF EXCHANGE

AUTHOR'S NOTE

This is a book, and what it says is not true. You will not find Slaka, Glit, or Nogod on any map, and so you will probably never make the trip there. The Heathrow air traffic controllers' strike of 1981 never took place, but was held in a quite different year. There is no resemblance at all between the imaginary figures here and any person who chooses to believe that he or she actually exists. So there is no Petworth, no dark Lottie, no Marisja Lubijova and no brilliant Katya Princip. Rum, Plitplov and the Steadimans have never existed, and probably never will: except insofar as you and I conspire to bring them into existence, with, as usual, me doing most of the work. Or, as the literary critics say, I'll be your implied author, if you'll be my implied reader; and, as they also say, it is our duty to lie together, in the cause, of course, of truth.

So, like money, this book is a paper fiction, offered for exchange. But, as with money, one contracts with it various debts. I must express mine to many helpful friends: Chris Bigsby, Anthony Thwaite, George Hyde, and others. But I especially thank those members of the British Council English Studies seminar who, over several summers, in various long rooms in Cambridge colleges, helped me in more than one sense to invent a language.

M.B.
1982

Narrative: Legal tender

– Roland Barthes

'You have a quarrel on hand, I see,' said I, 'with some of the algebraists of Paris; but proceed.'

– Edgar Allan Poe, *The Purloined Letter*

The language of this country being always upon the flux, the Struldbruggs of one age do not understand those of another, neither are they able after two hundred years to hold any conversation (farther than by a few general words) with their neighbours the mortals, and thus they lie under the disadvantage of living like foreigners in their own country.

– Jonathan Swift, *Gulliver's Travels*

It seems to me the further east you go the more unpunctual are the trains.

– Bram Stoker, *Dracula*

VISITING SLAKA: A FEW BRIEF HINTS

If you should ever happen to make the trip to Slaka, that fine flower of middle European cities, capital of commerce and art, wide streets and gipsy music, then, whatever else you plan to do there, do not, as the travel texts say, neglect to visit the Cathedral of Saint Valdopin: a little outside the town, at the end of the tramway-route, near to the power station, down by the slow, marshy, mosquito-breeding waters of the great River Niyt.

A city infinitely rich in this, and no less lacking in that, Slaka is, you will remember, the historic capital and quite the largest metropolis of that small dark nation of plain and marsh, mountain and factory known in all the history books as the bloody battlefield (*tulsto'ii uncard'ninu*) of central eastern Europe. Located by an at once kind and cruel geography at the confluence of many trade routes, going north and east, south and west, its high mountains not too high to cut it off, its broad rivers not too broad to obstruct passage, it is a land that has frequently flourished, prospered, been a centre of trade and barter, art and culture, but has yet more frequently been pummelled, fought over, raped, pillaged, conquered and oppressed by the endless invaders who, from every direction, have swept and jostled through this all too accessible landscape. Swedes and Medes, Prussians and Russians, Asians and Thracians, Tartars and Cossacks, Mortars and Turds, indeed almost every tribe or race specialist in pillage and rape, have been here, as to some necessary destination, and left behind their imprint, their customs, their faiths, their architecture,

1

their genes. This is a country that has been now big, now small, now virtually non-existent. Its inhabitants have seen its borders expand, contract and on occasion disappear from sight, and so confused is its past that the country could now be in a place quite different from that in which it started. And so its culture is a melting pot, its language a *pot-pourri*, its people a salad; at different times, these folk have worshipped nearly every well-known god, consumed almost every possible food (from the milk and eggs of the north to the spices and fruits of the south and east), spoken in numerous tongues, and traded in all the coins and currencies, stamped or embossed with the ever-fleeting heads of the uncountable emperors and princelings, thains and margraves, bishop-krakators and mame-lukes who have mysteriously appeared, ruled for a time, and then as mysteriously disappeared again, into the obscure and contorted passages of history.

As a result, in Slaka history is a mystery, and it is not surprising that the nation's past has been very variously recorded and the facts much disputed, for everyone has a story to tell. Perplexities abound, accounts contradict, and accurate details are wanting. But there is no doubt that that history goes back into the deepest mists of ancient Europe, back into the dark and virgin forest, where all history is supposed to begin, all stories to start. A certain reputable encyclopedia, consulted in an old edition, authoritatively observes (if I have read it accurately, and if my hastily scribbled notes, gathered amid the distractions of the great round Reading Room of the British Museum, where white-eyed Italian girls shout hotly for company around tea-time, tempting serious scholars, of whom I am not one anyway, into folly, are correctly transcribed):

No certain historical data exists for the period prior to the Xth. An obscure passage in a chronicle by Nostrum, Monk of Kiev, suggests a possible origin for these people some-where in the region of the Bosphorus, but even this much is disputed. The people are generally finely built, dark in the

2

southern part of the country, fair in the northern, inclined to spectacular deeds of heroism, but somewhat deficient in energy and industry. Long periods of outside occupation depressed the people, until the national awakening of the XIXth., led by Prince Bohumil the Shy, and celebrated by the poet Hrovdat, killed on his horse in 1848 as he declaimed epic verse in battle. The earliest specimen of the language occurs in a psalter of the XIth., but some seventeen different, regional languages presently exist in the country. Salt, gypsum and iron ore are mined. Principal cities are Slaka, the ancient capital; Glit, a seat of learning; and Provd, an industrial centre.

But this, as you see, is a long outdated account, written before two modern World Wars once more transformed the nation's history. Today, following more invasions, pillage, bombardment, jackboots and conquest, the nation is now a people's republic, issuing pretty stamps, in the Soviet orbit, a member of the Warsaw Pact and Comecon. It is a net exporter of beets, rose-water, china, timber, shoes, an excellent peach brandy (*rot'vitti*), glassware and brown suits, a net importer of oil, grain, machinery, manufactured goods, medical and sanitary supplies, meat and soft drinks (*sch'veppii*). Ballet and opera are good, footwear scarce, mostly going for export, literacy high, sporting achievements spectacular. Its swimmers win Olympic gold medals with regularity; its horse riders fall off less often than most. The units of currency are the *vloska* and the *bittii*, one hundred *bittiin* to the *vloska*. Hard Western currencies, especially the dollar, are scarce and much sought after. Money may be exchanged officially only at the change desks (*camb'yii*) of the state tourist board, Cosmoplot, found in all major hotels and at branches of the government bank (*Burs'ii Proly'aniii*). It should be admitted that, in the streets, bars and cafés, transactions of a more informal kind do occur, at very advantageous rates for the Western visitor; however, travellers should note that these transactions are serious crimes against the state, attracting the most severe penalties.

The voltage is 110. No *vloskan* may be taken from the country on leaving.

Of course in Slaka now history is perceived as a dialectical progress, and not, as in decadent Western thought, as a sentimental past. Even so, the national cultural heritage is taken very seriously, and, since much of it was destroyed in the battles of the Second World War, it has been rebuilt to the most exacting standards. As the guidebooks say, few, walking the city fine streets, can well tell which building have standed over the centuries and which are restituted in a living lifespell. However, if, as is likely, you are travelling with the guidance, and the guide, of Cosmoplot, you will probably not be taken to see the Cathedral. It is indeed some way out of the centre of town, at the end of the tram-route, down by the Niyt. And, though churchgoing is permitted and in fact much practised, secular materialism is the official state philosophy. It will therefore be assumed that, as a citizen of the present (which, like it or not, you are), you will want to see the triumphs of proletarian endeavour, the heroic achievements of socialist planning, the collective works of the people. So you will be taken to see the advanced glassblowing factory, perhaps the best in the world, with production targets that invite emulation; the reformed watercress industry, an oustanding example of agro-organization; the apartment blocks for the workers, erected in brief hours through miracles of pre-fabrication and pre-planning; the Park of Freedom, celebrating the friendship of all peoples; the tomb of Grigoric, who, when liberal elements hesitated, resolutely delivered the nation over to the Soviet liberator in 1944, and whose mausoleum, guarded by the soldiers of the state guard, in their fine feathered shakos, stands in Party Square (*Plazsci P'rtyii*); a neat, busy collective farm, with happy workers and clean tractors; the Museum of Socialist Realist Art, with pictures of the happy workers and the clean tractors.

And so, doubtless, you will; and you will understand the better the promise of the future. Even so, it is still worth going

4

to look at the Cathedral. It lies at the end of the Vipnu tram-route; tickets are not available on board, but must be bought in advance at the state tobacco kiosks (marked *Litti*). Mosquitoes are busy down by the river, so you would do well to spray before leaving your hotel. The Cathedral is, at first sight, not impressive, looking from the outside little more than a sombre domed warehouse of recycled blackened brick. The interior, however, is rich in splendours. Baroque finery illuminates the solemn darkness; beeswax candles splutter on the many small shrines; the altars are bright with plaster, silver and gold. Begun in the XIth., extended, under Bishop Wocwit the Good, in the XIIIth., vandalized in the XVth., restored in Baroque fantasy by Bishop 'Wencher' Vlam in the XVIIIth., briefly a mosque in the early XIXth., severely damaged by aerial and land bombardment in the XXth., and since rebuilt from medieval and Renaissance plans by attentive scholars, it enshrines many stages both of human and artistic evolution. Pillage and damage over the generations educated its priests and monks in the arts of survival and the tactics of hiding, preserving and, when the time was ripe, resurrecting its holy treasures. Much of excellence has thus remarkably survived: the many ikons, wonderful for the dark-souled expressions in the tortured saintly faces, in the crypt; the plasterwork cherubs in the nave; the medieval image of Christ Pantokrator painted and carved in the drum; the fine Flemish altar-piece; and, a little to the right of the main altar, the marbled tomb, a shrine and place of pilgrimage, of Saint Valdopin himself – patron saint of the church, bringer of the alphabet, Christianizer of the land, and the first of many national martyrs.

To Valdopin a great many stories attach; who is to know whether they are true or false? In the Xth., or just possibly the IXth., he came, from somewhere to the south, or possibly the west, to convert the prince or khan of the tribe that was settled in this middle terrain of marsh, forest and mosquito. In due course the prince was converted, to great political advantage; recognized by the Holy See, the tribe became a nation.

But Valdopin put his trust in more than princes, and brought his mission to the people. He set up the Holy Texts for all to read, translating them and devising his own alphabet for the purpose. This is the Valdopian alphabet, now little used: examples may be seen carved into the Cathedral's stone walls, though there is some dispute about the accuracy of the restoration. Thus the nation was won over to the ways of Christ – though later, it must be admitted, there was a pagan revival, when, according to the authoritative encyclopedia from which I have quoted, wild beasts made their lairs in the idle and desecrated churches. But to Valdopin the mission seemed complete; he now moved on to a tribe adjacent, still heathen and given to the most barbarous practices. And, story tells us, by these people – to the north, or the west, or just possibly the east (though for some reason this is particularly strongly disputed) – he was attacked, slain with stones, decapitated, and his body hacked with swords into very small pieces. A bas-relief in the Cathedral may be seen depicting this event, though modern scholarship questions the accuracy of the costume.

But, story further tells us, the faithful in the land of which Slaka is now capital had not forgotten Valdopin; they determined to recover their martyr and give him Christian burial. Emissaries were sent, and a contract arranged with the pagan. A set of scales was placed on the border between the nations: the mincemeat saint was to be placed on one pan, to be traded for an equal weight of gold from the prince's coffers in the other. However, you know stories, and how these legendary contracts always breed complications. The scales were raised, the portions of saint produced, ingot after ingot put into the pan; still the scales obstinately refused to tip. Gold was piled on gold until the treasury ran dry; the pans still failed to balance. Only a magical intercession could save the day; happily these were times when magic was still operational. The prince despaired and the faithful wept, but then, from the back of the crowd, there stepped a little old widow woman, dressed entirely in black, and leaning bently on a bent stick. In one twisted little hand she held out one tiny gold coin, her entire life's savings. The prince laughed and his retainers mocked, as in such stories they always do.

But you indeed know stories, and are quite familiar with the powers possessed by these little old widow women with their mites; I need hardly go on. Down went the coin, up went the scales, mad went the crowd, red went the prince. The pagans, who, as pagans go, had not done badly, loaded up their gold; the prince's retainers brought a coffin and filled it with hamburgered saint; the prince kissed the old woman, who did not turn into anything; the corpse was borne home, a marbled tomb was raised, somewhere in the marshy land down by the Niyt, where, for some reason, the first conversions had occurred, Valdopin won his martyr's burial, the tomb became a shrine, pilgrims came from distant destinations, miraculous wonders occurred, the sick threw off their crutches, the mad grew wise, the dumb began to speak. Sainthood was duly recognized, monks settled the site, a chapel was built, and then in time a cathedral, which you should not neglect to visit. The legend grew, as legends do. Even during Ottoman rule the memory of the saint survived in the minds of the people; and it survives still, even in these secular times, when miracles are usually economic, other kinds of sainthood are recognized, and Valdopin's tomb now has to compete for attention with that of Grigoric, with the shakoed soldiers around it, there in Plazsci P'rtyii.

Of the story, you may make what you like. Like all good stories, it can be read in many fashions. For the romantic nationalist historians it is of course a tale about the emergence of a people. For Christian theologians, it is a miraculous fable of divine intercession. For the Marxist aestheticians it is a classic socialist realist allegory displaying that power lies not with princes and their capital but with the combined power of the common people. For the folklorists it is – with its contract delay, magical intervention and happy outcome – a perfect example of the morphology of folktale. And for more

7

fashionable thinkers of the Structuralist persuasion, debating these matters in the Rue des Ecoles, well, is it not a perfect example of the *pensée sauvage*, of Lévi-Strauss's the raw and the cooked? And if you were to ask me, as well you might, since it is, just for the moment, my story, then I would probably pause for a moment, lighting my pipe to give an appearance of critical sagacity, think a little, and then suggest, very tentatively, that its deep structure is fairly apparent: mightn't we say, *shouldn't* we say, that it is a typical Slakan fable about rates of exchange?

For, if you should ever happen to make the trip to Slaka – metropolis of gypsy music, wide streets and rectorates of baroque accretion, where the trade fairs are held, the congresses meet, the languages criss-cross – you will still find everywhere an old Valdopian preoccupation with barter and transaction – a trading of goods, a shuttling of values, a fixing of rates. It is there in the currency checks (*geld'yii*) at the airport; at the change desks (*camb'yii*), found in the state banks or the lobby of your Cosmoplot hotel; in the great government department store, MUG, on Vitz'vitzimutu, where they sell shortages as well as plenty, so that many people solemnly visit it in order not to shop; in the endless commerce on the quiet park benches, where carefree children play on the sunlit lanes, pensioners enjoy their well-deserved repose, and briefcases open, to switch a pear for a cucumber, a pair of underpants for a bright pink bra; in the special foreign currency stores, WICWOK, where tourists compete with party officials for malt whiskies from rare Scottish glens and the Western blue jeans created by that other and far better known Levi-Strauss; in the dim-lit restaurants, where the waiters will ask 'You pay dollar?' before revealing whether or not they have any meat on the menu; on the wide pavements of the city, where passers-by will stop you as you walk and offer to exchange your suit for their antiques or, if you dress as badly as I do, vice versa. Yes, there are times in Slaka when it seems life is nothing else but making a trade, finding an equivalent, striking a bargain, forging a value, putting so much person into one pan and seeing how it matches up with so many goods in the other.

That is the way of things in Slaka; but then, where is life not like that? The world is full of money-talk; economists are our new wise men. The linguists, whom one meets everywhere these days, explain that every transaction in our culture – our money and mathematics, our games and gardens, our diet and our sexual activity – is a language; this, of course, is why one meets so many linguists these days. And languages, too, are simply invented systems of exchange, attempts to turn the word into the world, sign into value, script into currency, code into reality. Of course, everywhere, even in Slaka, there are the politicians and the priests, the ayatollahs and the economists, who will try to explain that reality is what they say it is. Never trust them; trust only the novelists, those deeper bankers who spend their time trying to turn pieces of printed paper into value, but never pretend that the result is anything more than a useful fiction. Of course we need them: for what, after all, is our life but a great dance in which we are all trying to fix the best going rate of exchange, using our minds and our sex, our taste and our clothes, according to Valdopian principles? So you, *cher lecteur*, with your customized Volvo and your Seiko quartz digital, your remote control telephone and your high opinion, so loudly expressed over the Campari soda, of Woody Allen up to but not including *Interiors*; or you, *chère ms.*, with your Gucci shoes, the tales of ego your analyst told you, and the buttons of your designer dress left strategically undone, to display the Seychelles tan and that tempting mammary inter-face, so raising the interest without lowering the price; or even you, *cher enfant*, with your Kids-In-Gear boilersuit and your endless new scram on Emerson, Lake and Palmer – what are you doing but putting what you like to think of as your self in the pan, bartering your mind and body, your youth and

9

opinions, on the economic frontier, in an attempt to find a meaning, invent a value, find your highest price, trade at the best possible rate of exchange?

So, if you were to press me about the story of Valdopin, this, or some such fashionable analysis of the same sort, is what I might answer; but really I prefer not to. I am a writer, not a critic, I like my fictions to remain fictions. No, let me rather recommend that one day you do indeed make the trip to Slaka, city at the international crossroads, capital of flowers and gipsy music, fine buildings and notable art, lying there in the warm wide declivity between the Storkian mountains, where the vegetation is lush and many pleasures are to be had. Admittedly ordinary life there can be drab at times; cold winds blow, tourism can be over-regimental, and the shops tend towards emptiness, but what is a holiday without its inconveniences? Flights that way are, it is true, not frequent, though the state airline, Comflug, operates from most Western capitals. The language can be difficult, for its grammar is much disputed and no two native speakers seem to speak it alike; but handy phrase-books help with simple transactions, and most young Slakans nowadays have a little English, even if it is only the lyrics of Pink Floyd songs. Currency rules are irritating, and you must exchange so much a day; but Western tourists have special privileges in the restaurants, and the crafts are notably good. The girls are generally pretty; the same is sometimes said about the men. And in general the people are lively and warm, the sights well worth seeing, the peach brandy (*rot'vitti*) not to be missed. As the Cosmoplot brochures say, here definitely is offered another kind of holiday, and when the nights descend and the motor cars swash along bright-lighted boulevards, only a short stroll in this fine old town will convince you at a start that there is much to be had.

And, if you do go, then don't omit the Cathedral. Look first at the ikons, which are down in the crypt; entry costs less than a *vloska*. Then go outside again and enter the nave, avoiding the reconstruction due to recent earthquake damage, and noticing the fine Christ Pantokrator in the drum. The altar is fine, and asserted, somewhere, to be Flemish. But do remember to look a little to the left of it, or was it the right, for the tomb of Saint Valdopin: first national martyr, bringer of the alphabet, founder of the faith, and source of many and many a legend.

CUSTOMER'S TRAVEL PLAN

DATE ..	FLIGHT ..	DEPART	TIME ..	ARRIVE ..	TIME
13 SEP	CF155	LONDON HR	10:40	SLAKA	14:30
26 SEP	BA231	SLAKA	13:30	LONDON HR	15:25

Please note that all times indicated are local.

12

1 – ARR.

I

The first thing one notices – as Comflug 155 from London,
two hours late, dips, touches down, bounces and brakes on the
runway, drops its raised wing-baffles, slows, turns, and begins
to taxi through the airport lanes toward the long, low, white
wooden buildings that have signs on their walls saying SLAKA
– is that a number of armed men stand about at various points
on the tarmac. At first, while the plane moves quickly, all these
men look alike; then vision through the round bowl of the
window improves, and it becomes apparent that they come not
just in one kind but in at least two. Some of them are soldiers;
they wear a military khaki, high-peaked caps with red bands
round them, long flared topcoats with white epaulettes and
black, rather baggy leather boots which reach up to their knees
in cavalry fashion. There is another kind who are probably
militiamen or policemen. These wear a rather dowdier uniform, in darkish blue, flat blue caps with white covers on them,
cross-straps of black leather over their chests, and trousers that
bulge out wide at the thighs and then taper down to fit into
very short black boots. As the plane comes nearer still, it
becomes clear that not only uniforms but offices are different
too. It is the function of the soldiers to cluster in groups around
the various aircraft – the shiny Ilyushins, Tupolevs and Antonovs, and the grey Mil helicopter gunships – that rest on their
stands along the airport apron, or on the grass beside it. Each
plane has four or five of these soldiers around it; they look

13

serious and attentive. The blue men, the militia, stand at or near the entrance doors to the various white airport buildings. Each doorway has two or three of them beside it, and they look stocky and solid. The two groups stand separately, do not talk to each other, and as the Comflug jet rolls in closer it is clear that the only reason for confusing them is that they all carry well-cleaned black Kalashnikov sub-machine guns of neat modern design slung on short straps over their shoulders.

Beyond the men and the planes there run the airport buildings, long and low, shining white in the late afternoon sunlight. They are buildings without any architectural conceit and only a modest appearance of functionality; they could be any buildings built for any purpose anywhere. The entrance doors where the armed militiamen stand are evidently kept locked, for no one goes in and out of them; above them one can see a sign in the Cyrillic alphabet, an incomprehensible code, and then another smaller one in the Latin alphabet, saying INVAT. The buildings are two storeys high, and have a flat roof with wooden railings around it; here on the roof are the people, a sizeable, busy crowd of them. The Comflug jet is still moving, and distances are hard to project, but they all seem to be fairly small and stocky people, dressed in a certain Sunday formality – though Sunday is, indeed, the day that this is. The men mostly wear dark double-breasted suits, cut square in the body, and dark ties, and hats or caps; the women are in large full cotton dresses, and look reassuringly round and bulky. They are all modest enthusiasts, looking out over the field and waving, with pleasure but without extravagance, at the plane as it comes slowly in closer to the terminal, or possibly at another one – for, though it is Sunday, the airport seems fairly busy, and a second Ilyushin from some other destination, fat, streaked with curdled lines from flight, its rivets shining, also in the blue and white Comflug livery, with Cyrillic tail colophon, is already following the London flight in off the runway.

The sun shines, the buildings are white, the world is in a

14

state of traveller's suspension. There are some people who will tell you that the world we live in now is converging, that everywhere is turning into everywhere else, that difference is giving way to universal similarity. At this moment, this seems both true and not. Airports, certainly, are everywhere airport-like, operating to much the same functions, expressing much the same signs, displaying the same abstract familiarities. Yet behind such similarities there are always the small differences, things that name the place. The air here has a distinct blueish quality; the airport grass is notably thick and coarse, and has the look of being planted for haymaking; indeed, an old tractor works between the runways. The uniforms of the armed men are not quite the uniforms of the other armed men in other places. Words are visible here and there, and they both explain and estrange; thus the van that has been leading the plane in through the airport tracks has a sign on its roof saying HIN MI, and the grey tanker nosing forward from the camouflaged sheds to the right of the terminal has a sign painted on the side saying BIN'ZINI. The empty blue buses that wait in a short row outside the terminal building, presumably to take the passengers from the plane and deliver them into the new country, are old and bulbous, with ladders up their backs, definitely other, created in a different, more ornate stylistic idiom. The people on the roof are short and stocky. Across the grass and cement, beyond the trees that line the airport perimeter, there pokes into the sky a golden onion, the spire-dome of a church. Over it, in front of the dropping sun, a great bird with white wings is flying. It appears to be a stork; however, vision through the dirtied globe-windows of the plane is difficult, and this could be an optical illusion.

And somewhere beyond the dome, and not too far away, there must be the city itself, which they have overflown and looked down upon only a few moments earlier. It lies in the middle of a wide green plain, not too greatly populated, with a jagged dish of mountains rising up all round it. Right across Europe this has been a wet summer, a summer of what

15

is called unusual weather, now usual. The plain, part-farmed, part-forested, part-bare, shows itself wet to the sky; across it, offered to the air-traveller in glints and flashes, runs one of those wide, twisting, European rivers that could flow either north or south, up to the Baltic or out to the North Sea, down to the Mediterranean or over to the Bosphorus, one of those famous rivers that stays in middle-aged memory from those old World War Two *Daily Telegraph* maps of advance and retreat, putsch and counter-putsch, as the war in Europe raged. Now it has flooded out from its banks, onto the green of the plain, into the forest-clusters, the stripes of green and brown field, the small huddles of communities which, with dark roofs, rising smoke, and surrounding busy farmyards, patternlessly dot the landscape, and even into the edges of the city itself, where the river tightens and is bridged, where the aircraft comes lower, where the people move.

The city itself seems only modestly big. From the air one sees a big brick power station with high metal chimneys, spurting orange smoke high into the bright blue sky; a distinct industrial section, with factory compounds laid out near the lines of long straight highways converging variously onto the hub of the city; a workers' district, with high rectangular living blocks in faceless contemporary style; many streets of high, square-windowed town apartments of the Continental type; on the streets, with their rows of shade trees, a small amount of traffic, moving quite fast; amid the traffic, many rocking pink trams, towing trailers behind them along metal tracks that glint in the sun. Then a cathedral, apparently unfinished, or having had its top knocked off; next an area of greater complexity, where the river turns round an outcrop, the bridges are several, and a crenellated castle from old storybooks sits up on a rock amid high trees, surrounded by streets that twist and contain old bright-painted buildings. Then a market place, with brightly coloured roofs to its stalls and a central edifice with a high tower; a vast square, surrounded on all sides by govern-mental-looking stone buildings, and having a *pavé* so very clean that it shines bright white in the late afternoon sunlight; more apartments, more factories, more countryside, looking lush and flooded, some intensive market-gardening, done under shiny polythene crop-covers, the onion church, the runway lights, the glide into the airport.

Now the plane comes in close to the terminal building, and begins to make its final turn. Out on the tarmac, down below, the armed men, the soldiers, stand and stare up at the big Ilyushin as it moves onto the stand; inside, the passengers, strapped into their highback seats, sit and stare down through the globed windows, at the armed men, and the waving people, and the baggage trucks and petrol tankers moving nearer, and the other planes, neatly arrayed on the apron, and the blue buses, standing quiet by the doors where the sign says INVAT, and the line of trees on the airport perimeter, and the possible stork on the skyline. The red sun shines in through the windows; the interior of the cabin smells, in homely fashion, of dumpling. On the forward bulkhead, green illuminated notices say LUPI LUPI and NOKI ROKI. A faint sound of martial music sounds through the intercom; the passengers sit very quietly. Three Comflug stewardesses have risen from their seats and stand at the front of the plane, by the kitchen area. Some international couturier has conceived them; their heavy bodies are clad in bright green uniforms, they wear a helmet-like headgear which makes them appear to have just got down from a horse. The world outside remains in suspension. The people who wave, wave, wave, the armed men, are not yet real. The notices on the buildings are mysterious hieroglyphics, for the comprehension of others. The eye collects but only partly understands. A life goes on here but one is not of it: people and houses, customs and habits have a shape that makes sense, but there is no sense to it yet. A reality of sorts is here, indeed a historical reality, the sort that Karl Marx promised as the regime of truth; but it is not yet real at all.

Preliminary descriptions exist. 'The airport at Slaka is in open countryside, situated 8km/5mi to the east of the city,' it says in a text, *Helpful Hints for British Businessmen*, which Dr Petworth, a cultural visitor, sitting in a high aisle seat, peering across two brown-suited bodies and out into life, has in his pocket, 'Buses to the central Comflug office, Wodjimutu 217 (no check-in facilities), are available. Tickets must be purchased in advance from the airport tobacco kiosk, marked *Litti*, and are not available on board.' Banks, government offices, and state trading organizations are closed on Saturday and Sunday. Only the orange-coloured taxis should be used. The voltage is 110. There have been many wars and battles here. Since the heroic liberation of 1944, about two million dwellings of the workers have been constructed, and per capita floor space is about 10^2 metres. The castle is particularly worthy of a visit. No vloskan may be taken from the country on leaving. Carefree children play in the sunlit parks, pensioners enjoy their well-deserved repose, and enamoured couples dream of the future. Art has developed here on realistic foundations, and few decadent tendencies have taken root among our patriotic worker artists and writers. Dances by peasants in regional costumes are regularly performed. Numerous marble plaques dedicated to those who fell in the national struggle remind us of those heroic days. Stalls selling flowers of the season delight the streets. The trade unions direct socialistic emulation, and are responsible for the sucesses of the 'rationalization' movement. Centres which offer 'vacation in saddle' delight horseloving fans, and large woods invite sportsmen. The work of the expressionist painter Lev Pric, to be seen at the People's Gallery of State Art (*Gal'erri Proly'aniii*), manifests that world thought-waves of the highest kind have passed through the nation. Especially lovely is the park in the month of May, when the magnolias bloom. An obscure passage in a chronicle by Nostrum, Monk of Kiev, suggests a Mediterranean origin for these people, but this is much disputed.

The flight-handler waving his bats to bring the plane into parking position has, beneath his great headphoned helmet the flat face of a Tartar. The big bird still flies on the skyline; on the roof of the terminal the people continue to wave, wave, wave. Lev Pric is not visible. On the intercom, the martial music ceases: 'Resti stuli, noki fitygryfici,' says a stewardess over the apparatus. The long rows of passengers, who have been sitting in great quietness, stir very slightly. On the tarmac, the Tartar waves his bats; then he crosses them over his chest in a final gesture. There is one last movement from the plane, one last roar of the engine; then it halts. Inside there is stillness, but outside movement: the armed men move forward to surround the plane, and the blue buses begin, very slowly, to move away from the door marked INVAT and come toward them; a flight of steps trundles forward. A great red burst fills the front of the cabin; the stewardess has pushed open the forward door. Unclicking his lap-strap, Dr Petworth, a cultural visitor, begins to rise and reach upward to the laced racks for his hand luggage, staring down the aisle that will lead him towards his new city.

II

Now this Dr Petworth whom we see peering out through the globed windows of Comflug 155, as it halts on the apron at Slaka airport, is not, it had better be admitted, a person of any great interest at all. Indeed, as brilliant, batik-clad, magical realist novelist Katya Princip will remark, somewhat later in this narrative, he is just not a character in the world historical sense. He is a man who is styleless; he wears an old safari suit, its pockets packed with pens and paper, Christmas present socks of a tedious rhomboidal design, and flat earth shoes; there is a certain baldness to his head where, in a better world, hair would be. He is white and male, forty and married, bourgeois and British – all items to anyone's contemporary discredit, as he knows perfectly well. He is a man to whom life has been kind, and he has paid the price for it. No military adventures enter his history, and he has struggled for no causes, taken no part in any revolutions. When the world went to war in the forties, he lay in a cot and played with soft toys; when the young in the fifties rebelled over Suez and Hungary, he played cricket for his school. When the students of the sixties saw the dream of a new Utopia, he quietly completed his doctoral thesis on the great vowel-shift; when the pill came and the sexual world was transformed, he promptly married a small dark girl met on a camping holiday. His service has been all on that most commonplace of battlefields, the domestic front; and he has the baggy eyes and saddened heart to prove it. He has known the Freudian hungers, received, at the age of twenty, a sound education in complicated misery from a bouncy-breasted Swedish girl friend, which still haunts his middle life, felt the desire for change and complication, but never satisfied it. He teaches; that is what he does. And his sole interest here is that he has also travelled much, for the British Council, and has had diarrhoea for that excellent cultural organization in almost all parts of the civilized or part-civilized world.

And it is as a cultural traveller that he now sits here, strapped in an aisle seat of an Ilyushin on the airport at Slaka, waiting to enter the world outside. He has left behind him, two time zones back, under different birdlife and a different ideology, a habitat of sorts: a small office in a Bradford college, lined with books, where he teaches the vowel-shift and the speech-act to students of many nationalities, including his own; a small, fairly modern brick house of faintly rising property values on a bus-route convenient both for the college and the city; in the house, a quantity of contemporary, which is to say already out-of-date, furniture; and a dark wife, contemporary too, a woman of waning affections, bleakly hungry for a revelation, evidently disillusioned, in these therapeutic times, with . . . well, what? It is a little shaming to say that he does not quite know, for his instincts are decent; but with him, perhaps, or the role of helpmeet-slave, or the patriarchial enslavement of women in society, or the incapacity of the

20

marital orgasm to make all life endlessly interesting, or her own ageing, or his absences, both symbolic and actual; a small sad wife in Laura Ashley dresses, who writes many letters to undisclosed friends, and belongs to Weightwatchers, who reads horoscopes in old newspapers, paints paintings of no recognizable, or at least recognized, merit in the lumber room, drinks solitary glasses of sherry at odd hours of the day or night, and sits for long hours in a sunchair in the garden, as if waiting – or so it appears to Petworth, as he peers, when he is there and not here, through the curtains of his high upstairs study at the lonely figure in the lounger – to be a widow, who makes him feel guilty when, as then, he is present, and quite as guilty when, as now, he is not.

He has also left behind, under another sky, in pouring rain, an England in fits of Royal Wedding. For this is the very late summer of 1981, one of the lesser years, a time of recession and unemployment, decay and deindustrialization. The age of Sado-Monetarism has begun; in the corridors of power, they are naming the money supply after motorways, M1 and M2 and M3, to try to map its mysteries better. The bombs explode in Ulster, the factories close, but it has been a ceremonial summer; the patriotic bunting has flown, the Royal couple whose images are everywhere have walked the aisle. The nuptials, it seems, have been celebrated much by foreigners, come for the season to enjoy the splendour and stability of British traditions, and the collapse of the coin. Shards and fragments, chaos and Babel; so summer London has seemed to Petworth as, up from the provinces the previous night, he taxied through it on the way to his hotel near Victoria. In Oxford Street, bannered and decorated, where the kerbside touts sell laurelled mugs with Royals on them and small signs that say 'Oxford Street,' the shoppers in the busy stores are mostly Arabs, buying twelve of everything, evidently furnishing the desert. By Buckingham Palace, the hi-tech cameras snapping the Changing of the Guard are mostly held by Japanese – reasonably enough, since their skills made them in the first

21

place. In the lobby of the Victoria hotel, the clerk speaks only Portuguese, and that not well; burnouses are mingling with stetsons, Hausa with Batak. In the high third-floor bedroom, no bigger than a wardrobe, where Petworth unpacks, the electric kettle which would once have been a maid offers instructions for use in six languages, none of them his. In the street, black whores in sunglasses and short tunics laugh in doorways, vibrators prod their plastic rocketry up in the sex-shop windows, and a troubled, chaotic noise of shouting people and police sirens sounds as he goes to dine on an American-style hamburger.

In the morning, after a breakfast of teabag and Coffeemate, London seems a fancy fiction, a disorderly parade of styles. There are Vidal Sassoon haircuts and Pierre Cardin ties in the Lancias halted at the traffic lights; meanwhile youths pass on the pavement with pink cropheads and safety-pins stuck through their ears. Green-headed girls with red-patch faces in clown's pantaloons and parachute suits walk along; a young black with his hair in a string bag skates by in headphones, with wires going down into his clothes, listening to his own insides. 'We'll take more care of you,' say the BA posters at Victoria, where Petworth gets on the single-decker Airbus; chadored Iranian women sit there, carrying designer dresses in plastic bags from Harrod's, beneath advertisements for home pregnancy testing, computer dating, the joys of being a personal assistant to an assistant person. The bus pulls out into Sunday London streets, past pizza places, topless sauna parlours, unisex jeans outlets. Vandalism marks the spaces, graffiti the walls, where the council pulls down old substandard housing, to replace it with new substandard housing. 'Fly poundstretcher to Australia,' cry the posters by the flyover, shining with sweatless girls in bikinis, drinking drinks with ice in in other people's bright sunshine; rain falls over factories which stand empty with broken windows. Beer advertisements display half-timbered cottages and old grey churches, the England of the heart; rubbish and abandoned cars litter the hard shoulder of the motorway out to the airport.

And at Heathrow, that city in the desert, the summer's stylistic pluralism has chaos added. The late summer tourists who have fed the economy are massing to go home; the assistant air traffic controllers, calling for their annual gold benison, have gone on strike. In the upper air, planes bleep for attention and, finding none, go elsewhere; below, on the wet pavements, a few strikers sit outside the European terminal, their legs out in front of them, holding a sign saying OFFICIAL PICKET, watched by one policeman. In front of Petworth, the automatic doors open, then close on his foot; inside the great sounding terminal, the summer spectacle is held in a state of suspended animation. Some flights are cancelled, yet more delayed, yet more uncertain; the crowds are gathered in confusion. Germans and Swedes, French and Dutch, Arabs and Indians, Americans and Japanese, sit on chairs, lie on benches, wheel suitcases round on small fold-up wheels, push airport carts here and there, laden with bags from Lord John and Harrod's, Marks & Spencer and Simpson, wear jeans, wear tartan pants, wave tickets, quarrel at check-in counters, wear yashmaks, wear kimonos, buy *Playboy*, buy *La Stampa*, wear beards, wear Afros, wear uncut hair under turbans, buy *Airport*, buy *Ulysses*, request *The History Man* but cannot get it, buy cassette recorders, model guardsmen, Lady Di pens from W. H. Smith, hold dolls, carry tennis rackets in Adidas bags, struggle with backpacks, hold up wardrobe bags, chatter into red telephones of modern design devised to make conversation impossible, wear safari suits, wear flowing robes, wear furs, wear headbands, wear tarbooshes, wear cagoules, sit on stools, eye girls, comb curls, tote small babies, hug old ladies, furiously smoke Gauloises or Players, gather in crowds in hallways or on stairs, depart, led by blue stewardesses carrying large clipboards, in the direction of aircraft, and then, led by yellow stewardesses carrying small clipboards, back into the lounge

23

again. Meanwhile, amid the post-Bauhaus chairs, the sounding spaces, the crying children, the meaningless announcements, a few Indian ladies in baggy pants, the only stable residents of the transient place, sweep the floors and empty the flowing ashtrays with an air of resigned and stoical patience.

Pushing hopelessly through the crowd around the BA check-in desk, Petworth manages to show his Comflug ticket. The girl behind the counter, busy fending off passengers, has no promises at all to offer; but, strangely, she does tag his blue suitcase with a tag that says SLK, feeds it into a metal maw that tastes and then digests it, and hands him a boarding pass, to go on to Immigration. Near the channel is the window of a bank; Petworth halts for a moment, wondering whether to get vloskan, but if he does not fly he will not need it, and if he does he will be met. He passes on, through the bottleneck of Immigration, into the stateless, duty-free hinterland beyond. 'Say Hello to the Good Buys at Heathrow,' declare the bright yellow signs on the shining duty-free shop, packed with glossy goods at their special prices. He looks at the long swatches of tartan and tweed, the Dunhill lighters and Jaeger scarves; he picks up a basket and wanders beneath the anti-theft mirrors, inspecting the bright bottles of Scotch and London Dry Gin, the long cartons of Players and Dunhills, the cans of Three Nuns and Player's Navy Cut – elegant British institutions laid out here, much perhaps like the strike itself, to spare the lazy traveller the need ever to step out beyond the small country of the airport in order to find them. The loudspeakers do not loudspeak; wandering, with nothing to do except buy, Petworth buys – a bottle of Teacher's whisky, a long thin carton of Benson and Hedges' cigarettes, delivered in a sealed bag he must not open until he gets onto the plane he may never get onto, the goodies of travel, which travel itself, that ultimate neurosis, makes us need.

Later, Petworth leans against a convenient bar, a pimple-sized English Scotch at his elbow, watching the flight-boards flutter desperately, the television information screens judder and go blank, as they rake the codes inside themselves for signs that are more than redundancy, waiting for his plane to take off or not, as the case may be. On the digital clock, flight-time comes and goes; Petworth orders another Scotch and finds himself caught by an old and nameless fear – the fear of being trapped here, for eternity, in the unassigned, stateless space between all the countries, condemned to live for ever in a cosmopolitan nowhere, on clingfilm-wrapped sandwiches, duty-free whisky, Tiptree's jam. It is a fate he knows he deserves; he is a man who has spent his life circling around and away from domestic interiors, hovering between home, where he sits and thinks, and abroad, where he talks and drinks. Travel is a manic cycle, with abroad the manic phase, home the depressive; there is some strange adrenalin that draws him into the fascination and the void of foreignness, with its plurality of sensation, its sudden spaces and emptinesses. He travels, he thinks, for strangeness, disorientation, multiplication and variation of the self; yet he is not a good traveller, abhorring tours and guides and cathedrals, hating cafés and beaches, resenting brochures and itineraries, preferring food in his room to exposed meals in public restaurants. He is a man given to sitting silently in the one good armchair in dull hotel bedrooms, smoking, drinking, thinking, improving his lectures, analysing, without conclusion, his relationships, inspecting what in some quarters might pass for his soul, peeping through blinds or curtains at the street-scene below, and waiting – for a happy interruption, a small invitation to work or entertainment, a step outside beyond the world of depression and anxiety, the world in which he feels that he, in this case, is not the case.

It is busy and confused in the departure lounge; well-suited businessmen stand waiting impatiently with Samsonite executive cases, fine women walk past in Gucci scarves and tight lamé trousers, those special exotic airport women one may always see but never have. The flight-boards are fluttering again, in a jumble of letters and digits, a chaos of signs. But, look, they are settling, out of redundancy is coming word: COMFLUG says the board, and 155, and SLAKA, and NOW BOARDING. He sets aside his glass; he picks up his briefcase, his overcoat, his yellow duty-free bag; he sets off down the long dreary tunnels of Sunday Heathrow – past moving walkways, now not moving; past bright advertisements from Smith's, displaying old Chester and the White Cliffs of Dover, Windermere with a steamboat, Wales with a sheep, the Britain he is not and has scarcely ever been in; past advertisements for Seiko watches that are programmed to the year 2000, when they will collectively stop. Luggage trolleys with squeaking wheels follow him along the linoleum; great arms prod off from the corridor into disconnected space; planes like stranded whales stand unmoving beyond the windows; 'Your Palace in the Sky,' says an Air India jumbo with Taj Mahalled windows, firmly trapped on the ground. He enters a lounge where his luggage is taken and X-rayed, by a machine that will not harm the film in your camera; an electronic Aeolian harp is passed under his armpit and across the secrecies of his groin. In the chairs sit his fellow-travellers, a group unlike the great display outside: men in brown suits, with flat, grainy faces, elderly ladies in black dresses with small cardboard boxes, several quiet children, a silent stoical baby. They sit without speaking; they rise in neat order when the stewardess comes to lead them down the long bending arm onto the wet tarmac, where a modernist bus with fizzing doors waits to drive them past catering trucks, police cars, petrol tankers, flights of steps going nowhere, toward the aircraft that awaits them.

The Ilyushin has been parked like a secret in some distant corner of the airport; two bottle-green stewardesses wait for them to get off the bus. They allow the passengers up the steps two at a time; in the cabin, two more stewardesses wait to seat them all in careful rows, filling each place in order, as if they are packing a box of persons. LUPI LUPI, NOKI ROKI says the illuminated sign on the forward bulkhead; a dismal martial music plays through the intercom. The luggage racks are of string, the seats high and stiff. Petworth straps himself into an aisle seat; between him and the window are two brown-suited men who smell quite strongly of onion. The aisle is narrow; at the back of the plane there is a section shut off by a green curtain, to which none of the passengers seem to be allowed access. The travellers sit very quietly; the stewardesses check them very carefully; the doors are closed, the service trucks underneath them slide away. It is quiet in the cabin, and a red bus moves on the road to Hounslow; then the engines fire and roar. An announcement in a language Petworth does not know comes through the intercom: the plane taxis a little, and then stops, taxis a little more, and then stops again. Then, suddenly, the plane's body throbs, and there is the great dash into airspeed; they leap a fence, overarch a wet bus, overfly a wet reservoir and a field of waste; London, that fancy plural fiction, tips crazily into sight through the opposite window. Then it is gone, the red buses, the big city, the Heathrow strike, the Royal Wedding, the topless saunas, the dark wife; clouds come round, rain runs down the windows, and Petworth is indeed going to Slaka.

III

In all cultures, Petworth is very shortly to be found reflecting – a man rising into the clouds somewhere above Gravesend or Dover – planes are much the same sort of thing: long metal tubes containing persons. In all cultures, planes may be over-booked or, like Comflug 155, take off, for whatever reason, late. In all cultures, stewardesses, those couturiered nurses, may suffer from swollen ankles, menstrual cramps, or short-ened tempers exacerbated by repeated encounters with foolish, bleating travellers; in all cultures, airline food seems to come from the same universal source, stewed in the same universal sauce. Plane travel makes all life alike; yet inside likeness there is difference. Thus, even now, after just a few minutes in the air, there is something about Comflug that makes it definitely Comflug. The same things that all airlines do have been done, the same grammar of flying followed. So 'Attention,' the pilot has said, just after takeoff, addressing the cabin in several languages, his, Russian, German, and Petworth's native English, 'Welcome here please on Comflug 155, destiny Slaka. We shall flight at a high of ninety-two pornys, airspeed forty vlods an hour. Our delay is because of economic inconsistencies in Britain, so we do not apologize. Through window, notice please grey sky and raining. For Slaka, forecast very sunny. In disaster, always obedience please your stewardess.' Yes, it is the same but not quite the same, just as the seats seem just a little narrower and higher than usual, the stewardesses a little firmer and more given to hair in the nostrils, the passengers a little quieter and rather less mobile.

More familiarities follow; at the front of the cabin a small balletic display has started, conducted by two stewardesses, short fat ladies in high hard hats. 'Tenti sifti inburdi,' says, through the intercom, the voice of some unseen female impresario; from behind their backs the two stewardesses have produced brightly coloured cards and are waving them gaily in the air. 'Plazsci otvatu immerg'nicina proddo flugsi frolikat,' says the voice; the ladies suddenly rise up onto their toes, put out both their arms, rotate their wrists in a complicated gesture, and point with sharp fingers at various corners of the cabin. 'Flattin umper stuli, op immerg'nicina,' says the voice on the intercom. Magically, the ladies summon up from nowhere bright plastic tunics of yellow, and draw them over their heads, tying them carefully at the waist. 'Imper flattin tuggu taggii,' announces the voice. The two ladies suddenly turn their backs to the cabin, prod out their dumpy behinds, and give mock-tugs to the rear of their plastic tunics. Then they take off the tunics; 'Mas'kayii icks'gen flipiflopa,' says the voice. The ladies now hold up in their hands curious, clear plastic objects, out of which dangles a yellow hose. 'Vono icks'gen uskaka por prusori, ot noki roki,' says the voice. The

28

ladies put the yellow plastic hoses to their faces, and suck at them erotically. Then, as suddenly as it has begun, the dance collapses; the stewardesses put away their props and resume their normal duties, walking up and down the aisle. Familiarity breeds familiarity; Petworth puts out his hand and stops one of the stewardesses, overcome by a primal bodily urge. 'Ha?' cries the stewardess, a very heavy lady with hair in her nostrils, looking down at him. 'Are you serving drinks now?' asks Petworth, 'I'd like one.' 'Va?' says the stewardess, staring down on him severely, as if stewardesses are really not meant to be spoken to, 'Kla?'

Perhaps it is language that poses the problem: 'Drinks trolley,' says Petworth, raising an invisible glass to his lips, 'Whisky soda? Ginnitoniki?' 'Ah, na, na,' says the stewardess, looking at him critically, 'Is not permitted.' 'Not permitted?' says Petworth. 'Only permitted is a Vichy,' says the stewardess. 'Very well,' says Petworth, 'I'll have that.' 'Na,' says the stewardess, 'No now.' 'Oh, when?' asks Petworth. 'Another day,' says the stewardess, 'Tomorrow. Now is Sunday.' 'I see,' says Petworth, leaning back in his seat, a man in a chair in the air over Brussels, perhaps, or Paris, trying to understand what the difference is. It seems to him that in the West, which is where he comes from, flying is invested usually with a sort of magical fictionality, an erotic and pleasurable texture. Economic forces clearly explain this: capitalist competition requires that a certain happy disguise, a sense of delights available here and nowhere else, be cast over all the gross and diurnal reality. So, on the planes, stewardesses serve drink and bargain-like commodities, offer smiles and adulterous glances, promises of intimate excess, display made-up faces and nice legs, utter cries of 'Enjoy your flight' and 'Fly us again sometime' and 'Have a nice day.' Indeed they transmit what a linguist – and perhaps it should be explained that Petworth, a man in the sky over Dusseldorf, or Strasburg, is actually himself a linguist – calls phatic communion, which is to say non-verbal intercourse, speechless communication, the kind of thing that babies and lovers, teachers and animals constantly use. But that is under capitalism, and such false allurements and disguises are evidently not necessary on Comflug, where a more rational economy prevails. So, it seems, drinks are not to be offered, nor food, nor friendship; indeed the stewardesses have now disappeared entirely, apparently behind the green curtain at the back of the plane, and the rest of the passengers are sitting stiffly, clearly expecting nothing at all.

And therefore even in the air, Petworth reflects, a person in the clouds over Munich, or Zürich (for his geography collapses totally east of the Rhine), the world can subtly turn and change. Down below there are frontiers and fences, Comecons and Common Markets, tariff walls and spheres of influence, politics and ideologies, language barriers and vowelshifts. There are spies and searches, arrests and imprisonments, iron curtains and Berlin Walls, Alps and butter mountains, oil and SALT. The world is divided, and divides more every day; missiles point and cluster-bombs cluster; Reagan and the Born Again are that way, Brezhnev and the Politburo are this. In the air it should not matter; grander detachments, larger objectivities, seem possible. But in the air the borders and barriers function too, in the mind itself; slowly, strangely, consciousness changes, and Petworth can feel the change taking place within himself. Nothing is happening, yet somehow his being is shifting: a Petworth life and a Petworth wife, a Petworth day and a Petworth way, are strangely slipping and disintegrating in his head. Perhaps it has something to do with that popping of the ears at altitude which – the medical men, who say so many things now, say – touches strange glands that make the brain function somewhat differently; perhaps it is the strange hysteria of travel, which changes the sense in which we see the world; perhaps it is Karl Marx who is right, and changes in material condition generate changes in mentality. Whatever the reason, there is no doubt that, somewhere inside him, an old world is beginning to go, a new one beginning to come. The sky has cleared, turned to bright blue, and new landscapes lie below them, by unfastening his seat-belt, and raising himself up a little, Petworth can just see out, to glimpse an extraordinary, high, mountain landscape, a raw cold world of blank ice-cap, where no roads run, no settlements stand, where peaks glint and stark rock shines, a voided place. It is a place that matches his head, emptying of familiar being; he sits back in his seat and looks around the cabin.

In the cabin, the other passengers sit, in stiff rows; Petworth looks at them and recognizes their actuality. The men sit in their weighty, pre-synthetic, rather crumpled suits; the women wear large, full-skirted dresses; the clothes are the clothes of convention and duty, not the light sensuous robings of provisionality Petworth has now grown used to, so lightly put on and so easily taken off. These people do not talk much, but when they talk, they talk assertively, poking each other with fingers; the accents are guttural, the words are sharp. Across the aisle an old man holds a beetroot in his lap, and a woman feeds bread to a child; these are peoply sort of people, and they remind Petworth of something – of, he realizes, the people of his childhood, a time when the world appeared remarkably solid, persons massive, individuals whole and complete, reality really real, buildings permanently in place, marriages made for ever, a fact a fact. It is in adult life that one conceives everything to be provisional, to feel oneself in the wrong bodily container, to sense the world as a shifting void; but these people do not seem to look or think like that. Petworth looks up; the heavy stewardess, hair in her nostrils, cake-crumbs round her mouth, stands above him like a severe mother; she is staring down at his groin rebukingly, as if he has committed some disgrace there, as, of course, one always has. 'Lupi lupi,' says the stewardess, pointing to the seat-belt; Petworth fastens it up. With reality shaping around him, Petworth decides he needs a fact: 'English newspaper?' he says to the heavy face above him. 'Ah, na,' says the stewardess, 'Not available. Only available here is *P'rtyii Populatiii*.' 'All right,' says Petworth, glad even of a foreign word, 'I'll have that.' 'Not in English,' says the lady, 'You will not like.' 'I will like,' says Petworth. 'So you want?' asks the stewardess. 'Yes, I want,' says Petworth. 'So I get,' says the stewardess.

P'rtyii Populatiii, when brought, proves very weighty: as much fact as you could wish for. It has a red masthead and heavy black type; evidently the government and party organ, it has photographs of authoritative solidity, showing firm men grouped around tables or under banners in strangely fixed positions. They shake hands in friendship, or they sign things; they are characters in the world historical sense. Petworth unfolds the big rough pages, staring down at the unknown words in their mysterious series, some in the Cyrillic alphabet, some in the Latin, all in the language he does not know. There are no pop stars, no women notable only for their tits, just fixed photographs, seamless text. From the text prod words of faint familiarity: *Mass'fin Manifustu* sounds recognizable, and *Chil'al Ecun'mocu* all too understandable. But *Gn'oui Prut* means nothing, or less: *langue* without *parole*, signifier without signified. The text flows, then does not; codes start, but will not unravel. Linguistic anxiety makes Petworth tense, as it does all of us; he reaches into his pocket for oral relief. 'Na, na,' says a voice above him; the big face of the heavy green stewardess is staring into his, hairs in her nose, 'Noki roki.' 'Pardon?' asks Petworth, a man in a chair in the air above Plupno, or perhaps Viglip. 'You smirk,' says the stewardess. 'No,' says Petworth, looking down at the paper, 'I didn't smirk.' 'Da, you smirk,' says the stewardess, snatching the unlit cigarette from his mouth and showing it to him, 'Of course you smirk. Smirking here not permitted.' 'I'm sorry,' says Petworth. 'Only permitted is having a sweet,' says the stewardess.

The single sweet, wrapped in cheap paper, comes to him thoughtfully, on a little silver tray. It has a sharp acrid taste, the taste of foreignness. Petworth sucks it, and stares on, mentally nudging and prodding at the mysterious system of hieroglyphs packaged so tightly in his lap. Here are subtle

32

grammars, cases, declensions and inflexions, an entire constructed universe that in turn constructs and orders the universe
itself. Without it the world would be senseless, and pointless;
yet for Petworth it does not mean, it simply is. It ceases to be
a closed system; it leaks. As linguisticians like Petworth like
to say, information without context becomes redundancy, or
noise. There is a noise: the aircraft wheels drop from their
casings. There is bright light: the grey sky and the raining have
all gone, and the sky is a luminous blue. The engine note
changes; the lights flash on the bulkhead; the intercom clicks,
and the voice of the captain gives a long message in the
language Petworth does not know, untranslated, graceless, cast
in the firm tones of socialist realism. The heavy green stewardess
comes and lifts up Petworth's newspaper: 'Lupi lupi?' she asks.
'Da,' says Petworth, proudly displaying his crotch. Outside the
harsh ice-cap has gone, and, craning, Petworth can see something else has come – a cup of jagged mountains, a green plain,
a glinting big river, flooded beyond its banks, a steaming great
power-station, the web of a city, not far beneath. Then down
they come low, over shining polythene crop covers, and the
Comflug flight from London, two hours late, touches down,
bounces a little, brakes on the runway, then turns, following
the van that says HIN MI toward the sign that says INVAT,
until the Tartar crosses his bats, the plane stops, the flight
handlers push steps toward the aircraft's side, the stewardess
opens the front door, to let in a great rosy circle of light.

Petworth folds up *P'rtyii Populatiii*, undoes his lap-strap,
rises, steps into the aisle, reaches up to the rack for his duty-
free bag and a large overcoat, quite mismatched to the bright
weather outside (but his geography collapses totally once east
of the Rhine). Outside, in the sun, the white bird continues to
fly toward a city, a new ideological world, a life he can't yet
know, a language he can't yet speak. 'Na, na,' says a voice by
his ear; the heavy green stewardess is beside him once more.
'Na?' asks Petworth, staring at her; now she is small, and he
big. 'Is not permitted . . . ,' she begins; but then, her mouth

33

open, she ceases utterance, her eyes staring, her brow furrowed. Petworth, who has taught many a seminar in language acquisition, knows these symptoms at once; the Babelian tragedy has struck, linguistic arrest, translator's block, has occurred. 'Yes, not permitted,' says Petworth patiently, 'Now, not permitted to do what?' 'Vistu ab stuli,' says the stewardess. 'Yes, well, try again, I don't understand,' says Petworth patiently. Big Petworth, little heavy green stewardess, they stare at each other for a moment, trapped together on the linguistic interface. Then two large green arms rise up from her body, and her big hands seize his shoulders in a tight grip. For a small woman, she is strong; she turns him a little, shoves him backward, pushes him down; this causes his knees to fold, his buttocks to smack heavily down into the foam-rubber aisle seat where he has been sitting, a pain to run up his spine, his overcoat to fly up over his face. But gesture is language too, indeed is probably language's very origin. 'Not permitted to get up from your seat?' suggests Petworth, removing the overcoat. 'Da, da,' says the stewardess, nodding vigorously, and putting the overcoat back onto the rack, 'Is not permitted to get up your seat.' And indeed, when Petworth looks round the cabin, he sees this is the universal understanding. For, though the doors are open, the steps ready, the blue buses moving toward them from the door marked INVAT, all his fellow-passengers have remained in their seats, strapped and silent, as if waiting for the next thing to happen.

IV

Now perhaps it should be explained that this Dr Petworth who sits with tingling buttocks on the apron at Slaka is, though a linguist, not that kind of linguist who knows many languages. He is competent in some tongues, but mostly dead ones: Old and Middle English, Middle High German, and, if pressed, a little Old Norse, a passable Old Icelandic. But otherwise he possesses no more than that conventional, minimal polyglotism that has, for centuries, taken the English, stammering and nodding, baffled and curious, speaking their own tongue very loudly and slowly in the belief that if spoken like this it will be everywhere understood, into every corner of the world. So Petworth possesses the words for *coffee* and *tea* in some thirteen different languages, those for *beer* and *wine* in some eleven or twelve, those for *please* and *thank you* in some nine or ten. He knows, for examination purposes, a lot of different Eskimo words for *snow*. Tourist words like *museum* and *cathedral*, travel words like *customs* and *check-in*, succour words like *meal* and *lavatory*, he can usually pick up anywhere with great facility. He knows his Norse from his Igbo; he has as many words of Hopi as he has of Greek. But it is all example and illustration; when it actually comes to learning and speaking to others the language they use and construct life through, Petworth has, to be frank, just as much trouble as the rest of us.

But this is not all. Petworth also possesses a rich international *sub*-language – he would call it an idiolect – composed of many fascinating terms, like *idiolect* and *sociolect*, *langue* and *parole*, *signifier* and *signified*, *Chomsky* and *Saussure*, *Barthes* and *Derrida*, not the sort of words you say to everybody, but which put him immediately in touch with the vast community of those of his own sub-group, profession or calling in all parts of the world – if, that is, he can find anyone who speaks enough English to lead him to them. Petworth may not be a master of languages, but he does know what language in its *Ding an Sich*, its languageness, actually is. He knows all about how we, as language-speaking animals, language speak. If you ask him about analogic and digital communication, the code of semes, or the post-vocalic /r/, he can tell you, would be delighted to do so. He is an expert on real, imaginary and symbolic exchanges among skinbound organisms working on the linguistic interface, which is what linguists call you and me. In his own mind, he knows whether the mind is, or is not, a *tabula rasa* before language enters it, though he will not be divulging his answer directly in this book. You may not worry about such things, but there are people who do; indeed Petworth is a valued commercial traveller in an essential commodity, a loyal worker in the service of the one British export that, despite the falling fishing stocks and the rising oil price, the strikes and the recessions, still booms in the markets of the world. The ideal British product, needing no workers and no work, no assembly lines and no assembly, no spare parts and very little servicing, it is used for the most intimate and the most public purposes everywhere. We call it the English language, everyone wants it, and in its teaching Petworth is an acknowledged expert. His books on TEFL and TESOP and TENPP, on ESP and EAP, are jostled for in bookshops from Tromsø to Tierra del Fuego. And this is why he is here, the acrid taste of a sweet in his mouth, a pain in his spine, his bag of lectures tucked under the seat in front, sitting waiting at Slaka airport.

Yes, Petworths are always needed, for isn't everything a language? The grammar of airports is a language: this bustle of vehicles, these structured operations, as the grey tankers come under the wing, and the toilet-cleanser comes under the body, and the air-waves crackle and the hand-sets operate. The code of coming and going is a language, though it is the nature of language to function differently in different cultures. So in some societies the opening of a plane door is a signal suggesting to passengers that they may get off. In others, like this one, the same signal may mean something else; for example, that armed men may get on. For this, Petworth notes, peering through the globed window, is what is happening now; up the steps, into the plane, are coming four soldiers, in flared topcoats and boots that come up to the knee in cavalry fashion. Large young men, they have to bend their heads and tilt their weapons to pass under the doorway; their hair under their caps is tight-cropped, to show the shape of their skulls, and make them look fierce. Behind them comes another man, smaller and in plain clothes, clothes so very plain that he must surely be a policeman from the state security system, HOGPo. These five stand at the front of the cabin for a while, talking to the heavy green stewardess. Then two of the soldiers, followed by the HOGPo man, begin to walk, their feet thudding on the thin carpet, down the cabin. The passengers do not look up; the cold metal of a sub-machine gun lightly touches Petworth's hand as they pass him by. They go right down the cabin, and into the forbidden green-curtained area at the end; Petworth turns discreetly, to see the curtain falling behind them.

When he looks forward again, he sees that the other two soldiers have now begun to walk very slowly down the cabin, side by side. One looks carefully to the left, the other to the right, examining, minutely, the faces of the travellers. Petworth, meanwhile, uneasily inspects theirs. They are young men, with primal-looking unstated features: their eyes are studs, their mouths raw, their expressions unchanging, like those in old photographs, when life was serious and exposures long. They take each row carefully, coming nearer and nearer. Now Petworth, in the service of the English language, has travelled much for the British Council. Once or twice a year, for several years, he has picked up his briefcase and gone afield with his lectures. In the process he has grown used to the hard outward face of modern travel. There are men with guns at Schiphol and Fornebu, Zaventem and O'Hare; soldiers with tanks and troop-carriers will suddenly surround Heathrow. He has walked through metal-detectors on several continents, pushed his luggage through hundreds of X-ray machines that do not harm the film in your camera, seen his lectures indifferently flipped through at innumerable security checks, watched the tablets in his medicine bag tasted by policemen in Dusseldorf and Rawalpindi, suffered, arms splayed, legs grossly apart, body-searches of all kinds, from the aggressive to the intimate, in countries of many ideological complexions. He understands the necessity behind these depersonalizations; airports are dangerous holes in all societies, and terrorists and hijackers, spies and political escapees travel the shuttling air routes, looking for all the world just like any ordinary linguist. The world seems to steam with growing anger and impatience; in some countries some people want an individuality they feel denied, in others a collectivity they feel they lack; some want less of self, others more. These are times when it is hard to know what a person is, and harder to be one; in many circumstances it is wise to be as little person-like as possible.

This, as the soldiers come nearer and nearer, stand over him, Petworth tries now. The stewardess, standing behind them, says something about him: 'Passipotti,' says the soldier. The soldier looks at the document, stares with black eyes at Petworth, through the face into the skull, feels the Heathrow bag, laughs at the clank of bottle, hands the passport back, and passes on. Some three rows behind him, there is a conversation, then a commotion; a moment later the two soldiers walk heavily back toward the front of the plane, between them a neat Burberry-ed businessman in a Western suit, carrying a code-locked leather briefcase, impregnable to all assault save that of being picked up and walked off with. He is an ordinary man, who looks a bit like Petworth; but he is in another story, a story of spies and betrayals, not, thinks Petworth, Petworth's story at all. The man goes down the steps between the soldiers, whose guns bob on their backs. There is a silence from the back of the plane, from behind the green curtain; there is a noise from the intercom, as the pilot says something in his gloomy monoglot. Slowly the passengers begin to rise, step out into the aisle, put on hats and berets, collect their cardboard boxes. 'Is permitted?' asks Petworth, waving at the heavy green stewardess, up the aisle ahead of him. 'Da,' she says, nodding. Petworth rises again, collects his Heathrow bag and overcoat, picks up his bag of lectures, jostles along the aisle to the entrance. 'Thank you,' he says to the stewardess as he passes her, hair in her nostrils, 'Have a nice day.'

Then he is at the top of the steps, looking down into the new country. Two more armed soldiers stand at the bottom of them, watching the passengers descend. Down he goes, till his flat earth shoes touch the new society, the fresh ideological soil. He pauses, sniffs the fresh, mildly aromatic air; one of the soldiers points him to the bulbous blue bus that stands waiting. Inside are just a few gun-metal seats, occupied by moustached men, old ladies carrying parcels; the smell is of disinfectant. The crowd jostles in; the grey-shined driver presses a button, and the doors hiss and close. Very slowly, the bus begins to move, bouncing on poor tyres past the Ilyushins, the Tupolevs, the Antonovs, guarded and in their places, toward the white terminal and the door that says INVAT. Draped with his luggage, Petworth hangs onto a metal pole and looks out, through the wavy imperfections of the glass, with flat eye, flat mind. There are colleagues of his at home who would regard this country, the ground of which he has just touched with his flat earth shoes, as the model of the desirable future, the outcome to which a benevolent history points; there are others who would see it as the bleak end of things. Petworth, who sees himself as an open-minded man, a voter for modest improvement, only political when roused, has no urgent views, merely a mild irony at the expense of all societies, each with its own fiction of having improved history. The bus bounces, the passengers sway, and not far off is the terminal, where he will, he trusts, be met and attended to, taken off on his tour.

Hanging on the pole, he feels the usual small disorder in his stomach, the predictable pressure pain from the aircraft in his ears, the familiar gloomy confusion about why he has come to be lonely here, rather than being lonely somewhere else. He is away again, in the state of foreignness, which is a universal country, simply the opposite to home and domesticity. The two worlds both mesh and contend. So, waking at night in Bradford, next to his sleeping dark-haired wife, dreaming, probably, of someone or somewhere else, he will suddenly feel intensely the stupidity of linked flesh, the incompleteness of human bonding, the prison of property, the foolish sameness of days, the hunger for a bigger and less exact world. Waking at night in double-bedded hotel rooms, under duvets for two covering only one, in the central square of some not really apprehended distant foreign city where the trams rattle, night-club music blurts, and the lights of cars reflect crazily on the ceiling, he will feel the wastefulness of displacement, the tug of domesticity; he will pick up the telephone and, through distant switchboards, place calls to Bradford, frequently not con-nected, lost amid the spacious buzzes and clicks of inter-national wiring. Domestic and foreign, manic and depressive, never become one; between the states there is all this: the signs in unknown languages, the security checks and body searches, the armed men, the shifting landscapes glimpsed through wavy imperfections in glass; the great tankers saying COMOIL or BIN'ZINI; the duty-free lounges, the safety instruction pam-phlets, the gins-and-tonic, the terminals.

Here is the terminal, white and wooden; before the door marked INVAT, two blue armed men stand, not moving. For a while, the bus doors remain closed; the passengers – the moustached men, the elderly ladies – remain silently in their places; evidently this is a culture where people are used to waiting. Then, inside the building, behind the glass of the door, there appears a girl in a blue uniform, with the word COSMO-PLOT on her hat; she unlocks the INVAT door, comes outside, presses a button on the bus side, and the doors hiss open. They go, the passengers off Comflug 155, down the steps, between the armed men, through the door that says INVAT. Inside, as well as out, the terminal is a building of little distinction, its walls and partitions of rough wood, its ceilings of crumpling tile, its floors of worn linoleum. The air has a faint dusty consistency; there is an endless boom of noise from various functions. Some semiotician has designed a system of wordless signs – arrows through squares, crosses in circles, ladders in oblongs – to guide bemused strangers through the labyrinth, the web of partitions and channels Petworth sees ahead of him. More functionally, another blue armed man stands there,

40

pointing his sub-machine gun to help the passegers toward a place where stands another blue armed man, guarding a black line painted on the floor, behind which the passengers from London have formed a queue, long, slow, polite, orderly. From time to time, this armed man waves one of the passengers forward, toward one of a row of small curtained stalls; over the stalls is a sign saying IDENT'NII.

Groups of green stewardesses go by; an old tractor drags through the hall a row of luggage-laden rubber-tyred barrows. The roar of planes taking off seems to shake the wooden frame of the building. The wait is long, but at last Petworth comes to the black line; the armed man waves him forward into one of the cubicles. He lifts the curtain; the cubicle contains a glass-fronted booth; in the booth sit two more armed men of the militia type, one with his hat off. 'Passipotti,' says the man with his hat off; the other man stares beyond Petworth to a mirror hanging behind his back, which discloses him from the unguarded rear. Into the hand that has come through an aperture in the glass, Petworth puts his British passport, blue and hardback; stapled into it is his visa, issued just ten days before at the London consulate of the country where he now stands. In several copies, it bears the formal seal of this people's republic (Ryp'blicanii Proly'aniii) and a good deal of elegant script in Cyrillic. On each of the several copies is a small photograph of Petworth, showing a blotched and haunted face, caught in that strained expression one assumes behind the curtains of a railway station photo-booth not unlike the place where he waits now, when (*flash*) one is desperately trying to adjust the stool to the required height and (*flash*) the train one can just hear departing the platform is probably one's own. The two armed men look, from photograph to Petworth, Petworth to photograph, image to what passes for reality and back again. Then the man without the hat looks up at Petworth: 'Dikumenti?' he says. Since the plane, Petworth has lost his taste for transient linguistic encounters, verbal one-night stands, but words are called for. 'Professori,' says Petworth.

41

'Ah, da, prif'sorii?' says the hatless man, 'Prif'sorii univer-
sitayii?' 'Ja, or da,' says Petworth, 'Prif'sorii universitayii
linguistici.' The other armed man leans forward, interrupting.
'Dikumenti?' he says. It is now that Petworth recalls another
document: a letter, very ill-typed, written in stiff and inaccurate
English on rough grey paper, an invitation to himself from
his formal hosts in the country, the Min'stratii Kulturi Komitet'iii. The letter has smudged badly in the pocket, and he
has scribbled notes on the back; but the hatless man takes
it, unfolds it, very carefully, and inspects its contents. 'Kla?' he
says, passing it to the other armed man. 'Da,' says the second
armed man. The first armed man picks up the visa again and
looks once more at the photograph, then at Petworth. Evidently his face has now acquired the same blotched and
haunted expression the photograph depicts, for the first armed
man tears a page from the visa, stamps, one by one, the other
copies, and then hands the passport and the folded letter neatly
back to Petworth through the aperture in the glass. 'Danke,'
says Petworth, smiling at the wonder of language, its seductive
art for linking man to man. He lifts the curtain, steps out of
the booth: to find before him another line of waiting passengers, another black mark across the floor, another armed
man, another small row of curtained booths. The situation is
the same, only the sign above different; the notice here says
GELD'AYII. The wait, as before, is long; the queue moves
forward slowly. Outside, planes roar, and there is a drumming
on the roof presumably from the waiting crowds above. It is
not, thinks Petworth, to whom the doors of language seem to
be slowly opening, hard to judge what GELD'AYII means. This
is a country where balance of payments problems are severe,
and currency offences serious crimes against the state; indeed
on the plane Petworth has been issued with a document, which
has required him to list all the money he carries, and reminded
him that the ordinary visitor must change so much foreign
currency every day, at the official exchanges, or the offices of
the state bank.

He is ushered into the cubicle; inside is another glass booth. In it sit two more blue armed men, one wearing a jacket and the other not, the other wearing a moustache and the first one not. The man wearing the moustache and not wearing the jacket puts his hand through the aperture in the glass and says: 'Dikumenti?' Petworth hands in the passport, the visa, the letter, the currency form – a document on which he has in fact written nothing, all his expenses in Slaka being, as he understands it, the responsibility of the Min'stratii Kulturi Komitet'iii. The man with the moustache looks at the blank paper; he passes it to the man with the jacket. 'Geld'ayii na?' asks this man, looking at Petworth with some amazement. 'Na, hospitalito,' says Petworth, spreading his arms wide. The man without the moustache and the man without the jacket observe Petworth for a moment: then 'Hippi?' says the man without the jacket. 'Na, na,' says Petworth, 'Prif'sorii univer-sitayii linguistici, hospitalito officiale.' 'Vloskan na?' says the man without the moustache. 'Look, dikumenti,' says Petworth, pointing to the grey letter in the passport. 'Ha,' says the man without the jacket, reading, very slowly, the letter, 'Ka? Con-gressi internat'yayii?' 'Colloquiale didactico,' says Petworth. 'Na geldin ab pitti?' asks the man without the jacket. Petworth thinks he understands; he reaches in his pocket, and takes out a small wad of green and blue paper, samples of falling sterling, brought to buy Scotches on the plane. The man without the jacket counts it, and laughs; the man without the moustache writes something on the currency declaration, tears off the top copy, puts it in a drawer, stamps the remaining sheets, and hands it back to Petworth, together with the passport and letter. 'Grazie,' says Petworth, lifting the curtain: to find yet another queue of passengers, another armed man, another black line on the floor, and, instead of a row of booths, a single white doorway, which is marked DONAY'II.

But the third labyrinth is different; the doorway, when Petworth is allowed to pass through, leads to a place of luggage, with open benches surrounded by waiting passengers;

there are no armed men. Instead there is a big dapper lady, in dark blue skirt, white blouse, black tie, inspecting baggage; she works alone, and takes much time to get from passenger to passenger, for she is dedicated, poking severely into every bag, lifting out shirts, interrogating underwear, asking many questions. Petworth finds, on a bench, his own blue suitcase, with its tag saying SLK; he stands by it, he waits. Beyond the walls is a ferment of voices, the roar of a crowd. It is probably the noise of the meeters from the roof, waiting to greet the arriving passengers. Among their number must be an emissary to him from the Min'stratii Kulturi Komitet'iii, waiting there to give him money, take him onward, lead him to his lectures; the end is in sight, or hearing. 'Va?' says the dapper lady, reaching him at last, tapping his suitcase. Petworth unlocks it; she probes briefly into the intimate world of his changes of sock, his small case of medicines, his formal suit and spare set of shoes. Then she glances briefly into the plastic bag proclaiming 'Say Hello to the Good Buys from Heathrow.' The briefcase, however, does detain her attention. Unlatching it, thrusting its jaws wide, she stares down curiously into the mass of papers and books that are shoved untidily inside. She pokes a little, looks at Petworth. Then she says: 'Ot.'

'Ka?' says Petworth. 'Ot,' says the lady, putting both her hands out, then turning them over. Gesture is language; this is unmistakable. 'Ah, ot,' says Petworth, resignedly, upturning the bag. Its contents spill out, a chaos of papers and paragraphs. Lectures lose their paperclips and disintegrate; script blows across the floor; books fall from the bench and fall flat on their faces in the dust. The books are what the lady attends to first. She lifts them and looks at each one: Chomsky on Transformational Grammar; Lyons on Chomsky; Chomsky on Chomsky; Chatman on socio-linguistics; Fowler on Chomsky and Lyons and Chatman. 'Pomo?' she asks. 'Na, na,' says Petworth, 'Scienza, wissenschaft.' 'Ha,' says the lady, lifting one of the books (Fowler's, actually) and looking doubtfully through it; then she lifts another and inspects it page by page.

'Ka,' she says, handing it out to Petworth. There is an illustration of writhing human organs. 'It's a speech act,' cries Petworth, 'The mouth engaged in a speech act.' 'Ha,' says the lady, setting the books aside, suddenly seeming to find them dull. Instead she turns her attention to the scattered texts of Petworth's own lectures. She spreads them, ill-typed texts, roughly held together with rusting paperclips, texts that have travelled in many parts of the world, known the extremes of heat and cold, passed before many sorts and conditions of men, along the bench in front of her. Then, going through the tidy piles, she picks one out, lifts it onto her clipboard, and attempts to read it.

It is probably not one of Petworth's best, a well-worn, anodyne piece entitled 'The English Language as a Medium of International Communication.' Its audiences have, however, been large, and it has been with Petworth for some time, as is the way with lectures. Many changes of thought, refinements of feeling, have been scribbled into its margins: Petworth, the author himself no less, has difficulty in reading it. So, evidently, does the lady. She furrows her brow, turns the pages backward and forward, as if the end might be in the beginning or the beginning in the end; she holds it up by the paperclip and shakes it, as if its meaning might emerge this way. What does come out is a few sheets, which fall onto the floor; she picks these up and looks at them with special attention. It is now Petworth is struck with a professional thought, worth, in less anxious circumstances, a lecture in itself. The written word, it occurs to him, does not simply have a different *meaning* in a different culture, because of its changed relation to the total vocabulary of that culture; it also has a different *weight* or *status*. So in some cultures – like, for example, Petworth's own – words are expended very freely, readily spoken and fairly easily published; they have a *low* weight on the market. In other cultures – like, for example, this one now – words are traded more selectively and carefully; hence, according to a familiar economic principle, they have a *high* value on the market. In such cultures, text can be trouble, books small bombs. Moreover, it is possible for *low-value words* from one environment to become *high-value words* simply by changing not the words but the *environment* – for instance, by putting them in a bag and taking them somewhere in a plane. Hence environment determines the worth of words; this can be seen from what is happening to his own, right now.

For the lady looks, and frowns, and is not happy. Petworth senses he must establish that these words at least are worthless and irrelevant: 'Lectori academico,' he says. 'Poy,' says the lady, reading on. There is, actually an old argument, sometimes used in language teaching, that fear and anxiety can improve people's language acquisition. Petworth doesn't believe it, but something is happening to his own competence now. 'Lectori academico pri'fissori universitayii hospitalito officay'alii congressi intemat'yayii colloquiale didactico,' he says desperately. 'Moy,' says the lady, not looking up from the text. It is not easy to tell, from inspecting her expression, whether any comprehension at all is taking place, though the length of time she is taking with each page makes it seem doubtful. Despite the long delay, the other passengers continue to wait patiently, casting only the smallest and most oblique of glances at the events at his bench. All look foreign, none look as though they might help; he has no other rate of exchange but his own. 'Exchangi amicati,' says Petworth, taking out the grey letter from the Min'stratii Kulturi Komitet'iii, and handing it to the lady. 'Voy,' says the lady, taking it and putting it on the clipboard that rests against her hard, white-shined breasts, which seem clearly designed for this purpose and no other. She stares at it, shakes her head. Only now does Petworth recall that this letter, too, is in English, and hardly likely to solve his problems.

Petworth looks round, at the walls, at the other passengers, who patiently wait for what will happen next. When he looks back again, the lady is walking away, toward one of a wall of roughly partitioned offices that lines the room, where men in white shirts and black ties work or stare out at him. She carries both his letter and his lecture on 'The English Language as a Medium of International Communication.' On the bench in front of him flutter his remaining lectures, their pages in disorder, their content in recollection absurd: he tries, a little, to order them, but the spirit is somehow not there. A few moments later, he sees the dapper lady walking back from the office toward him: she is now accompanied by one of the blue armed men. She takes up her position on her side of the bench; the armed man, boots squeaking on the tile, comes and stands beside Petworth. The lady now begins to collect up all the papers scattered in front of her, doing it with a notable neatness, uncreasing the bent corners of the rough and pen-corrected texts, smoothing the covers of the books; this is evidently a culture where care and time are taken. She slips them into the briefcase in neat and sensible order, closes the top, hands it to the armed man. 'Da?' asks the armed man, pointing to the blue suitcase and the Heathrow bag. 'Da,' says the lady. 'Hin,' says the man, nodding to Petworth to come; the other passengers watch, with some curiosity, but not too much, as Petworth and his escort march off through the sounding shell of the low-roofed wooden building, the armed man in his thudding thick black boots, Petworth in his pattering flat earth shoes. 'Exchangi amicato,' cries Petworth desperately; the armed man does not respond, but leads Petworth to a small white door, which has a sign on it saying DIRIG'AYII.

Inside the room, behind a desk, sits another, very big blue armed man. Near the desk, in a plastic easy chair, sits, under a sign saying NOKI ROKI smoking a sweet-smelling cigarette, a small man in plain clothes, clothes so very plain he must surely be a policeman from the state security system, HOGPo. Both are reading. The big blue armed man, who has a scar down his nose, has the grey letter from the Min'stratii Kulturi Komitet'iii. The man in plain clothes has 'The English Language as a Medium of International Communication.' 'Exchangi amicato,' says Petworth, standing in front of the desk. The big

47

man rises and walks slowly forward; his eyes are blue, his gunstrap seems too tight for his swelling chest. The plain-clothes man stubs out his cigarette. The blue armed man stops in front of Petworth, looks him up and down. His arms spread wide, he thrusts them forward; suddenly Petworth feels himself seized in a maelstrom or turbulence; his nose is being pushed hard into the leather cross-strap over the man's shoulders; his breathing is stifled on the thick worsted of his uniform; his hands touch the cold metal of the machine gun on his back; their thighs come together, prodding each other. His groin is being bored, his back being beaten; the man has a sweaty stench; sweat, too, pours down Petworth's body inside his clothes as these things happen to him. The armed man pushes him backward for a moment, holds him out at arm's length, like a large doll. His blue eyes stare, around them the creases wrinkle. 'Camarad'aki,' he cries, 'Velki in Slaka.' And then Petworth is dragged forwards again, into the great fraternal maelstrom. Comrade is not a word he is fond of, never having had one, but 'Camarad'aki!' he cries when, breathless, he emerges.

'Rot'vitti!' says the plain little plain-clothes man, gaily standing behind the desk with four glasses and a bottle. A full glass of bright clear liquid appears in Petworth's hand. 'Snup!' says the big armed man, raising a glass to him. 'Kulturi!' says the plain-clothes man, raising his. 'Musica!' says the armed man who brought Petworth here, pretending to bow a fiddle. 'Exchangi!' says Petworth, raising his glass and drinking it down, with a choking cry; the local peach brandy is not to be missed. The others are laughing; perhaps the word is senseless, or even obscene, it does not matter. He is in the middle of some great masculine joke; it is, in the circumstances, well worth joining. The four men, two armed, two not, stand in the room and laugh together, in full male roars, like the roars of adults in the living-room when Petworth was a child. After a while, the laughing stops; through the window, Petworth sees the Western businessman, with the code-locked briefcase, being marched by two soldiers towards a black car. 'Please have good visit, Mr Pitwit,' says the plain-clothes man, handing Petworth the briefcase, 'Such interesting books. Do not leave them with any of our people.' The big armed man gives Petworth a last comradely hug; the other armed man lifts his baggage and guides him from the room. They go down a corridor, back into the customs hall; the big dapper lady turns to watch him go, with his guide, to a door marked OTVAT. Here another armed man, sitting on a stool, unlocks it, and allows them through. The armed man who is his guide puts down his baggage, bows a little, goes back through the door. It closes, a key clicks; the sign on this side of the door says NOI VA.

Sweating, Petworth turns. Beneath him is his luggage tumbled at his feet. In front of him is a long thin concourse, packed with people, too many, indeed, for its confined and narrow area, for they push, jostle a little, tread on each other's feet. The men are mostly in double-breasted suits, the women are round and bulky. They carry flowers, wave handkerchiefs, and cluster hopefully round the door marked NOI VA. Faces bob into sight in the turmoil, and then subside again. Beyond the people are long dirty windows, lit by the now fading sunlight; beyond the windows Petworth can see yet more armed men, walking up and down a forecourt to inspect yet more people – who lift luggage, carry flowers, tote backpacks, enter small orange taxis, or wait patiently at a place marked BUSOP, where more battered blue buses with bulbous noses stand with their doors tight shut. And further on still, beyond all the busy people, there is a landscape, of wide hedgeless fields, trees, wooden houses, a small hill; poking up in the middle is the golden onion. And beyond the onion there must be the city, with its lives and realities, cemeteries and cathedrals, ministries and museums, hotels and bars, customs and conversation. He is here, within the gates, come, in his flat earth shoes, to visit.

2 – RECEP.

I

Now this Dr Petworth, whose arrival in Slaka we have just witnessed, is in fact an old and practised cultural traveller. Today, in this late summer of 1981, he stands in the lobby of the airport at Slaka, but really he might be anywhere; year after year he has been coming, coat over arm and bags at knee, through the arrivals labyrinths of airports with wildly different names – Madrid or Helsinki, Tunis or Teheran – but with the same fluttering flight-boards, the same sea of faces, the same incomprehensible, polyglot announcements, emerging, pausing, putting down his luggage, in the firm expectation that his coming will be noticed. He is a person of no great interest, not a character in the world historical sense, a man waiters neglect and barmen save till last; yet he believes that someone will always step forward from the crowd, shake his hand, lead him to the car park, and put him in the way of a familiar plot of days, quite as familiar as the domestic world he has not been sorry to leave behind. He confidently expects to be taken to the city, signed in at some downtown hotel already apprised of his coming, handed to a bellboy, left for a while to shower, shave, freshen and change knickers, be collected again, driven to one of the town's better quarters, taken upstairs to an apartment, with a good view, a maid holding a tray of drinks, a host in something formal, a hostess in something ethnic; where, in the rooms, the professors come and go, talking of T. S. Eliot, professors who will seize on him, reminisce about the Oxford colleges they long ago went to, say Lacan to his Derrida, Barthes to his Saussure, and discuss, quite as if they had read them deeply and long ago, and not just glanced at them hastily that afternoon in expectation of his arrival, the several books that he has published.

All this Petworth expects, as he comes through the arrivals labyrinth, because he is a man with a sign. From the handle of his briefcase there dangles a puce and magenta tag; it is the identification tag of the British Council, an organization designed to bring scholars like himself to the cities of the world. Between him and the Council, a compact exists. The Council representatives have their responsibilities: meeting and greeting, driving and arriving, tending and mending, liquoring and succouring, showing slides and fixing rides, detaching and onwardly despatching. And Petworth, in turn, has his: coming, meeting, chatting, eating, drinking, talking, listening, walking, imparting and finally departing, on to the next place, so that the cycle can resume again. A simple system, it has always worked well; hotels of modest comfort have always been found, with a booking in his name or one like it. Restaurants of pleasant ambiance have from time to time been frequented. At appropriate times Petworth has been taken to academic buildings, where the stairwells are alive with the smell of disinfectant, been offered coffee or something stronger, introduced to those who in turn will introduce him, then led through long corridors past student posters everywhere much the same, advertising exhibitions of Expressionist art and attacks on the regime, their own or someone else's, into sudden large lecture halls: where students, their physiognomies, clothes and skin-pigmentation differing somewhat, though by no means as much as you might think, from country to country, according to which one this happens to be today, are stacked in rows to stare at him, look at his tie, and listen as well as they can or they care to while Petworth stands on the podium and divulges, in the complexities of the English tongue, the complexities of the English tongue.

Like the students, the countries differ in detail. Some allow no mention of Jesus, and some no mention of anyone else; some have statues of long-dead scholars in the courtyard and students whose eyes are always on the ground, and some have tanks and armed troop-carriers in the forecourt, and students whose fists are always in the air. Yet the impression – because it is an impression of lecture rooms, hotels, restaurants and receptions – is always rather much the same. There are moments that do stand out: a certain affair of a suitcase lost in Bogota once; a certain matter of a girl called Irina in Bratislava (but that was in another country, and the wench now has tenure); a meal composed of grass in Kyoto, another of poisoned seafood in Singapore; a notable performance of Hamlet in Belize, a notable performance of belly-dance in Hammamet. As in life itself, familiarity is occasionally fractured and transformed by surprise and variation, sometimes but not usually in the form of pleasure. And today, in Slaka, there is one. For here is Petworth, sweating, red-faced, troubled, fresh from Slaka's turbulent labyrinth of arrival. He stands in the crowded lobby, his back to a pillar, the busy faceless crowds around him, the meeters and greeters, the pushers and jostlers, clustering round the small white door marked NOI VA. His coat over his arm, his luggage below his feet, his face turns expectantly, this way and that; the puce and magenta tag hangs from the handle of his bag of lectures. The sun diminishes, the armed men walk up and down. But Slaka is the capital of a hardline country of the socialist bloc, a member of Comecon and the Warsaw Pact, suspicious of the Western cultural agencies; as a result, there is, in Slaka, no British Council office or representative at all.

II

Now all this has been explained to Petworth at a very brief briefing, given him by a grey-haired lady smoking Player's

Number Tens from a tiny packet, in a dark old office with high cupboards somewhere high up in the British Council building in Davies Street, London, some ten days before his present journey. It is, this day ten days gone, a very bleak wet day; Petworth, down from Bradford on the early morning train, with visas yet to collect and flights to check, sits damply on a wooden chair, staring at a lithograph portrait of Shakespeare and an old poster for the Berliner Ensemble. He holds a plastic cup of coffee of very murky consistency; a secretary in a ra-ra skirt keeps stepping in and out with files; water from his mackintosh is making a puddle on the Council floor. In Oxford Street, round the corner, the usual ambulances and police cars heehaw; he can see, through the window, the Royal Wedding bunting, dripping rain onto the sheikhs and their spouses who are shopping below. 'There's no British Council there?' he says, shaking the coffee and pondering the impossible thought. 'No, we're not represented in several of the socialist countries,' says the grey-haired lady, dropping ash over a thick file which is, Petworth presumes, his own, 'They think we spy and bring in bad books, perish the thought.' 'How is this tour arranged, then?' asks Petworth. 'What we have is a cultural exchange agreement,' says the grey-haired lady, patiently, 'It's directly negotiated each year between their government and HMG. Our part's minimal, we just arrange your travel out there and point you to the plane. After that, you're in the hands of their Ministry of Culture. They'll look after you, rather well, I expect, unless the political climate changes. You know how these things work. They flow when it thaws and block up when it freezes, just like the lav down the corridor.' 'I see,' says Petworth, 'So money, my hotel, my programme?' 'All their responsibility,' says the lady, cheerfully.

'Tell me,' says Petworth, sitting in his puddle, 'Would you say now things were thawing or freezing?' 'Well, thawing, really,' says the grey-haired lady, 'Or they wouldn't have asked you. On the other hand, they are beginning to freeze again. Since Afghanistan and the Reagan hard line and the failure of détente and the collapse of SALT. Actually we're very interested in your visit, because it's rather a test of the mood. If it goes well, we'll hope for more. Or course if it goes wrong, we'll reassess the whole programme.' 'Goes wrong?' asks Petworth, looking up, 'How might it go wrong?' 'Well, it does happen,' says the grey-haired lady, opening up the file in front of her and looking into it, 'Tell me, my dear, you aren't a bugger, are you?' 'Pardon?' asks Petworth. 'There's nothing here about your sexual tastes,' says the lady. 'I see,' says Petworth, 'No, I'm not.' 'Not that we're against buggers in the Council,' says the lady. 'I always thought not,' says Petworth. 'One's all for life's pleasures,' says the lady, shaking out the match with which she has just lit a fresh cigarette, 'The trouble is there's very high surveillance there, and their security police – they're called HOGPo, actually – are rather keen on that sort of thing. They find it very good grounds for blackmail. One can hardly blame them, really, they've done rather well out of our British taste, as you well know.' 'I suppose so,' says Petworth. 'Yes, if one were asked to sum up Eastern Europe in a phrase,' says the lady, 'one would say it was their buggers listening in on ours. So you're totally hetero, my dear.' 'Well, I am, yes,' says Petworth, staring down into the gloomy grounds of the coffee. 'Well, in that case,' says the lady, 'do be careful. Practise out of sight, and above all avoid the whores in all the main hotels and nightclubs.' 'I will,' says Petworth. 'And they'll undoubtedly give you a guide-interpreter,' says the lady, 'Sometimes they're tough old biddies, but sometimes they go for rather attractive young females. Think of her as totally forbidden fruit, it's probably a plant. Remember, in this world, everyone reports to someone; them to theirs, us to ours.' 'But I don't,' says Petworth, 'And I have no information worth having whatsoever. Except about linguistics.' 'Yes, well, we'll come to that in a minute,' says the lady, 'More coffee.' 'No, thank you,' says Petworth, steaming in his chair.

'Yes, well, now, my dear,' says the lady, 'I'm not sure what hotel they'll put you in, probably the Europa. But do assume as a matter of course that the room is bugged, most of them are. There's not much you can do about it, except take care. But I always like to hang a towel over the mirror when I get into bed. They photograph through them, you know, and you never are sure what you'll be doing. Of course nowadays they've got these advanced multi-directional microphones that can pick up anything at enormous distances, so if they're interested in you they can usually find you. But if you're talking to anyone, or worse, try banging spoons on the woodwork, or run the shower and do it in the bathroom. Better still, go outside. The only real place to chat or make love is in a newly ploughed field, but they're not always easy to come by.' 'I suppose not,' says Petworth. 'There are all sorts of ways of getting you if they want you,' says the lady, 'But do avoid illegal currency transactions. Everyone will try to buy your Western money, but it's a crime against the state and they can put you in prison for years. And don't bring papers or documents out of the country, however compassionate the story; that's another favourite. Always stick firmly to the titles of your lectures, don't comment on national events, and try to keep all politics right out of it.' 'Well, there aren't many politics in linguistics,' says Petworth. 'I expect that's why they chose to ask you,' says the grey-haired lady, 'But you'd be surprised. If you should get picked up by HOGPo at all, try not to eat anything. They're particularly fond of drugged chocolates and poisoned cigarettes, for some reason. Of course all these are just common-sense precautions; nothing's likely to happen to you. Unless they suddenly decide they want to trade someone for someone, or something.' 'I see,' says Petworth, 'I think I will have another cup of coffee.'

'Sorry I couldn't offer you lunch,' says the lady, 'I've found the most marvellous Indonesian round the corner, but you know our budget's been cut, like everyone else's. Georgina, Dr Petworth would love another cup of your coffee. I say, dear, haven't you had your hair done? I think it's super.' 'Thank you,' says Georgina, 'Same again?' 'Black this time,' says Petworth. 'Well,' says the grey-haired lady, snapping shut the file in front of her, and smiling at him. 'I'm sure you'll have the most marvellous tour there. I was posted there, you know, I loved it. Slaka's a very delightful city, you know, lots of old buildings and parks and flowers and gipsy music. And you're perfectly entitled to dismiss your guide when you're not working, and get in lots of sightseeing. Incidentally, let me recommend the cathedral. It's just out of town, but the ikons are marvellous, and I always say you can't get into much trouble in a cathedral. There's a lot of very nice craftwork, some of it you can't bring out, but do watch out for the handmade embroidery. Your wife, you've got one, haven't you, will love it, and you might as well buy masses, since you can't bring any money out with you, you know. Ah, here's Georgina with your lovely coffee. And, look, here's a little booklet you might find useful. It's not actually for academic visitors, but it's full of wise saws and modern instances. You know, like the voltages, and so on.' 'Well, thank you,' says Petworth, taking the coffee, and *Helpful Hints for British Businessmen.* 'And if you should get into trouble,' says the grey-haired lady, 'we've telexed the British Embassy to forewarn them about your tour. Of course it's a very small embassy, Slaka's not exactly the centre of the world, but there's a second secretary there named Steadiman who does traffic accidents and a bit of culture. He'll give what help he can in any emergency. I've put the address in your papers, and you'll find the number in the Slaka telephone book, I expect. If they allow you to see one. Yes, I loved it there, marvellous posting. The only thing was not being able to talk to anyone. When I got back, I just talked and talked and talked, for twenty days. And ate chocolates. As you know, their economy's weak, and you don't find many delicacies.'

It is gloomy in the British Council office, with its dark old corners, on this exceptionally bleak day. The rain falls outside; and the sunshine is not shining in Petworth's heart either. He knows and has read the stories, of frontiers and guardposts, spies and imprisonments, beatings and treacheries, that we delight ourselves with in this dark world; and perhaps if he were a stronger character than he is, or is said to be, he would protest now that he does not really wish to be put into one. But then he knows he is not being put into one, rather a version of the old and familiar story, the lecturer's tale, with stock theme and minor variations. He drinks the coffee, the lady blows smoke: 'Well, I think that's really it,' she says, 'It's all common sense. No currency deals, no buggery, no political statements, no private talks, in bedrooms or public places, no documents, towel over the mirror. And do watch the ladies; I think you get the point.' 'Yes, I think so,' says Petworth, 'Beware of foreign parts.' 'Exactly,' says the lady, 'And just one more thing. We'd like a brief report when you get back. Purely on academic matters, state of the universities, and so on. Don't make your notes while you're there, of course, keep them in your noddle and then jot them down when you're back in, where is it, Bradford?' 'Yes, Bradford,' says Petworth. 'Well,' says the lady, standing up, and walking him toward the door of the dark office, 'Have a marvellous time, enjoy yourself. And do let us know when you return safely.' 'I will,' says Petworth, 'If I do.' 'Well, of course you will,' says the lady, 'It's a terrific experience. Georgina, he's going.' 'Bye,' says the secretary, picking up the file from the desk, 'Sorry about the coffee.'

And so, his face looking a little bleak, and not unlike the day, Petworth walks, in his damp mackintosh, out of the dark British Council office and across the corridor toward the rickety British Council lift, which stands waiting. At the back, a sign forbids more than six people to travel in it at once; ten laughing Japanese, blue airline bags hanging over their shoulders, cameras round their necks, beckon, excitedly to him to get inside. He steps into the elevator, as if into an unwanted future; around him, the Japanese now all begin to press conflicting buttons at the same time, with the result that the lift jogs up, jogs down, and visits every single floor in the building before it descends at last to street level, where

Petworth, *Helpful Hints for British Businessmen* held in his hand, steps out into Davies Street, amid the decorations and the gloom, and past the newspaper seller at the tube station, who is advertising some new strike for the summer silly season, to go on about his business, find his visa, check his ticket, make his plans. And it is in consequence of all these arrangements, or the lack of them, that he now finds himself in the dusty airport concourse of the airport at Slaka, standing against a pillar near the door marked NOI VA, his luggage tumbled by his feet, while the great crowd bobs around him, and the clock on the wall ticks away the time.

And away the time goes; it is thirty minutes since he came through the door, thirty minutes in which nothing has happened. The puce and magenta tag still dangles from the briefcase at his feet, a sterile sign, a meaningless meaning; the crowd mills, and faces swim into existence and then fade again. The other passengers of Comflug 155, the besuited men, the elderly ladies, have all long since come through the doors behind, to be welcomed and kissed, hugged and enfolded, laughed over and given flowers, taken off through the crowd, led through the exit doors, hurried off into the forecourt, removed into life. But nothing of this sort has happened to him; there has been no meeter to meet him, no greeter to greet him. Outside, beyond the dusty glass, the red sun has been steadily slipping down, and most of the blue buses in the parking lot have long since been driven away; in the coming dusk, the golden onion has ceased to be golden, but has begun to turn toward a shade of black. From Petworth's face too a certain glow has gone: the confident expectation he wore as he came out from the arrivals labyrinth has turned to doubt, and even to a tiny touch of fear. Things, of course, should be well; there is an organization behind all this. For somewhere, if the typist of the grey letter in his pocket has got matters clear, and translated the information correctly, if the dates are accurate and the British and Slakan calendars analogous, if he has himself comprehended all facts correctly and those with whom he has been dealing have done the same, then he should be passing now from the hands of Davies Street to the hands of Stalingradsimutu, from the closed file of the British Council to the open one of the Min'stratii Kulturi Komitet'iii

On the other hand, it is apparent that certain things could have gone wrong. He has, after all, come on a flight that, thanks to the Heathrow strike, many thought would not take off at all; he has come on a plane that has descended two hours late, and on top of that he has been delayed for an hour in the labyrinth of entry; he has arrived on an arrangement which, if one closely inspects – and by now he has very closely inspected – the grey letter, actually appoints no specific places of rendezvous, means of contact, type of encounter. The chances for confusion are many, and confusion in these matters is not unknown, even when travelling with the British Council, which he is not. The clock ticks on; he has been here forty minutes; the crowds, the noise, the dust rage around him in the long concourse. Airport lobbies all over the world are, if one passes through them quickly, as one usually does, much the same anywhere; but the more time one spends in them, the more minor variations grow apparent. Thus, at Schiphol, Amsterdam, there is a Diamond Shop; at Frankfurt one may find Dr Muller's Sex Shop; so in either place one may pick up that last-minute present she has always wanted. And other airports, when recalled offer a similar infinitude of delights; bars and banks, radio shops and ski shops, shoe-shine parlours and fast-food outlets, souvenir stalls and bookstores. By comparison, the arrivals hall at Slaka is simplicity itself; its services are minimal. There is, to one end, under the clock that ticks away his time, a small kiosk, displaying some pens, a few postcards, and some copies of *P'rtyii Populatiii*, with a sign over it saying *Litti*. In the centre, there is another stall, with a girl in a blue uniform behind it, writing on a form; the sign over this says COSMOPLOT. At the further end is a third stall, marked AVIS; it has a notice on it saying, in English, 'We Try Harder,' and no one on duty.

59

Beyond this, there is nothing. There is, for example, no telephone kiosk, from which, if he had money, he might call the Min'stratii Kulturi Komitet'iii on Stalingradsimutu and declare his arrival, though even that would presumably be unprofitable, since, as *Helpful Hints for British Businessmen* helpfully hints, banks, offices, and state trading organizations are closed on Saturdays and on Sundays, the day that this is. There is no place to get money, no bank or change desk (*camb'yii*) to which he can turn for local currency, though, if there was, it would, this being Sunday, probably be closed anyway. Having no money, there is no way he can take the airport bus to the Comflug offices in the city (no check-in facilities) where it is just possible that his meeter might even now be waiting, nor take a taxi to Stalingradsimutu, where he might find a guard or a porter who could find a host or a receiver who could find a hotel, or just sit on the steps. There is no place marked *Information*, where he might get some, or even *Enquiries*, where he might try to. Another sort of man might do something; grow angry, take action, leave arrivals and go to departures, there to try to change his return ticket and get back on the flight back to London, if there is one, or even go back through the door marked NOI VA and ask for assistance. But Petworth, in his dogged way, knows the sort of story he should be in, and he is prepared to wait and let it come to him: a story not of frontiers and guardposts, spies and imprisonments, beatings and treacheries, but a simple story, commensurate with his talents and limitations, a story of small hotels and large lecture rooms, of faculty lounges where grey professors talk about incomprehensible educational reforms which are hardly worth comprehending anyway, since they will be transformed again within the year, and bright girl assistants discuss the deeply dull theses they mean to write, and of occasional evening receptions where, drink in hand, Petworth can chatter brightly on about matters of common fascination, Hobson's Choice and Sod's Law, birds in the hand and frogs in the throat, a story of, in short, everyday life.

And so he stands there in the lobby of Slaka airport, with fifty minutes gone since his arrival, his luggage at his feet, with no meeter, no greeter, no money, no city, no hotel, no food, no bed, no lectures, no professors, no, in a sense, future. A fresh flow of passengers, men in dark suits, women in dark dresses, entire families of six or seven, all dressed in their Sunday best, a complete football team in their blue blazers, streams out through the door marked NOI VA. He turns to see; when he turns back, someone is standing in front of him. It is a small unshaven man, in dirty black trousers, grey shirt, exposed braces, a small denim cap. He smiles at Petworth, with a twisted smile: 'Private Tacs,' he says, bowing slightly. It seems to Petworth that Private Tacs is an odd emissary; but messages come everywhere in strange packets, and this is a proletarian country. 'Petworth,' says Petworth, holding out his hand. The man does not take it: he shakes his head. 'You like private tacs to Slaka?' he says, 'I take dollar, Anglisch pount, very cheap rate.' 'I see,' says Petworth, temptation flowering suddenly in his mind; a path to survival opens before him. 'You like stay private house?' asks the man, 'Very cheap, dollar only, pount.' Temptation grows, but currency offences are crimes against the state, attracting the most severe penalties: 'No, thank you,' says Petworth, standing solidly against his wooden pillar. 'Okay,' says the man, stepping back and disappearing, with a magical rapidity, into the crowd. A hope come, and then gone again, Petworth leans sadly back against the wooden pillar, staring up at the clock, which has now ticked away an entire hour since his arrival here.

But now another plane must have come in, for in front of him the crowd mills and eddies frenziedly; he stands there with his feet protectively set over his luggage as the people press busily by. Then in the mass a space appears; in the space he sees, some little distance away, someone standing there, halted, looking across, smiling at him questioningly. It is a lady, in her middle years; she wears a big black coat with a fake fur collar. Petworth smiles faintly in return; the lady looks and twists her hair, which appears to be a large blonde wig. Again it is not the sort of emissary that Petworth has expected, but letters come in strange envelopes, and this is a different land, under another ideology; he raises an eyebrow. The lady, smiling a little more, begins to step toward him through the crowd; as she does so, she allows her coat to fall open, revealing a very low-cut dress struggling to hold in a very large bust. Petworth stares; the lady, coming closer, puckers her mouth in the gesture of a kiss. It is now that Petworth suspects temptation of another kind; the whores in the main hotels and nightclubs should be avoided at all costs. The lady comes close now, wreathed in a pall of distinct scent; now she pushes her arm through his. 'Chaka, chaka?' she says. 'Sorry, my mistake,' says Petworth, trying to retrieve his arm, 'I thought you were . . .' 'Chuka, chaka, na?' asks the lady, 'For dollar, very cheap?' 'Na, na,' says Petworth firmly, this is not what he has come so far to exchange. 'Ah,' says the lady making a *moue*, 'Very nice.' 'I'm sure,' says Petworth, getting his arm free, 'But I'm an official visitor.' The lady goes into the crowd; exhausted by his temptations, Petworth leans back against the pillar. He is tired of false messages, and wants only a true one. Then he looks up, and realizes that it has very probably come.

For there, standing in front of him, smiling politely toward him, is a far more probable emissary: a middle-aged man with grey in his hair, refinement in his face, wearing a smart rectangular suit, with an honour of some sort in the button-hole, and over the suit a topcoat, which is loosely draped over his shoulders. 'Feder,' says the man, looking at him. 'Ah, Petworth,' says Petworth. 'Please, Feder,' says the man. 'From the Min'stratii Kulturi?' asks Petworth. 'Ah, Min'stratii Kulturi Komitet'iii?' says the man, 'Man, na. Feder? Cueta?' 'I don't understand,' says Petworth. 'Ah,' says the man, raising a finger; then he lifts his hand into the air, and seems to scribble with it. 'Oh, you have a message for me?' asks Petworth. 'Na, na, not a message,' says the man, scribbling again in the air. 'A letter?' asks Petworth. 'Na,' says the man, shaking his head.

'You have a book?' says Petworth, 'A story, a history?' 'Na, ma,' says the man, encouragingly. 'A poem, a play, a novel,' says Petworth. 'How you write?' says the man, 'Für schriften?' 'A pencil, a brush,' says Petworth. 'Na, stylo,' says the man. 'What, a pen?' asks Petworth. 'Da, da,' says the man, with delight, 'A pen. Please, your pen.' 'Ja, ja,' says Petworth, agleam with the glow of literate contact, and he reaches into his pocket and produces his silver Parker ballpoint: an old travelling companion, and the true author of so many of his lectures. 'Ah, da,' says the man, gratefully, taking the pen, 'English so hard. I do not really speak. So, slibob. In our tongue, thank you.' And then the man bows, smiles, holds up the silver pen, and moves off into the crowd with it. The afterglow of literate contact remains with Petworth for a moment; then, 'Here, my pen,' he shouts, hurrying off after the loose overcoat, which is disappearing, with some rapidity, around the corner of the kiosk that is marked COSMOPLOT.

Another new flight has evidently come in: a busy new flow of passengers – old ladies, men in ties, an entire orchestra carrying their instruments in cases – streams from the doors marked NOI VA and blocks Petworth's way as he hurries in pursuit. Petworth stumbles over double basses, falls over euphonium cases; when he reaches the corner of the stall marked COSMOPLOT, the man in the topcoat has quite disappeared. The stall is decorated with posters of peasants dancing in blousy costumes, the women in trousers, the men in skirts; of a market place with a high clock tower in it; of pinnacled castles high on crags in some Transylvanian wonderland, where all stories are said to start. The girl in the blue uniform still writes away behind the desk at her document; as Petworth comes up to her, she looks up with suspicion. 'Did you see a man go by, with an overcoat over his shoulders?' Petworth asks, breathing hard. 'A man? You want a man?' asks the girl. 'He's taken my pen,' says Petworth. 'Oh, yes?' says the girl, returning to her document, 'Do you say a man has taken your pen? Well, I hope you do not want to borrow a pen of me. I have only one pen, and it is an official one.' 'No,' says Petworth, 'I don't want your pen. I want to find that man and get mine back.' 'Oh,' says the girl, 'Do you tell that this man steals your pen?' 'He took it away from me,' says Petworth. 'Well, it is not my business,' says the girl, 'I am not policeman. You must go to that policeman over there and make a document, if you like to.' The girl points – with her pen, not his pen – to one of the blue armed men, who stands a little way away from the Cosmoplot desk, his Kalashnikov automatic rifle over his shoulder, talking to a girl in a grey coat, with a shoulderbag.

'Yes, I see,' says Petworth. 'Of course, if you do this, you will spend many hours at the police house, and they will make very many questions of you,' says the girl, 'Perhaps it is not so important, just for one pen.' 'It was a Parker,' says Petworth. 'Also I wonder if that man truly steals your pen,' says the girl, still writing, 'In our country such crimes are not permitted. Perhaps he likes to think you gave it to him. Perhaps if they ask him he tells you try to change it for something illegal, for dollar. Often when such things happen it is best to buy a new pen. You can buy one at this place over here, do you see it, it is marked *Litti*? There they can sell you pen. Now, do you see how busy I am? I must write on my document with my pen.' 'I don't suppose,' says Petworth, struck with an idea, 'you've had any messages for me? My name's Petworth. I'm an official visitor, and I've not been met.' 'Are you turstii?' asks the girl. 'Am I thirsty?' asks Petworth. 'No,' says the girl, tapping with her pen on the desk, 'Are you turstii? Do you make here a tour by Cosmoplot?' 'No,' says Petworth, 'I'm an official visitor.' 'Then, please, not here,' says the girl, 'Here for turstii only.' 'You can't suggest any way I can get in touch with my hosts?' asks Petworth, pleadingly. 'Not here,' says the girl, bending her eyes to her writing, 'You are in wrong place. And now you see I am busy.' For a crowd of large middle-aged women, most of them with dyed blonde hair and garish plastic luggage, have suddenly swarmed around the stall, picking up leaflets and asking many questions in Russian. 'Well, thank you,' says Petworth hopelessly, turning back into the crush.

An hour and a quarter has passed now since he first came through the door marked NOI VA, a door which opens again, to emit many more new passengers: elderly men, young ladies in headscarves, a whole bevy of priests in cowls, wearing grizzled patriarchal beards. Petworth stands, looking two ways: somewhere ahead of him in the crush is his silver pen, somewhere behind him his piled luggage, the blue suitcase the briefcase of lectures, his yellow Heathrow bag, his grey overcoat. Beyond the moving throng is the pillar where he has stood for so long, waiting for his meeter to meet him, his greeter to greet him. Jostling the old men, pushing at the priests, he pushes his way back to his territory. The pillar still stands there, with a space around it; it is only his luggage – the suitcase, the briefcase, the yellow bag, the grey coat – which has gone. He looks around, walks to the next pillar, walks back, and knows the low point of human fortune. He is here, in a foreign country, under a changed ideology; but, like some old car abandoned on the motorway, he has been stripped of all his functional equipment. He has no money, no hotel, no friends, no contacts, no pen, no property, no lectures, no books, no clothes, and, in a sense, no future at all. For a moment he thinks, not knowing what to do. 'You will spend many hours at the police house, and they will make very many questions of you,' the Cosmoplot girl has said, but questions are all that are left. Petworth turns and walks slowly through the moving flow of people, the black-dressed ladies, the dark-suited men, the priests in their orthodox robes, toward the armed man with the Kalashnikov, and the police house where they ask the questions.

III

Just behind the Cosmoplot stall, the armed man still stands there, talking to the girl in the grey coat. 'Please,' says Petworth to him, 'Do you speak English? Someone has stolen my luggage.' 'Va?' says the armed man, turning, his nose hard and fierce, his gun swinging on its short strap, 'Va?' 'My luggage,' cries Petworth, 'Stolen!' 'Please,' says the girl in grey, 'He does not understand you. But I know how to interpret. Describe please these luggages to me, and I will explain you.' 'Thank you,' says Petworth, turning gratefully to the girl, who has a white tense face, a mohair hat on her head, a shoulderbag over her shoulder; and in her hands and at her feet a blue suitcase, a bulging briefcase, a heavy overcoat, and a plastic bag which says 'Say Hello to the Good Buys at Heathrow.' 'What consists your luggages?' says the girl, patiently, 'Please explain it. He is a policeman and likes to help.' 'That's my luggage, there,' says Petworth, 'You've got it.' 'These?' says the girl, staring at him, 'No, these are not your luggages.' 'I left them over there, by that pillar,' says Petworth. 'But they are not your luggages,' says the girl, firmly, 'They are the luggages of another. They belong to Professor Petworth.' 'Exactly,' says Petworth, 'Me.' 'He comes from England to make some lectures,' says the girl. 'Yes,' says Petworth, 'I'm Petworth.' 'Oh, do you like to think so?' says the girl, looking at him, and laughing, 'Well, I am sorry, you are not.' 'I'm not?' asks Petworth. 'No, really you are not,' says the girl, 'I have his photograph, sent from Britain. Do you think you are that man?' Petworth looks at the photograph; it shows a large round balding face, of late middle age, wearing heavy glasses, and underneath it the legend *Dr W. Petworth*. 'Well, no,' Petworth admits, 'That's someone else.' 'I have looked three hour for this man,' says the girl, 'Now I find his luggage. But it is not you. You do not even look like a professor.' 'I'm not, yet,' says Petworth, 'But I am Petworth.' 'You are not,' says the girl, 'Please go away.'

'Wait, I think I know who that is,' says Petworth, pointing at the photograph, 'There's another Petworth, who teaches sociology at the University of Watermouth, I get his mail sometimes. He's not very well known.' 'And you, who are you?' asks the girl; the armed man steps nearer. 'Well, I'm an even less well-known Petworth than he is,' Petworth admits, 'But I'm the one they sent.' The armed man pokes Petworth with his fingers: 'Dikumenti,' he says. It is a happy intervention, for out comes the grey letter from the Min'stratii Kulturi Komitet'iii, which the girl seizes. 'Oh, oh, yes, you are the one, really!' she cries, 'Oh, Petwurt, you have confused me, you do not look like yourself. And there I waited for two hour at INVAT, to bring you past the custom, but I looked for that man with the big head. Well, no matter, it is just a small confusion, quickly solved.' 'Then you're from the Ministratii Kulturi Komitet'iii?' asks Petworth. 'Oh, Petwurt,' the girl says admiringly, looking at him with her white, saddened face, 'You are in Slaka just three hour and already you speak our language. Actually we say it so: Min'stratii. Do you see the difference? You intrude a redundant "i." But that is natural error for an English. Yes, I am from there, your guide for this tour. My name is Marisja Lubijova, Oh, dear, that is hard for you. Do you think you can say it?' 'Yes,' says Petworth, 'Marisja Lubijova.' 'Very good,' says the girl, 'But I think it is too long for you. You call me Mari, like all my good friends. And in Slaka it is your first time? I don't think so, you speak our language so well.' 'Yes, my first time,' says Petworth. 'Then I welcome you to my country,' says Lubijova, 'Do we do it the English way? How do you do, shake the hand, I wish you very nice visit?' 'What's the Slaka way?' asks Petworth, 'In customs they gave me a comradely hug.'

Marisja Lubijova stares at him: 'Oh, I see, Petwurt,' she says, 'You are only just come but already you want everything. Well, of course, the Min'stratii will not be outdone.' 'I just meant . . .' Petworth begins, but his words choke; for two arms come firmly round his neck; he is tugged, forward, downward, into Lubijova's grey coat. This time it is nicer: no male sweat, but the scent of healthy soap; no belt of hard leather, but a delightful soft mammary cushion; no prodding male groin, but a better mesh of bodily economy, a fairer rate of exchange. 'Camarad'aki,' Lubijova cries, thrusting him back, 'So welcome in Slaka! Oh, dear, Petwurt, your face goes quite red. Perhaps you are shy, like all English.' 'It seemed the right colour for the country,' says Petworth. 'I think you like our customs,' says Lubijova, 'That means you will make good visit. Now, I just tell this policemen all problems are solved. Please take some of your luggages, and we go somewhere. Do you like a nice hotel of the old kind, I hope so?' 'Yes,' says Petworth, sensing he is back on the old course of things, 'I do.' They begin to go, Petworth carrying his recovered luggage, walking with his recovered guide, toward the evening light, the doors marked OTVAT. 'Oh, dear, you must think I am bad guide,' says Lubijova, 'Did you think no one comes for you? I think you did, but you shouldn't. Of course someone finds you, you are important visitor. Everywhere people are waiting to see you, and expecting remarkable talks. Often there are confusions in these places, but no matter. Now we find a very nice taxi. Oh, I please you are here.'

But it is now, as they come up to the doors marked OTVAT, and are about to step outside, that Petworth realizes that someone has been watching him – indeed has been inspecting him, and the process of meeting and greeting, for some time. By the entrance doors, against the light, a small dark-eyed man, in his thirties, with a neat curve of beard round the line of his chin, stands, arms folded. He wears a white sweater with a small animal-like symbol sportively decorating the left nipple, sharp black trousers with a white chalk stripe. His bird-like face holds a large curved pipe; it is a face Petworth has caught sight of several times before, in the tidal movement of the crowd, feeling he almost knows it, though not how, or where, or when. Now the face responds, beams at him, removes its pipe, moves toward him, speaks. 'Well, my good old friend Dr

68

Petworth,' it says, 'I see you are getting very well received. But always with the ladies you are lucky. And how are you?' A hand comes out, which Petworth shakes, having put down his luggage: 'Very well, thank you,' he says. 'Of course,' says the man, 'And the lovely Mrs Petworth, what of her? Perhaps you have just left her, I hope she does not put on some weights. When thin, her figure is very good. But that is a lady who must watch always the plates.' 'Very well also,' says Petworth, staring at the face grinning at him. 'You must not let such ladies spoil themselves,' says the man, 'Often I think of her. And of course of wonderful Cambridge. How is it these days? Of it I have the very best memories.' 'Cambridge?' says Petworth, 'Oh, Cambridge is very well too.'

Beside him, Lubijova impatiently shifts her shoulderbag; Petworth stares at the face in front of him, with its sharp little grin, its bird-like look, and finds that certain small things are beginning to come back to him. There is the place, Cambridge, England, in the summer, the sun shining, the greenfly busy, the language-school season at its peak, the streets full of noisy youths from many cultures, speaking multi-lingua; a long room, hot and sunfilled, packed with easy chairs, windows open, admitting the noise of student transistors playing pop music on punts and the bright cries of blonde Swedish girls as they fall, with great regularity, into the river; at the front of the room, at a podium, Petworth himself, lecturing on some linguistic crux or other; somewhere at the back of it, in a chair by a door, this same sharp face, with its bird-like eyes and curve of beard, moving busily, nodding, grimacing, beaming at wit, shaking from side to side in dissent, nodding up and down in affirmation. The time is vague: this could be any one of a long succession of British Council summer schools, annually held, where university teachers from universities abroad are invited, to bring themselves up to date with contemporary writing, and criticism, and linguistics, and the detailed stuff and custom of English life, like going regularly into pubs. For a number of years now, Petworth has done his stint there, staying for a few days, lecturing on such questions as whether the mind is, or is not, a *tabula rasa* before language enters it, drinking in rooms, wandering in Heffer's, bringing with him his dark wife – who, glad of the chance to leave domestic routine, and Bradford, comes to explore the wickerwork of Joshua Taylor, the cramped flowerprint of Laura Ashley, the wine bars, the college chapels, the mirrored, musical boutiques.

Over the years Petworth has met many students, made many friends, there; but, once remembered, this one can only be recalled as memorable – for his sharpness, wryness, slyness, for his interventions, his omnispresence, his readiness with an issue at a lecture's end, his demanding face looking over the plates in the college hall at dinner. 'What a place!' says the man now, at Slaka, 'Of it I have the most extraordinary recollections. But especially I recall some excellent literary conversations we are making together. Oh, Dr Petworth, you were acerbic then, I remember, quite caustic. We look forward to those qualities again. I hope you don't forget my name, my good old friend. Plitplov.' 'Of course, Mr Plitplov,' cries Petworth, 'How nice to see you again.' 'Well, Doctor Plitplov now, you will please to learn,' says Plitplov, putting his head down in humility, 'Things change for us all, for the better or the worse. And thanks in no little part to you. Perhaps you remember a certain small writing – small, that is, for you, large for me – you assisted with? To you I owe many important footnotes, references I cannot at all obtain at the libraries of Slaka. You know for us books are a problem, we must fight to see them. But you are very kind, and that work has appeared now in my country, to create, if I do not be immodest, some stir.' 'Splendid,' says Petworth. 'Of course I reserve a copy for you,' says Plitplov, 'And you find in its openings acknowledgement of your contributions, a gratitude for scholarly and not-so-scholarly assistances. Also to Mrs Petworth. I do not overlook her great help to me.' 'Really, she was a great help to you?' asks Petworth. 'Indeed,' says Plitplov, 'what a fine person.'

In the lobby at Slaka, Petworth thinks once more of Cambridge, and something else comes back: an occasion in the courtyard of a pub, probably the Eagle, on a summer's night, with cockscombed punks and louche youths from the language schools drinking and sitting on the cobbles all round, and the fingers of his dark wife tapping in irritation on an empty gin glass, while this same engrossed face has held them both and discussed, at great length, over the potato crisps, an enterprise in the linguistic analysis of nineteenth-century fiction, something on the imagery of food and drink in ... 'Wasn't it Trollope?' Petworth asks. 'Ah, my friend, I see your recall is total,' says Plitplov, beaming, 'Trollope, your great and too-much-neglected novelist of the bourgeois realist era, now I think over. Well, I like to believe I have restored his interest, secured his reputation again.' 'Good,' says Petworth, 'Splendid. Tell me, I've forgotten: do you teach here at the university in Slaka?' Plitplov takes a pouch from his pocket; slowly he lifts vegetable matter from it and deposits it thoughtfully into the bowl of his large curved pipe. 'You might say I hold certain posts in my country of pedagogic kind,' he says after a moment, 'In fact you also might say it is not accident you are invited to come here. Evidently some influential person has spoken somewhere of your talents, had a finger in that pie. Perhaps a person not so very far from you now.' 'I'm most grateful,' says Petworth. 'Well, if your visit here is very good,' says Plitplov, 'I hope you will remember that person very nicely, and perhaps give a little more help. If not so good, then remember that also others have been involved.' 'I'm looking forward to it,' says Petworth, 'It's my first visit.' 'I know it,' says Plitplov, 'I have researched you, quite a little bit. I have some schemes for you, plans of every kind. Also I know many good lectures will come now our way.'

Marisja Lubijova has been standing, fidgeting, at Petworth's side. 'Let us find now your taxi,' she says, 'They wait you at the hotel.' 'Oh, excuse please,' says Plitplov, turning, beaming, 'This pleasant young lady. You have not introduced me. Perhaps she is your guide. How is it, when I see you, you have always the most attractive female companies?' 'Oh, please excuse me,' says Petworth, 'Yes, this is Miss . . .' But it is too late: Plitplov has already bent forward from the waist and has seized Miss Lubijova's hand. Now he is putting it to his lips and lightly kissing the back of it – a grace-note, Petworth suddenly remembers, that went down exceedingly well, like some others, with his dark wife when Plitplov made just this gesture in Cambridge. 'Plitplov,' says Plitplov. 'Lubijova,' says Lubijova, 'I think we perhaps meet somewhere before.' 'Before?' cries Plitplov, 'Oh, no, not possible. One does not forget to meet such a nice young lady.' 'I think so,' says Lubijova. 'No,' says Plitplov, 'Perhaps you know my small articles in the newspaper. Or perhaps you read a book of me.' 'Book of me?' says Lubijova, 'Do you really say "book of me"? And there is rumour you like to teach English. Yes, I think there was a time once when I did have to read a book of you.' 'Oh, please!' cries Plitplov, slapping his brow with the heel of his hand in a theatrical fashion, 'Did I say "book of me"? Oh, my good old friend, do you see how much your arrival has excited me? You know from Cambridge my English is well-nigh faultless, better than many British. But emotion can have such an effect.' 'Well, I think your good old friend wants to go now to his hotel,' says Lubijova, briskly, 'I think he is quite tired of his journey.' 'Ah, now, that is interesting question,' says Plitplov, turning his bird-like eyes on her, 'Is our good friend tired *of* his journey? Or is he perhaps rather tired *by* his journey? There are two different things. Well, we have here expert in such questions, a dab hand. Let us ask him. Pronounce for us, please, Dr Petworth.'

Tired or not, Petworth senses a diplomatic crux when he meets one, calling for the best exercise of his talents. 'Yes, fascinating, isn't it?' he says, there in the airport at Slaka, 'One of those delightful English cases where two idioms meet and both are relevant. Yes, I'm indeed tired *by* my journey, and I'm also tired *of* my journey.' 'And wants to get taxi to his hotel,' says Lubijova. Taking his pipe from his mouth, Plitplov stares at Petworth. 'Yes, I recall,' he says, 'Always you like to be diplomat, to please everyone. This was noticed in Cambridge. Of course not always everyone is pleased. But, excuse me, I am not considerate. You like to go to the hotel. My dear young lady, do you find for that purpose a taxi. Meantime I stay here and amuse our tired and diplomatic guest.' 'I expect you will amuse very much,' says Lubijova, hitching her shoulderbag high on her shoulder. Then she goes through the glass doors and out into the world outside: Petworth and Plitplov, two gentlemen scholars, stare out through the dirty and finger-printed glass as she goes across the forecourt to yet another armed man, who stands in the road, invigilating the cars and the taxis, the Ladas and the Wartburgs, that pick up and put down. 'Oh, this is good guide,' says Plitplov, pointing with his pipe, 'Sometimes the guide is not so suited. Sometimes it is an old lady or a man. That is not half so amusing.' 'No,' says Petworth. 'Also, look, she treats you like important visitor,' says Plitplov, 'She makes that police stop a taxi for you, so you do not wait in a line with the people.' 'How nice,' says Petworth. Outside the militiaman raises his baton, and blows whistles; an orange taxi screeches to a stop. Inside, Plitplov turns suddenly, so that his back is to the window. 'Of course with that one we must both be very careful,' says Plitplov, staring at Petworth, and putting a forefinger to his nose.

'Really?' says Petworth. 'I think you notice my small ruse to send her away,' says Plitplov, chuckling, 'Of course she is very suspicious of me, because I have come here to meet you.' 'Is she? Why?' asks Petworth. 'Well, of course,' says Plitplov, turning and looking through the window, 'I do not come so many miles to the airport just to see those planes go up and come down. I do not wait here three hour just to exchange some little memories. No, in my country, we have a saying. Certain matters are certain matters.' 'I see,' says Petworth. 'This is not your very nice Cambridge,' says Plitplov, 'There you can play your games of the mind, I remember them. Does the reality exist, or is it just a construct of the head? Here we know some answers to that. There is reality everywhere, the art is to survive.' 'Yes, I see,' says Petworth. 'Do you notice how that one pretends we have met before?' asks Plitplov. 'Hadn't you?' asks Petworth, 'Why did she do that?' 'Of course,' says Plitplov, sucking on his pipe, which fumes like a small bonfire, 'She likes to find all out about me. She has her duties. Why do they give to her such a job, to escort an important intellectual of the West?' 'I don't know,' says Petworth. 'Well, I know some things of her,' says Plitplov, 'No matter how. Slaka is small city. Everyone knows a little of someone else. Her father is a high party member.' 'What duties?' asks Petworth. 'Oh, there is always a way to embarrass everyone,' says Plitplov, 'For example, I have certain positions. Here, with positions, there are always enemies. Someone works to replace you. Of course these things are not done directly. One approaches always a matter by a corner.' 'Yes, I understand,' says Petworth.

'So you must be very cautious,' says Plitplov, 'It is for instance well you do not say anything about me to this girl. Perhaps I am indiscreet already. Now they know I am once in Cambridge.' 'Yes,' says Petworth. 'And then with you,' says Plitplov, 'I have said you are my friend. But how do I know your intentions? Perhaps you will say in your lectures many bad things about my country, or use ideologies that are not correct. Perhaps you have some orders.' 'Not at all,' says Petworth. 'Remember, I have pulled some strings for you at a very high level. If you commit some wrongs here, that will be bad also for Plitplov,' says Plitplov. 'I don't think you need worry,' says Petworth, 'They're very ordinary lectures.' 'Or if you make some wrong friends,' says Plitplov, 'Well, a wink to a blind horse, as you say. Or is it a nod to a blind horse?' 'It probably doesn't matter,' says Petworth, 'If the horse is blind.' 'Even to talk here to a foreigner at an airport, that is a risk for me,' says Plitplov. 'Surely not,' says Petworth, turning – to see that, beside them, there now stands another blue armed man.

74

Plitplov's face whitens; the armed man speaks to him. 'He likes to see our documents,' says Plitplov, 'Do not worry. A small matter.' The armed man inspects the papers of both of them. 'I have broken some small rule,' says Plitplov, knocking out his pipe into his hand, 'They are such bureaucrats here.' 'What rule?' asks Petworth, as the armed man, apparently satisfied, goes off. 'Oh,' says Plitplov, 'Not to smoke in public place. But I explain him I am with important government visitor who likes me to smoke.' 'I see,' says Petworth. 'You observe now one must be here an artist in relations to survive,' says Plitplov, 'Luckily I am such artist. I do not embarrass you, I trust? You don't think, my good old friend tries to compromise me?' 'Not at all,' says Petworth. 'Good,' says Plitplov, 'Because I think we can make both some profits from this visit. I expect you will find me by your side quite often.' 'How nice,' says Petworth. 'But do not surprise if sometimes you do not see me,' says Plitplov, 'Or if we meet and I say I do not know you. I like to take care, I have a nervous wife, who cannot live without me. Now, tell me please, the transformational grammar of Chomsky, that still convinces you? Or do you join the army of structuralism, which has cut such a wide swathe in the thinkings of the West?'

But that large and crucial question is never answered: for, at Petworth's side, Marisja Lubijova, in her grey coat, is quietly standing once more. Behind her stands a small man in a plastic black cap and a grey shirt. 'Oh, my dear young lady, so soon you are back?' cries Plitplov, turning in apparent surprise, 'We are having such good talk about optative counter-factuals in elegiac works. But I think we continue it now in your taxi.' 'I do not think it goes in your direction,' says Lubijova, firmly, 'It is a very small taxi that goes to the hotel only.' 'At least I bring your luggage, my friend,' says Plitplov, bending to grasp Petworth's baggage, which now dangles lightly on the ends of his fingertips. 'The driver comes for them,' says Lubijova. 'Oh, please, I have such strong arms,' says Plitplov, striding out toward the door that is marked OTVAT. 'I am afraid your good old friend is a nuisance,' says Lubijova, with a frowning brow, a lady with a tough side, following behind. 'Quite a character,' says Petworth, opening the door to let out the taxi driver, and then colliding very briefly with a tall, neatly besuited man, carrying a furled umbrella, who has come running from a brown Ford Cortina parked at the curbside on some urgent and frantic errand. But it is a small delay; Petworth is out now, beyond the terminal, in the world to come. The asphalt spreads, but beyond is nature: fields, trees, the jagged curve of the mountains. A football team is getting into one blue bus, an entire orchestra with its instruments into another, a row of grizzled priests into a third: the sun is dipping, the evening light growing blue, the low-watt forecourt lights coming on, the wind sharpening. There are two distinct smells in the air: a rustic odour of rot and dung, and an acrid stench of industrial pollution.

Down the forecourt, a small orange taxi stands, its rear door politely held open by a topcoated armed man. 'Oh, this is a very big taxi,' Plitplov is saying, 'I think we can all get in it.' 'It goes to Hotel Slaka,' says Lubijova. 'By an interesting coincidence, I must go just by there to a chemist, with a recipe for my wife,' says Plitplov. Petworth follows his two contending guides. He is tired, *of* his journey, *by* his journey; he feels dismantled and deconstructed, like some fictional sentence; but he has companions, directions, somewhere to go. The scented smell from Plitplov's gross pipe, the orderly common sense of Lubijova, a good if tricky guide, not an old lady or a man, which is not so amusing, reassures, familiarizes. The taxi is a small home from home, a domesticated place: its vinyl upholstery is protected by furry blue nylon covers, with pink cushions on top of them; from stereo speakers in the two corners of the back window comes the stirring chorus of some massed choir unable to contain itself. 'Slibob,' says the armed man, ushering him into the rear seat. Meanwhile Plitplov and Lubijova are thudding his luggage into the trunk; from them, over the noise of the music, comes a familiar noise, the sound of a quarrel, intimate, violent, almost marital. Then, to his left, Marisja Lubijova slams into the taxi, her shoulderbag swinging furiously. A moment later, and the right-hand door opens; Plitplov gets in, his bird-like face grinning. Pushed to the middle, knees high over the transmission shaft, Petworth suddenly finds his head neatly caught at that point between the two stereo speakers where it becomes a perfect booming receiver. 'Oh, this is very nice music, do you like it?' asks Lubijova to his left, 'It is a military song of the people.' 'Oh, no, such noise, too much, I think,' says Plitplov to his right, 'I think we like it turned off, don't you, Dr Petworth?' He is tired, very tired, but always the diplomat: 'It's very nice,' he says, 'But perhaps he could turn it down a little.'

Lubijova taps the shoulder of the driver, sitting in front in his plastic black cap; he lowers the sound and roars the engine. At the same moment another sound replaces it: a sort of demented tapping, as if someone were beating fingers on the roof. The car begins to move; simultaneously Petworth notices a pair of human hands scraping at the glass of the window, beside Plitplov's face. 'Someone is here,' says Plitplov, winding down the window a little; a small hand wriggles in, waving in the fingers a bright silvery pointed object, looking like . . . 'It's my pen,' says Petworth. 'Slibob, slibob,' shouts a voice through the window; the little creased face of the man in the topcoat beams in through the glass as he runs along beside the moving car. 'Slibob,' Petworth calls back. Plitplov turns the pen in his hand, and stares at it: 'You lent to him this, your good pen?' he asks. 'Yes, I did,' says Petworth, taking it. 'Well, I think you are lucky he brings it back to you,' says Plitplov, 'That is Parker, very good.' 'Of course he turns it back,' says Lubijova, 'You don't think in our country the people will steal?' Meanwhile Petworth, with difficulty, turns to look through the rear window. The topcoated man, still waving, stands on the forecourt; he has been joined by a companion, a big, fine, fair-haired young woman, in boots and a batik dress. 'Oh, really, you believe our people do not steal,' says Plitplov, 'Do you read it in the newspaper?' 'He brings it back,' says Lubijova, crossly. 'Because he sees this is important government visitor, with a guide,' says Plitplov. 'I hope you don't criticize your country to a foreigner,' says Lubijova. 'I think this is intelligent person who has been in Cambridge and can make up his own mind,' says Plitplov. The intelligent person who has been to Cambridge stares on, through the back window: under the forecourt, the couple wave and wave. Then they stop, for a third person joins them, and holds them in conversation. He is familiar, this third person; he is the besuited man with whom Petworth had just a moment ago collided, at the door marked OTVAT, as he came out and the man went in. He still carries his furled umbrella, but for some mysterious reason he has added to it a large sack.

The taxi stops at a sign; the besuited man raises his umbrella in the air and, carrying his sack, starts to run, in pursuit of it. The driver roars the engine, and swings round a corner. Behind, the man, indeed all three of the wavers, have dropped from sight. It occurs to Petworth that this small drama is a matter worthy of comment; but he is tired, tired of the journey, tired by the journey, and in any case his companions have other matters to discuss. Having left the public space of the airport, the taxi driver has tuned to another station: the sound of woodchoppers' music is replaced by a jazz track, by someone called Henry James and His Imps. 'Ah, Western,' says Plitplov. 'It is decadent,' says Lubijova. 'You like it?' asks Plitplov. 'You don't want it,' says Lubijova. 'Of course he wants it,' says Plitplov. 'I don't think so,' says Lubijova. In front of the taxi, a long, thin, straight road lies ahead, pointing toward the horizon and the mountains; along the way, a high stack of orange smoke rises like a marker from the tips of the chimneys of the power station. 'Tell me,' says Petworth, rousing himself from lethargy to minor conversation, 'What's the rate of exchange here?' 'You don't have some money?' asks Lubijova. 'You like change?' asks the taxi driver, turning round in his black plastic cap. 'You know,' says Plitplov chuckling,

78

'We have here a saying: why is Slaka like the United States? Because in the United States you can criticize America, and in Slaka you can criticize America also. And in the United States you cannot buy anything with vloskan, and in Slaka you cannot buy anything with vloskan also.' 'You criticize your country,' says Lubijova. 'I make a joke,' says Plitplov, 'Really I do not criticize my country.' 'Of course, it is a crime,' says Lubijova.

The bitter chatter goes on, trouble to the right of him, trouble to the left. In the middle, Petworth sits, holding on tightly to the plastic seat covers. In front of him points the long straight road, directed straight at the jagged rim of the mountains. And ahead too there lies, he knows, function, definition, who are you, why are you here, what do you think, why do you think it – the questions that, if he can summon up enough belief or identity to do so, he has come all this way, over two time-zones and to new skies, to answer. Somewhere behind him, back at home, there is the identity that he should be able to summon up those answers from, if only he can remember what it was, or if he ever really had it. Caught in the fragile universe of his own gloom, Petworth bounces, over the hard transmission shaft, up and down, up and down, staring forward at the red setting sun that, falling over the mountains, gilds the long straight road ahead.

3 – ACCOM.

I

As the travel texts say, the journey of 8km/5mi from the airport
to central Slaka offers indeed a journey of the most interesting
contrasts. Here, on the famed Vronopian plain, one may see
peasants in typical costume following the rural praxis of times
immemorial; also evidence of the industrial achievement of this
energetic and reformist people. In the taxi, bouncing over the
transmission arch between the muscular sporty thigh of Plitplov
and the soft silky-textured leg of Lubijova, Petworth stares out.
The straight, thin, rutted road ahead, pointing to the power
station chimneys, the far-off mirage-like towers of what must
be workers' apartments, the glaring red of the sun, runs between
gnarled old trees with heavily whitewashed trunks; beyond the
trees, large muddy unhedged fields stretch out vacantly. In the
fields are strange shapes, the shapes of haystacks that look like
round loaves of bread; among them, white ducks wander freely.
By the roadside, here and there, sit, in scattered groups, a few
low wooden unpainted houses, very weathered, their window-
holes covered with mesh screens; round the houses are small
fenced yards where vegetables grow, geese cackle, a child or two
plays, dogs bark, and strange semaphoric arms, tilted over
wooden uprights, rise up – the poles, presumably, of wells. At
the side of the long, straight, rutted road, a few peasants, men
in blue overalls, old ladies in black, bundles on their heads,
walk slowly along; these leap suddenly into ditches or deep
puddles as the taxi, klaxon hooting, comes up to them at high

speed. Radio blaring, black plastic cap at a rakish angle, the little driver screws his eyes up to face the red sun and pushes down the accelerator. Out of the sun, detail comes up very suddenly: like the ancient horsedrawn farm-cart, laden with hay, topped off by two lounging children, which is suddenly in front of them, causing the driver to brake violently, Petworth to bounce high in the air over the transmission.

'So your flight on Comflug, very good, I think,' says Lubijova, the thigh to his left. 'I hope your mother is very well,' says Dr Plitplov, 'You mention her to me once.' Nudging forward, the driver inspects the red glare round the obstacle. 'And many strikes now, in Britain, I believe,' says Lubijova, 'Here of course our people like to work. They have the moral for it.' 'Also no food if they don't,' says Plitplov, chuckling, the thigh to his right. Now the taxi swerves and swings round the cart; Petworth bounces again as the wheels hit the rutted road-edge; from behind there comes a shrill whinnying of horses. 'In the West now, many economic difficulties,' says Lubijova, 'What a pity it makes late your plane.' 'I'm sorry you both had such a long wait,' says Petworth, seeing ahead of them now a long, long line of grey trucks with huge tailboards, on which are painted white numbers and Cyrillic letters, and which is moving very slowly toward Slaka. 'They told me your flight is cancel,' says Plitplov. 'I hope you did not believe it,' says Lubijova, 'They know nothing, those people.' On the other side of the narrow road, another line of great grey trucks, with big blunt noses and small shining headlights, has appeared, moving toward them with equal slowness. 'Notice please in our fields we make a very good harvest,' says Lubijova, as the taxi driver, adjusting his plastic cap, begins an ambitious overtaking manoeuvre, cutting in between the first and second of the oncoming trucks in order to pass the last of the ongoing ones. 'Your very nice wife, she still smokes the little cigars?' asks Plitplov, as the driver goes on to cut between the third and fourth of the oncoming trucks, to overtake the next to last of the outgoing ones.

81

'The rain affects our production, but is still a record,' says Lubijova, pointing out of the window. 'Her name is Lottie, I think,' says Plitplov, chuckling reminiscently, and beginning to stuff his curved pipe with garbage, 'Always I found her the most amusing company.' The driver is overtaking again; stones explode in the wheel arches, dust rises, headlamps flash, horns blare, Petworth bounces, up and down, up and down, his head hitting the roof. 'Isn't he driving rather fast?' he asks, shutting his eyes. 'Here we like in cars to go with a little adventure,' says Plitplov. 'Also it is good, because we are late at the airport,' says Lubijova. 'It is a very boring airport,' says Plitplov, 'Not as in the West.' 'I do not think it boring,' says Lubijova, 'I found a seat and read almost one hundred pages of Hemingway. Comrade Petwurt, please. Your eyes are shut and here is coming Slaka, don't you like to see it?' Petworth opens his eyes: the sun's glare has died, the grey trucks have all disappeared, the road in front has widened out and is busy. To the left the big power station stands up, with its vast metal chimneys; webs of power line thread away from it in every direction across glinting marshes. There are low factories at the roadside, surrounded by high fences and barred gates, each one having a board outside with a list of figures on it, topped with hammer and sickle. 'Our state industrial enterprises' says Lubijova, 'Do you see their remarkable figures of production?' 'Really, Hemingway,' says Plitplov, leaning across Petworth, and chuckling quietly, 'My dear young lady, do you really like to read him?' Now, beyond the factories, huge blocks of prefabricated apartment buildings, thirty or forty storeys high, rise up above scoured and naked earth. 'Here they build a great and startling project,' says Lubijova, 'Do you surprise I like Hemingway? Perhaps you think he is decadent.'

Petworth looks out at the apartments, which look duller from the ground than from the air. Dust blows between the blocks; there is the Eastern European spectacle of much vacant open space. Few cars are parked here, few people walk, no children play; no shops are visible, and on the ends of the apartments are great maps of the complex for the guidance of the residents. 'No, he is a fine writer, and his style good,' says Plitplov, grinning round his pipe, 'But I do not think he is very tolerant of women.' Behind the apartments the river has over-spilled its banks; amid the marshland is a large brick building, resembling a sombre domed warehouse. 'The river, it is the Niyt,' says Lubijova, 'And also there the cathedral of Valdopin, not very interesting. Well, I am not professor, but I think he makes his women very well.' Now the taxi races at speed down a long tree-lined boulevard, with tram-tracks running down the centre, and on either side old, dirty-faced apartment blocks in the familiar Continental style, from which balustraded balconies stick out, like Victorian corseted breasts. 'Don't you observe his suspicion of female treacheries?' asks Plitplov, puffing at his pipe, 'Don't you notice his hairy-chested hero?' 'The old part of Slaka, really not the best,' says Lubijova, 'You can see here there were many fightings, where our people made a heroic stand of 1944. Well, perhaps I do not know so much about these things, but I think Hemingway would like very much to be a woman.' Petworth peers out at the bullet-pitted stucco, broken balconies, eyeless façades, mostly unrestored. 'You are talking of Hemingway?' cries Plitplov, leaning across Petworth in excitement, 'The author of *Whom the Bell Tolls For* and *Men With No Women*? Don't you observe his cult of the masculine? The buildings break, a view appears, of the wide river, crossed by a long suspension bridge, hung by wires from a gantry to one side only, and beyond it a craggy outcrop, where there are spires, old roofs, the crenellated mass of a castle. 'Now the Bridge of Anniversary May 15,' says Lubijova, 'Also the castle of Vlam, from century eighteen, I hope you try hard to go there. Perhaps his works have only subjective ethical realizations, but I think he well understands the plight of the modern woman.'

They have crossed the great bridge, entered the heart of the city. 'His women are stony bitches, and the men must resist their destructive tendencies,' says Plitplov. There is a park, and greenery. 'To the right, the state operhaus,' says Lubijova, 'Do you know, you will go there in your programme. You are wrong. His women are of a new kind, and he understands them well.' Outside the state opera house, a heavy building of ornate nineteenth-century splendour, built in the Germanic style, large posters announce the performance of a work called *Vedontakal Vrop*. The boulevard leads on into the city; on central tracks a bright pink tram, towing a trailer, both vehicles ancient, survivors of more than one war and revolution, rattles along. The taxi driver speeds to pass, on the inside, the tram, tight-packed with people, some riding on its wooden steps or clutching onto its ornate ironwork. On the forehead of the tram, a sign says VIPNU; enthroned in the prow, ringing her bell violently at the taxi, is a hard-bosomed, uniformed young woman. The tyres skid on the cobbles; the taxi sways. 'Well, we do not lack an expert,' says Plitplov, puffing up thick smoke, 'Let us ask Dr Petworth for his opinion.' 'The statue of our great revolutionary poet of 1848, Hrovdat,' says Lubijova, 'There you see him on the horse he falls from when he recites his great poem in the battle. Beyond, you do not see it very well, the university, where teaches Dr Plitplov, I think.' 'Well, Dr Petworth, you do not speak,' says Plitplov, 'Perhaps you like to be diplomatic? But give us please your serious critical assessment. Do you say Hemingway really likes to be a woman?'

'Now our monument of solidarity with the Russian people,' says Lubijova, gesturing to a vast mass of statuary in the centre of the boulevard: in a mixed mass of styles, constructivist and abstract, realistic and epical, a big stone soldier holding aloft a rifle stands amidst a huddled mass of venerating stone women. 'Well,' says Petworth, 'Obviously he did like to emphasize the masculine role, with all the bullfighting and big-game hunting.' 'We do not forget their help,' says Lubijova. 'On the other hand, he had the instincts of a great writer,' says Petworth, 'And there's something very androgynous about his work.' 'Yes, androgynous, what is that?' asks Plitplov. 'Oh, you don't know that word?' asks Lubijova, 'Well, it is not so common. It means when a man likes to be a woman.' 'It means thus?' asks Plitplov. 'Well, it really means possessing male and female in one,' says Petworth, 'As so many writers do.' 'So you are agreeing with this person?' asks Plitplov, turning. 'I understand both points,' says Petworth. 'I see, my friend,' says Plitplov, 'Well, I do not think this is a very solid critical assessment. Really we had much better literary conversation when we are in Cambridge. You are much shrewder then.' 'Here almost the centrum,' says Lubijova, 'Don't you like very much our trees?' But now Plitplov is leaning forward, and saying something to the driver; the tyres screech on the cobbles, and the taxi stops suddenly, producing much loud hooting from behind, and a clanging of bells as the tram marked VIPNU clatters past them the white-bloused driver gesticulating from the prow. Plitplov now sits there, his hands pressed to his head, his face in a grimace; he turns one eye and looks at Petworth.

'Excuse me, my friend,' he says, 'All of a sudden I am having a headache. Perhaps this loud music you like does not suit me. I think I make excuse and leave you.' 'Really?' says Petworth, 'I'm sorry.' 'Well, you are nicely looked after, by this lady you like to agree with,' says Plitplov, 'She makes sure you find your hotel. But for me it is better to rest. Also my wife is a very delicate person, who is very nervous that she does not see me for more than five hours, while I struggle to the airport to make my duties to my good old friend.' 'But how will you get home?' asks Petworth. 'I think he manages,' says Lubijova, unconcerned in her corner of the taxi. 'My apartment is one block from here,' says Plitplov, 'It is lucky coincidence.' 'Yes, I should have a rest,' says Petworth. 'Please, my good friend, do not worry,' says Plitplov, stretching out an arm, 'My pain is severe, but does not concern you. You are very important guest, with major tasks to perform.' 'Perhaps better you come with us to that chemist shop,' says Lubijova, 'They will give you a mixture.' 'Those things are no use,' says Plitplov, 'Beside, I am strong and will be better soon. So I leave you. Madame Lubijova, look please well after my friend. He is nice man, and really his lectures are sometimes quite good. Even if I do not agree at all his poor assessment of Hemingway. Well, Dr Petworth, goodbye.' Plitplov opens the door of the taxi, and gets out 'Shall I see you again?' Petworth asks as he stands above him on the curbside, 'I do hope I haven't . . .' 'As we say here, the days will tell what they will tell,' says Plitplov, 'But one day our paths could cross again, fate is like that. Perhaps I come to one of your talks, unless I am too busy. Perhaps even you come to hear at the university my famous lecture; it is on the hairy-chested hero of Ernest Hemingway. Now please, put inside your head, I shut this door. Oh, but one thing.' 'Yes?' asks Petworth. 'Remember, when you telephone to your nice wife, to Lottie,' says Plitplov, 'Give her the love of Plitplov. Tell her you see me, and all is well. No need to mention that headache.'

Plitplov slams the door; the taxi jerks forward; Petworth, face to the glass, stares out at Plitplov as he stands at the roadside, putting, in a final gesture, one forefinger to his nose. Then there is a screech as the taxi, moving out into the traffic stream, narrowly misses a brown Ford Cortina, passing them at speed; when he looks back through the rear window, the pavement where Plitplov had stood is quite empty, as if he has departed in some great magical leap. 'Now the new part of the city,' says Lubijova, in a tone of improved good humour, 'Here do you see our new shopping and commerce street, all the world knows about it. Who can wonder many congresses like to come here?' 'Quite,' says Petworth, staring down a great wide central boulevard built in the style of international modernism, 'Do you think I offended him?' In the violet dusk, the showpiece buildings line the great street, in glass and steel; there are office blocks and stores, goods in half-lit windows, high flashing neon signs saying WICWOK and JUGGI JUGGI, MUG and COMFLUG. 'I thinks he likes it very well, to get a free taxi right next to his apartment,' says Lubijova, 'Our department store, MUG, you must buy some glass there. Also the foreign currency store Wicwok.' Many pink trams fill the boulevard; traffic lights flash; a few passers-by with overcoats on walk by the stores in the darkening and now windy evening. 'I shouldn't have said that about Hemingway,' says Petworth. 'Of course,' says Lubijova, laughing, 'You were very good. He thinks he is famous critic, always writing in the newspaper. And his bad lecture on Hemingway, I heard it twenty times when I was student. That is why I teased him. Look, here the Sportsdrome, of Olympical standard. It holds ten thousand spectator all at one time.' 'So you do know him?' asks Petworth. 'Of course,' says Lubijova, 'He knows me well. He gives the examen on my thesis.'

Over the wide boulevard, great flagpoles project; onto them men on hydraulic platforms, elevated over grey trucks, are hanging great banners. 'Look, do you see, they put out the nice flags?' cries Lubijova, 'Do you know why? Don't you guess?' 'A parade?' asks Petworth. 'Oh, Petwurt, you are clever,' says Lubijova, 'Now I know why we ask you. Yes, soon it is our Day of National Culture, when our writers and painters and teachers march the streets. Of course you will spectate it, it is on your programme.' 'When do I see my programme?' asks Petworth. 'Later, at the hotel,' says Lubijova, 'And so this Plitplov, he is your good old friend? Perhaps you know all about him?' 'No, not at all,' says Petworth, 'He's just a chance acquaintance.' 'Here we turn to the old part of the city, all the buildings in the older style,' says Lubijova, 'There a museum of old pianos, there the state theatre, there the Russian Embassy. But he tells he knows you very well.' 'He doesn't,' says Petworth. 'Well, perhaps he likes to make himself more famous, by knowing you,' says Lubijova, 'And now you disappoint him, how very sad. Oh, look, those up there, do you know them?' The taxi is now moving down a narrow street, with high, creeper-clad public buildings hemming in each side; above the street there hang, many times life-size, great stylized photo-portraits of the faces of several solemn men. Depicted in the mode of heroic realism, the faces wear beards, moustaches, expressions of moral seriousness, the conviction of being characters in the world historical sense. 'Marx, Lenin, Brezhnev,' says Petworth. 'Please, *Comrade* Marx, *Comrade* Lenin, *Comrade* Brezhnev,' says Lubijova rebukingly, 'Also Comrade Grigoric, our great liberator, and Comrade Wanko, president of the praesidium of the party. But he seems to know very well your wife.'

Petworth stares up at the solemn photographs, flapping above: 'As far as I know, he's only met her once,' he says, 'In a pub in Cambridge.' 'Oh, beautiful Cambridge,' says Lubijova, 'Of it he has the most happy memories. Of course, he would love it. He likes history so much he wants it all for himself. But why does he say that? He is not a foolish man.' 'I can't imagine,' says Petworth. 'Over there the puppet theatre, there the Military Academy,' says Lubijova, 'And your wife, Comrade Petwurt, do you know her very well?' 'We've been married thirteen years,' says Petworth, looking out at a large building, with a colonnaded entrance, on the steps of which many crop-headed young soldiers in uniform sit, smoking, holding portfolios under their arms. 'Well, that is long?' says Lubijova, 'But people are secrets to each other. In my country, men and women do not get on so well. Of course our divorces are liberal and marriage is not so important a thing any more. Is it so in your country?' 'A bit like that,' says Petworth. 'Perhaps that is why you like to travel to Slaka,' says Lubijova, 'You have some wishes you cannot make real at home, so you go to somewhere and hope they will happen. Often I feel so. Look, here, the square where is your hotel. It is Plazsci Wang'liki, remember it, please, because you will need to find it again. I hope you like it?' 'Yes,' says Petworth, looking out; the square has high old buildings round it; a café with tables sits on a corner; signs flash, saying РЕСТОРАН, and СЛОРТ, and SCH'VEPPII, and HOTEL SLAKA. There is a gravelled area in the middle, with shade trees; under it there is a stopping and meeting place for the pink trams.

'Please look round, do you see any chemist shop where

your good old friend can go for his recipe?' says Lubijova, sitting in the far corner of the taxi, 'I don't think so.' 'Yes, he's an odd sort of chap,' says Petworth. 'I wonder if your wife thinks also he is an odd sort of chap,' says Lubijova, 'Do you call her Lottie? It is a nice name. How is she, your Lottie? Also a nice person? Would she like one like that for a friend?' 'She's dark, very private,' says Petworth. 'And also she smokes the small cigars,' says Lubijova, 'Here, see, your hotel. Isn't it grand? Do you see now you are important visitor?' And the Hotel Slaka, under the portico of which the taxi now moves, is clearly a hotel in the old grand manner, with fine stone façades and many balconies. 'Very nice,' says Petworth. The glass entrance doors open, and two limping doormen walk toward the taxi; the driver switches his radio from jazz to massed choir music, and gets out. Petworth is about to get out too when, in the half-darkness, a hand seizes his arm; in her corner Lubijova, holding him, is staring at him urgently. 'Comrade Petwurt, before you get out, I tell you one thing, for your good,' she says, 'This odd sort of chap, I think you shall be a little careful of him. Always in my country there are those who want something. Perhaps he makes for you some trouble.' 'Trouble?' says Petworth, looking at her. 'I am your good guide, I like to help you,' says Lubijova, 'I do not know what he plans, but remember, it is good to be cautious. I hope you understand?' 'I think so,' says Petworth. 'I think so too,' says Lubijova, putting her forefinger to her nose, 'Now let us get out, and you see your nice hotel.'

II

The Hotel Slaka, located in Plazsci Wang'liki (somewhere toward the top of your map), is indeed a hotel in the old grand manner. Imperial times have made it, and the grand travellers of an older Europe; its façade is stone, its portico wide, its lobby vast, its ceilings high, its ferns abundant. Archdukes and hussars, duchesses and décollettée ladies must once have passed through these fine halls, beneath these cut-glass chandeliers, beside this faintly erotic statuary, up these grand staircases, into these discreetly curtained alcoves. But history, sparing no one and nothing, affects even hotels. Now portraits of Lenin, Brezhnev, Grigoric hang over the reception desk; at it work girls in the blue uniform of Cosmoplot. Today's visitors have contemporary political significance: a group of Vietnamese women in dark blue worksuits, cadre pens in their top pockets, hair fringed over their eyes, stand and talk quietly in one corner, and a cluster of black Africans in long flowing robes laughs and chuckles in another. In Petworth's path, as he goes toward the desk, which is marked R'GYSTRAYII, two men stand silently facing each other, holding red carnations, while the two interpreters beside them talk fluently. A limping doorman takes Petworth's luggage to the desk, which is surrounded by a crowd of large women, several with dyed hair, most in dresses of pink and green. Large suitcases stand at their feet; they look at Petworth curiously. 'Ivanovas,' says Lubijova, 'Push through them, push, push, push. They like to make their factory outings here, we are so cheap. But you are important visitor.'

There is a girl behind the desk in blue uniform, with dark red hair, spread fanlike from her head in lacquered splendour; she looks at them without interest. 'Hallo, dolling,' says Lubijova, 'Here is Professor Petwurt, reservation of the Min'stratii Kulturi, confirmation here.' 'So, Petvurt?' the girl says, taking a pen from her hair and running it languidly down the columns of a large book, 'Da, Pervert, so, here is. Passipotti.' 'She likes your passport, don't give it to her,' says Lubijova, 'Give it to me. I know these people well, they are such bureaucrats. Now, dolling, tell me, how long do you keep?' 'Tomorrow,' says the girl, 'It registers with the police.' 'No, dolling, this is much too long,' says Lubijova, 'I do not love you. You can arrange, do it for me tonight. Tomorrow he goes to the Min'stratii Kulturi, and they don't let him in without it.' 'Perhaps,' says the girl,

'I try.' 'Comrade Petwurt, remember, come back in three hour and ask it from her,' says Lubijova, 'Remember, here if you do not have passport, you do not exist. And I expect you like to exist, don't you? It is nicer.' 'Here, Pervert,' says the lacquered-haired girl, pushing a form across the desk, 'I need some informations.' 'It is not English, he doesn't understand it,' says Lubijova, 'We do it together. Put here: name, address, where born, how old; so old, are you really, I didn't think it. Now where you come from, London, didn't you, and how long you stay, that is three nights. Now where you go next, do you know, I tell you: Glit. Write it down, four letters, G-L-I-T. She can do the rest herself. There, dolling, is good?'

Taking the pencil from her hair, the girl checks the form. 'Okay, is good. Now, Pervert, this card I write for you, it is your hotel ident'ayii, ja? Only this gives you your key. If you lose, no replace. And don't forget, no this, no key, no break-fast.' Petworth picks up the card, which has a name, A. Pervert, written on it, and a room number, and on the back a message saying: 'Bienvenue à Hotel SLAKA, une Hotel «COSMOPLOT». Services gratuits: transports du bagages jusqu'à et depuis la chambre; brosses à habit, aiguilles, fils; information sur la température de l'air.' 'Thank you,' he says. 'Dolling, let us find out if anyone loves him,' says Lubijova, 'Does he get some messages?' The lacquered-haired girl inspects the pigeonholes behind her: 'One letter,' she says. 'Oh, from Slaka?' asks Lubijova, 'You have some more good old friends here?' 'No,' says Petworth, putting the letter into his pocket, 'I can't think who could know I was coming.' 'I expect it is some nice girl who remembers you,' says Lubijova, 'Now is everything good? Do you need anything? Do you want perhaps to call your wife, your dark lady? If so, please tell me. There are certain regula-tions, they are such bureaucrats here. We must book it before.' 'Yes, I would like to call her,' says Petworth. 'Of course, you must give her the love of Plitplov. I will make arrangements while you are upstairs. Please write down me the number.' The lacquered-haired girl leans over the counter and bangs on it with a large key: 'Sissi funvsi forsi,' she shouts to a large bald hall-porter, who comes over, takes the key, and drapes himself in Petworth's luggage.

'It is not permitted that the guides go upstairs,' says Lubijova, 'So you go there, take a time, do a wash, what you like. I sit here in these chairs and read some more pages of Hemingway. Then you come down and we make some business.' 'Business?' asks Petworth. 'Oh, don't you like some money?' cries Lubijova, 'And a programme? Don't you like to make some objections and changes? Look, go quickly, you will lose your luggage again. See, the man gets in the lift, be quick.' Petworth pushes back through the crowd round the reception desk; the big Ivanovas, smelling of musk, stare at him, though whether they are struck by his charms or his sagging Western clothes he cannot tell. The elevator has great copper doors, embossed with modern reliefs showing peasants and factory workers happy in their activities: the scowling porter holds them apart. Petworth gets in; so do three more Petworths, in baggy safari suits and flat earth shoes, staring at him from the mirrored walls. Slowly, jerkily, the doors close, and the downstairs world of travellers and tours, guides and delegations goes from sight; slowly, jerkily, the elevator, its decor evidently in excess of its technology, begins to bump and grind upward through the building. Then the big doors tug open again, to reveal an upstairs world: a silent wide corridor, carpeted down the middle, flanked with vases on pedestals, holding plastic flowers; an old wooden desk with an old wooden chair, on which sits an elderly floormaid, in white overall, mobcap, black socks, white shoes with the heels omitted, who looks up from an old paperback book to inspect him.

The porter leads the way to a large mahogany door with 654 on it, which opens to three turns of the key. Inside is a big airless anteroom, bigger than last night's entire hotel room in Bayswater, but furnished only with a large sprouting hatstand with a crop of coathangers on it, a large cheval glass, and a doormat for the feet. Another mahogany door leads on into a room of considerable nobility: a vast, high-ceilinged bedroom with two balconied windows, facing out over the large square below, with the trams and the signs saying СЛОРТ and РЕС-ТОРАН. An empire sofa stands against one wall; a directoire table holding a bowl of roses stands against another; a dressing table with a large mirror faces across to a vast bed, more treble than double. A fresco of raucous nymphs decorates the ceiling; a great brass light like an upturned bush dangles from the centre of their sport into the room. On the wall hangs an old and vaguely erotic line-drawing, showing the image of a decorative female foot, and the inscription 'Salon Damenschuh um 1890.' Apart from that, the decoration consists largely of mirrors; some twenty Petworths and their bald porters move frantically in all directions through the disproportionate space. 'Camarad'aki,' says the porter, opening another mahogany door and switching on the light of a vast inner sanctum: in it is a throne-like toilet; a bidet; a very large bath with shower-pipes, ascended to by means of tiled steps. It seems strange, under a new and egalitarian ideology, to be granted such space, more than he has ever had in a hotel before, more even than his ego can fill; it seems difficult, in a proletarian world, to know how to reward the bald porter and the floormaid, who peers in from the doorway. It seems well that he has no money; what he does is to reach into the Heathrow bag, take out the carton of cigarettes, crack it open, and offer a packet each to the porter and the maid. The porter puts down the large key on the directoire table, and inspects the packet gloomily; the maid puts hers unenthusiastically into the pocket of her over-alls. Then they are gone, leaving Petworth to occupy, as best he can, the vast space.

He looks around. Already the room does not look quite as it did before, as if it is emptying to match his own vacancy. More closely inspected, the grandeur displays small flaws. There is a marked smell of dustiness. Moths inhabit the velvet curtains to the balconied windows. In the rose-bowl on the directoire table, processes of vegetable decomposition have begun. A large crack runs down the wall opposite the bed; another zigzags between the reaching hands of the nymphs cavorting on the ceiling. A wall-lamp has fallen down behind the sofa. The cornice droops off the ceiling in one corner. The glinting mirrors are bloomed, discoloured, and cracked. The rattling windows fit badly, admitting metallic noise from the trams below. The signs saying РЕСТОРАН and СЛОРТ flash stark bright light into the room. When tried, the great radio like a cinema organ at the bedside proves to have only one audible channel, the others giving off the noise of static and bagpipe jamming. The bathroom light the porter switched on will not switch on for Petworth, so that the door must be kept open. The fine European toilet, which has one of those high inner ledges that permit scientific inspection of one's most basic daily achievements, has an American addition: a slip across it saying SANIT'AYII, which has spared someone the trouble of cleaning it. As Petworth drops his trousers and sits down there, drips from the ceiling, twenty feet above, fall generously onto his head. And when he reaches out to the toilet-roll holder for paper, that simple provision – quite unlike the temperature of the air – proves not to be a free service of the establishment. From above the washbasin, a cracked mirror stares at Petworth, inspecting this predicament; so probably too, Petworth reflects, does some nearby HOGPo man, peering through a screen.

Yes, there are, Petworth goes on to consider, sitting there, travellers who are adept at travel. And travel is in turn adept with them, so that for them switches always work, keys move easily in doors, telephones function. There are others who travel too, but travel does not sympathize; and for them bedsprings always fail, wardrobe doors never shut or, more probably, take one's clothes and then will not open again, lightbulbs fail, toilet paper runs out. Perched there, in front of the HOGPo man, Petworth knows himself to be of the second class; once again, he feels in his pocket for a piece of paper that will solve his problems. There is the grey letter of invita-

94

tion; there is his currency declaration. And there too is his hotel ident'ayii, which proves to say on the back: 'Welcome to Slaka, city of trees and art, flowers and gipsy song. No doubt all will be satisfied with their sojourn in this beautiful place. In HOTEL SLAKA, do not neglect to visit: ***RESTAURANT SLAKA: offered are such delicacies as, Kyrbii Churba (mutton soup), Cotelette de l'Amateur (chop-lover's chops), Sarkii Banatu (folded pate), and the notable Boyard Plate, animated with folkloric singeress and typical orchestra; ***NIGHTCLUB ZIPZIP: the personal are clothed as peasants from mountains and national fame artists give remarkable performances of, jiggling, songing, art-strip, ect.; ***BARR'II TZIGANE: the personal are in cutumes Romany, and both spiritual and non-alcoolical drinks are availed.' There is the letter he has just been given downstairs, in an envelope which has an official crest on the back, as well as an air of having been unstuck and refashioned, though this could be an optical illusion. The envelope contains an engraved invitation card, from a Mr and Mrs Steadiman of the British Embassy in Slaka, inviting a Mr A. Petworth to dinner at their apartment the following night, in order to meet a Mr A. Petworth. The card is too stiff, the envelope too sharp, to serve the occasion; happily there is also last night's bill from the hotel in Bayswater, to resolve the problem.

Petworth washes, soaplessly, for this is one of those European nations that thinks it unwise to risk giving soap to people; then he goes back into the great bedroom, where bright flashes from the gantries of trams keep lighting up the dark ceiling. The spaces of hotel rooms bring out trouble and unease, there is trouble now in his mind. He is no longer lost, but found; he has two guides, but each warns him against the other. Removing his pyjamas from his blue suitcase, and placing them on the treble bed, he tries to remember Cambridge, and summer school, to recall some occasion, some opportunity of an occasion, for real intimacy between Plitplov, that beaming bird-like man, and his dark wife; but memory fills only with lectures given or listened to, college lunches, small wine parties in tutors' rooms, a short trip in a punt, a longer visit to a pub, and nothing more. Replacing his travel-stained shirt with a new one, he thinks of Lubijova, severe but gay, tense but laughing, waiting downstairs for him now in her mohair hat, helping but enquiring, protecting but probing, watching his luggage and his contacts; they report to theirs, and ours to ours. Picking up his briefcase, laden with Chomsky and Chatman, Lyons and Fowler, and putting it away in the back of the wardrobe, the door of which will not shut, he tries to think of the strange purposes for which he, or perhaps even another Petworth, bald and bespectacled, from another university, in another subject, might have been brought here; no sense comes to his head. The mirrors glint, in a place where mirrors are dangerous. Plitplov leaves the taxi, Lubijova checks his messages. The lights flicker, as if weary of their business; Petworth looks round the room and recognizes in it, for all its space and grandeur, a true hotel room, a fitting landscape for solitude and misery, an appropriate outward architecture for the psychic world within.

Petworth goes over to the window and looks out, to glimpse the city to which he has committed himself; a trapped bee buzzes fitfully between the double panes. Below is the square, paved with cobbles, and quiet, save for the sound of the pink trams that grind from track to track and halt to let a few overcoated travellers on and off. Over where the sign says PECTOPAH, a few empty tables with their umbrellas downfolded stand on the pavement. A man stands selling balloons, which bob above his head, to two small children; another offers newspapers and magazines from a makeshift wooden stall on bicycle wheels, though no one stops to buy. A number of crop-headed soldiers from the Military Academy, holding their portfolios, talk to a group of girls in cotton dresses and dark jackets, in an age-old fashion. Across the square are high houses with pointed, twisting gables; around their bottoms are a few dull shop façades, with small lighted signs that say LITTI

96

and FILIATAYII. Beyond, on the skyline, a few domed knobs in the eastern taste stand out, perhaps the tops of the governmental buildings close by. The blue daylight is shading off to black, and a dusty wind blows through the square, stirring the gravel. Down a street to one side, Marx and Lenin, Brezhnev and Grigoric and Wanko, solemn-faced and replete with historical understanding, bounce in the breeze. Now the balloon man is pulling down his balloons and going home; the newspaper seller covers his newspapers with a plastic sheet, folds his stall so that it magically becomes a bicycle, and wheels it away. Petworth turns too, picking up his key, and going through the anteroom and out into the corridor.

This, too, has grown gloomy since he left it. Bleak yellow wall lights illuminate it thinly; the plastic flowers stand grimly in their stone bowls. Petworth struggles with his key to lock the door; the elderly floormaid, as if expecting him, stands in her white pinafore a few feet away. She watches him as he goes to press the button for the elevator, as he steps into the mirrored box to make his descent. The buttons are mysterious, but he presses one near the bottom; he descends, stops, and the doors open, just a little, to give a second's glimpse of a great room where some dance is in progress, men in military uniform dancing with girls in lurex dresses. Then they close, descent occurs, they open again: to reveal the familiar lobby, where the bald porter stands, smoking a cigarette, the sign saying LITTI flashes, Arabs in burnouses crowd round the reception desk. Big ferns stand in pots; small men sit in red plasticated armchairs, reading *P'rtyii Populatiii*. In one of the red armchairs is a grey shoulderbag, and a copy of Hemingway's *Men Without Women*; but Marisja Lubijova is visible nowhere, nowhere at all. Petworth sits down in the adjoining chair; the man in the next chair along drops his newspaper. 'You are English, I think, it is the shoes,' says the man, 'I have doctoral qualifications, and perfect taste. If antiques interest you, I know some good ones, for dollars or pounds.' A big-hatted man in a raincoat sits down in the next chair along. 'No, thank you,' says Petworth. 'My tram,' says the man with perfect taste, getting up. Behind the long registration desk, a door marked DIRIG'AYII opens, and a girl in a mohair hat comes out.

'Oh, Comrade Petwurt,' says Marisja Lubijova, walking brightly toward him, 'Only a moment ago you are gone, and now you are come again. How please is your room, do you find it comfortable?' 'Fine, almost too grand,' says Petworth. 'I told you, you are very important visitor,' says Lubijova, 'This is our best hotel, right next to the government places; all the high offficials come here and make their business and their pleasures. Petwurt, Petwurt, I have been trying to arrange your phone-call. Really they are such bureaucrats. I have to book a time and you can only call at that time. I have told them eleven o'clock tonight, is that good, is that all right for you?' 'Very good,' says Petworth. 'Well, now, shall we be like the party officials, and make our business?' asks Lubijova, lifting up Hemingway and sitting down herself. The big-hatted man in the raincoat stands up, moves one chair nearer, and sits down again. 'Why don't we do it in the bar, over a drink?' asks Petworth, 'I see there's one in the hotel.' 'Oh, you see that, do you?' says Lubijova, 'I think you check all the important things. So, you like to drink and make business at the same time.' 'Unless you have to go quickly,' says Petworth. 'Petwurt, in my country, here we always put our work before our homes,' says Lubijova, 'That is why we make such a good economical progress. You are my work, if you must go there to the bar, then I must go there also.' 'We don't have to,' says Petworth. 'Comrade Petwurt, don't you think I am teasing you, just a little?' asks Lubijova, getting up and seizing him by the arm, 'Do you like a bar with some gipsies? It's over here, down the steps. And who did you talk to when I was in Dirig'ayii? Did you find a friend?'

III

So Petworth and his guide go down the steps, beneath the hotel, and into a dark, dank, barrel-roofed area which once must have been cellars. But, like so many cellars in the modern world, this has been transmuted into a place of delights. A narrow stone passageway is lit with dim red lights; it leads to a low doorway, a heavy curtain, a hat-check girl, a scrolled ironwork sign saying *Barr'ii Tzigane*, and, through the curtain, the bar itself, which has been done out in gipsy style. On the rough whitewashed walls, murals depict the joyous footloose life of the wanderer, the fiddling Romany, the happy piping shepherd. In round-roofed alcoves are small red tables with small red-checked tablecloths; on them stand small red table lamps with small red-checked shades. The waitresses who pass about serving the clientele wear small, red-checked dresses; the clientele itself is on the sombre side, consisting almost entirely of besuited gentlemen, some drinking alone, some in large male groups of the commercial kind; evidently this is where Rumanian oil drinks with Russian grain, Albanian olives with Vietnamese rice. Half of a gipsy caravan has been inserted into one wall, to form a bar where, in bright Romany costume, a very gloomy barman stands, slowly shaking drinks. It is on the high stools in front of him that there is one touch of joy; here is sitting a bright row of girls, in colourful dresses and silvery eye make-up, drinking, giggling, and swinging their long legs.

'Well, it is very typical,' says Lubijova, as they sit down together in one of the alcoves, 'Of course such places are a little bit touristic, and the drinks are expensive. But perhaps that is quite interesting for you, because you are a foreigner. Also here it is possible to get all your favourite Western drinks. What do you like? Perhaps a ginnitoniki or a bols?' 'No, I think something local,' says Petworth, lighting a cigarette, 'I like to try the local things.' 'Yes, also you like to smoke, I see,' says Lubijova, loosening her long grey coat, to reveal a long grey dress, 'I wonder what else you like to do before you leave my country? First you make embraces, then you want to drink, now you smoke. I wonder: do you mean to be trouble to me?' 'I don't think so,' says Petworth. 'Well, it is good you wish a Slakan drink,' says Lubijova, 'Perhaps it means already you are liking it here. I hope so. Well, tell me, what do you wish better? A peach brandy, we call it *rot'vitti*, or a wodka?' 'I've tried the *rot'vitti*,' says Petworth, 'So I think the vodka.' 'Oh, of course,' cries Lubijova, 'You have been here already a whole four hour, of course you have tried *rot'vitti*. Well, wodka, tell me, what do you wish better? Wodka simple or wodka scented? Scented comes from a bottle with a long herb inside it, do you never try it? Then I get that for you. I am sorry, there is no music for you, what a pity. Often there is tzigane music, but even our gipsies like to make a little rest for Sunday. It is not too dull for you?' 'Oh, no,' says Petworth, looking round, at the men in their suits, looking contemplatively down into their drinks, the commercial groups chattering, the glowering barman, the girls along the barstools.

Sunday seems in the soul. The girls, at least, are exotic: two are blonde, with bouffant hair, low white blouses, tight black skirts and high boots with decorated tops; the other three are raven-haired, and have great dark eyes shining through silver make-up, tight velvet dresses, net stockings, and high-heeled shoes. Their laughter trills; they glance all round the room; they swing their long legs. 'And vodka for you?' asks Petworth. 'No, I think for me, just a *Sch'veppii*,' says Lubijova, 'Sometimes I like to take those strong drinks. But tonight we must make our business together, so I think I mind my head. Beside, some of the other guides might see me drinking strong drink with my official visitor.' 'What about those girls there?' asks Petworth, pointing to the girls at the bar, 'Are they guides too?' A sudden sharp slap falls across Petworth's wrist: 'Oh, Petwurt, Petwurt,' says Lubijova, laughing at him, 'Really, do you think I am one of those? Don't you really know that kind? Those are the lovely ladies.' 'Ah, I see,' says Petworth. 'Guides in a way,' says Lubijova, 'Of course really they are not permitted. But this is good hotel, and many foreign visitors arrive here, and they have not their wives, and we do not want life to be too dull for them. Oh, here is our waitress. Perhaps you like to make the order? I think so, I believe you speak very well our language.' 'No, not at all,' says Petworth. 'And yet you are linguist?' says Lubijova, 'Well, I do it this time, you next, so listen how to say it. Vidki fran'tiska, da, ei sch'veppii, froliki, slibob.' 'Ah, da,' says the red-checked waitress. 'There, it is not so complicate,' says Lubijova, 'All you must know is the nouns end in "i," or sometimes two or three, but with many exceptions. We have one spoken language and one book language. Really there are only three cases, but sometimes seven. Mostly it is inflected, but also sometimes not. It is different from country to town, also from region to region, because of our confused history. Vocabulary is a little bit Latin, a little bit German, a little bit Finn. So really it is quite simple, I think you will speak it very well, soon.'

'I doubt it,' says Petworth. 'Then perhaps you need your guide,' says Lubijova, smiling at him, 'And I will take you to nice places. Don't I bring you here to see the lovely ladies? Which do you wish better, the fairs or the darks?' 'I hadn't thought,' says Petworth, looking over at the bar. 'No, please tell me,' says Lubijova, 'I like to find out all your tastes.' 'Well, the dark ones, I suppose,' says Petworth. 'Oh, yes, you like the arabesques?' cries Lubijova, 'That shows you are not an Ivanov, they like better always the fairs. Well, you know, I am a little bit arabesque myself, did you notice? Dark is typical here. It is from Turkish times, when many atrocities against us were committed.' 'And the blondes, are they typical too?' asks Petworth. 'Oh, yes,' says Lubijova, 'Typical of a bottle. Some things are not what they seem, even in my country. Oh, look, she brings us our drinks. Now, please, Comrade Petwurt, do not drink it. I like to teach you a little lesson. You do not mind if I am your teacher?' 'No,' says Petworth. 'Good,' says Lubijova, 'Now, when we take drink in my country we like to make toast also.' 'Toast?' asks Petworth. 'With the glass,' says Lubijava, 'Mine is Sch'veppii, that is not right, but I will show you. Please do just as I do. First the glass, it goes in the air so. Now the eyes, look at me, straight, serious, no, it is not right, you are laughing. Be very sincere, have a good feeling, I like you. Now, back with your head, back more, the drink goes straight there to the throat. Oh, no, the choking at the end is not at all correct. The rest very good. But I think you try once more. Are you ready?' 'Yes,' says Petworth.

'So now, very serious, please, my dear,' says Lubijova, 'Lift the glass, make the stare. See how I think of you: I like you, you are fine, I want you for my bed. Now drink, straight to the throat. Yes, that is very good, Comrade Petwurt. Your self-criticism is excellent, that time perfect. And now I think we are very good friends, don't you say?' 'I think so,' says Petworth. 'And also now I know some things about you, like a friend,' says Lubijova, 'You drink, you smoke, you like darks. Well, of course, you said your Lottie is a dark. And your marriage is not so easy for you. And you like to go to Cambridge, and meet a certain good old friend. And you like to make some travels.' 'Yes,' says Petworth. 'And perhaps all is not so well with you in your relations,' says Lubijova, 'Well, that is like here, we are fond of our families, we like to be close. But our marriage, not so good. I do not think our men like really the ladies. Of course they like to bed, but for other things they like better to be with men. Well, our apartments are small, and there is not so much time when people are together, but perhaps they do not really like us. For you perhaps it is different.' 'Perhaps a little,' says Petworth. 'Do not move quickly,' says Lubijova, dropping her voice suddenly, 'But please take a small look in the next alcove. Do you see some trousers? Did you ever see some like that before?' Petworth turns slowly; at the bend of the alcove, a leg is swinging in and out of view. It is a leg in black trousers with chalk white stripes; a male handbag lies on the end of the table. 'Perhaps,' says Petworth. Lubijova reaches into her shoulderbag, and takes out a spectacle case, from which comes a pair of red-framed spectacles; large, they cover the top part of her face. 'Comrade Petwurt,' she says, looking over them severely, 'I think we must make our business. Here, please, inspect your programme.'

Lubijova hands Petworth another grey letter, much like the one he has in his pocket, and bearing the same insignia from the Min'stratii Kulturi Komitet'iii. Headed 'Vyag'na Priffisorim Petworthim,' it is clearly the plot of his days, the plot he has wanted. It records an orderly destiny; this Petworthim is evidently going to be a busy fellow. Few hours of his waking life are unfilled with some form of activity: lecturing and meeting, travelling and sightseeing. Here he is visiting a Min'stratii, there a kloster; here he makes reformist didaktik recommendation at a Fakult'tii Fil'gayiim, there he attends an oper. His days are mobile and moving; here he goes by car to Glit, there by train to Nogod, then by train to Provd. It is, to Petworth, a likeable story, lively, familiar, harmless, well suited to his talents. 'Please read it very carefully,' says Lubijova, looking at him over the spectacles, 'We make here our proposals. You can object and ask for changes, but tell me now at this time. Or else it is our contract, and you must do it.' 'Yes, it's fine,' says Petworth, putting it down on the table. 'Do you look at it carefully?' asks Lubijova, staring at him, 'Please notice, all days are taken care of. All the places you attend have good academies. All are very nice. Glit has towers on an old castle. In Nogod you can see an old kloster with paintings, and forest with hirsch. Provd is modern, and has a fine steelwork.' 'Good,' says Petworth. 'You come back to Slaka for our day of national rejoicerings, you saw those flags,' says Lubijova, 'You make seven lectures and go to four places. It is clear?' 'Yes, it's excellent,' says Petworth.

Over her spectacles, Lubijova is staring at him in exasperation. 'It is all right, four places, you don't want three?' she asks, 'You accept all those titles for your lectures? You have brought them with you? You don't like to change them? No

103

places you want to go are not included? There are no people you like to meet who are not in your programme?' 'No,' says Petworth. 'Really?' asks Lubijova, 'And you don't wish another day of quiet to yourself? You don't like to ask for some more pleasures, as some fishing? Perhaps you do not like this oper, *Vedontakal Vrop*? It is sung only in our language and takes five hours. Perhaps you have some criticisms of our procedures?' 'No,' says Petworth. 'Then I expect you have many questions?' says Lubijova. 'Well, not really,' says Petworth. 'Comrade Petwurt,' says Lubijova, looking at him crossly, 'Do you really pay attention? I think all the time you are looking at those lovely ladies. You know you must do all these things? Then why aren't you difficult, like all the others?' 'Well, I'm happy,' says Petworth, 'I like being organized. I'm pleased my days are full. I like not being on my own. It's all very satisfactory.' 'And so you accept it?' asks Lubijova. 'I look forward to it,' says Petworth. 'It is good, I also,' says Lubijova, 'You know I shall go to all of these places with you! Or perhaps you object?' 'No, I'm pleased,' says Petworth. 'It is as well,' says Lubijova, 'To go without a guide is not permitted. You know, for me it will be very interesting. So, do we finish our business? Do you like now to order a drink?'

With much prompting, Petworth orders two drinks from the red-checked waitress; she brings them, along with a small saucer with the bill. Lubijava picks up the bill: 'Did you invite me?' she asks, holding it up to Petworth, 'Do you like to pay?' 'Oh, yes,' says Petworth, 'But I haven't any money.' 'Of course,' says Lubijova, 'That is because you do not make your business properly, you forget something. Now you see why you need so much a guide. Here is some money for you, in this envelope. I wait you to ask for it. No, Petwurt, please, please, don't put it in your pocket. Count it now, and sign me you receive it.' So, onto the tablecloth, Petworth pours the money from the envelope: there is a stout wad of paper vloskan decorated with images of muscular men wielding sledgehammers, and yet more muscular women tending vast machines;

there is a jingling handful of silver and copper bittiin. 'Is it enough? Do you manage?' asks Lubijova, 'You know your hotels are paid already.' 'I expect so,' says Petworth, 'Of course I don't know the rate of exchange.' 'All right Petwurt, look, I explain you,' says Lubijova, 'This little one is one bittii, with it you can have one box of matches, or a nice postcard. Here the blue one, one vloska, with that you may take twenty times the tram, or buy eight kilo of tomatoes, or six loaves of bread, or perhaps a book. Now show me how you pay this bill. Oh, Petwurt, fifty vloskan for two drinks? No, just put there two of the blue ones. Also a small silver one for the girl. It is not permitted here to tip, but they are angry if you do not. And now, do you sign this paper for your money? Oh, what a nice silver pen, I hope you look after it. Nobody steals in my country, but often such things disappear. So, now we really finish our business. Put please away the money, in your pocket, good boy. And I take off my glasses. Has he gone now, that one?' Petworth peers into the next alcove, and sees it is vacant, except for an empty glass and a full ashtray: 'Yes,' he says. 'Do you think your good friend follows us?' asks Lubijova, 'Perhaps he is mad, that man.' 'Was it really him?' asks Petworth.

'I don't know, but now I think we make one more toast,' says Lubijova, her glasses off, smiling at him, 'Comrade Petwurt: to a good journey between us, amity and concord.' 'Yes,' says Petworth, 'A good journey together.' 'And even if you do not think it, because of that airport, you will find I am very good guide. Perhaps a little bit strict with you; but really, Petwurt, I think you are someone who needs a guide. What do you do now? I think you must eat. In Slaka are many good restaurant, but on a first night it is best to stay at the hotel. There is a place upstairs, the best to eat is ducks. The word for this is *crak'akii*, just like a duck makes. Can you say it?' 'Crak'akii,' says Petworth. 'Yes, you are quite good,' says Lubijova, 'Now you must improve. Only he who speaks survives. I hope you will. Well, now is late, do we go?' They walk out, past the caravan bar, where the barman glowers and one of the blondes turns to give Petworth a bright smile. They climb the stairs to the lobby, busy with new travellers: a crowd of turbanned Sikhs talks to the lacquered-haired girl at the desk. 'Remember, Petwurt,' says Lubijova, halting to button her coat, 'Go to that bitch there in two hour, and make sure she gives back to you your passport. At eleven, please ring your Lottie, and give the love of Plitplov. And now can I leave you? Do you remember all these things?' 'Of course,' says Petworth, 'And what happens tomorrow?'

'Oh, Comrade Petwurt, already you are a problem to me,' says Lubijova, looking at him, 'Did you read at all your programme? Does any of that stay in your head?' 'Travelling abroad is confusing,' says Petworth. 'Especially I think to you,' says Lubijova, 'So, I come at nine, to this place. I take you to the Min'stratii, where is an official welcome. Put on your nice suit, if you have one. Remember to take first your breakfast, or must I come here to help you with that too? Drink your milk up, eat nicely your egg, Comrade Petwurt?' 'No, I'll manage,' says Petworth. 'I know I am mad to leave you,' says Lubijova, shaking her head, 'But you are not all my life, you must live sometimes on your own. Or, if you don't like it, you can go back to those lovely ladies.' 'Well, no, I think it's best to be cautious,' says Petworth, putting his finger to his nose. 'Yes, I think so,' says Lubijova, laughing, 'I ask in the morning whether you have been good.' Then she turns and goes out past the doorman, out into the dark square, where the signs flash. Petworth watches a moment, as a lighted pink tram turns the corner; in her long grey coat, she runs towards it, and jumps aboard, going to whatever kind of life she lives in the dark city. The tram's tail-light fades, and Petworth turns too, following through the lobby the signs that lead him toward the Restaurant Slaka.

IV

It is over an hour later, and Petworth still sits in the vast, chandeliered dining-room of the hotel, awaiting, as he has long awaited, the meal he has once ordered. It is a grand room, with some sixty tables, each spread with white tablecloths, which cast up a damp smell of recent laundering in the water of some brackish river. The tables are laid, creating an atmosphere of vast vacancy, for all but six of them are empty. Nonetheless the maître, in the way of maîtres, has chosen to seat Petworth in a dark corner, under a noisy air vent, and next to the smells of the kitchen. The doors from the kitchen open frequently, to let out black-suited waiters who carry peppermills ceremonially about the great room, carefully avoiding all contact with the diners. 'Crak'akii,' Petworth has said, some time ago, to one of these, as he passed incautiously close to the table. 'Negativo,' the waiter has said, stopping, shaking his head, and removing most of the cutlery from the table. 'Na?' Petworth has said. 'Na,' the waiter has said, 'Kurbii churba, sarkii banatu. Da?' 'Da,' Petworth has said. 'Tinkii?' the waiter has said. 'Tinkii?' Petworth has asked. 'Da, tinkii,' the waiter has said, pointing to Petworth's glass, 'Pfin op olii?' 'Well,' Petworth has said, 'Pfin.' 'Da, pfin,' the waiter has said, raising his peppermill and entering the kitchen. He has not, since then, appeared again, though others have, carefully curving their paths away from his table. The cloth on the table in front of him steams faintly; on it is a small stand holding the flags of twenty nations, none of them his own. The door to the kitchen now opens, and the waiter appears, comes over to his table, takes away the flags, and disappears again.

Petworth sits, waiting, as travellers do: waiting for wonders to happen, drinks to come, adventures to occur, the surprising lover that comes from nowhere, the dark coach that suddenly stops to pick one up, those things that travel always seems to promise and never seems to give. The table is vacant in front

107

of him; opposite is a single empty chair. In the middle of the room is a small podium; on it has appeared the typical orchestra, five frilly-sleeved gipsies who have been trilling violins without enthusiasm, occasionally looking at their watches. Now, as he waits, they are joined by someone, evidently the folkloric songeress, a lady with a curve of hair from a fifties film that falls down tantalizingly over one eye. She has very red lips; she wears a frilly wide ballgown, cut down to the bosom, which lays bare the stately square shoulders of some other, older era. Taking the microphone, her lips in a sulky pout, she begins to sing, some dark and ancient ballad. She half-weeps, half-chants, dipping her knees, tossing her hair; her breasts enlarge with breathed-in air, and then subside. The performance is imperfect, the gestures are clumsy, but the song she sings is of vacancy and emptiness, and there is vacancy and emptiness in Petworth, too, as he sits there, a personless person. There are few to hear, but he hears, admitting that, on a dull Sunday night, in a distant foreign city, when one is alone beneath new stars and a different ideology, in an empty grand duckless restaurant, there is something finally very convincing about a songeress who sings of pain and agony, lovelessness and betrayal and neglect. She looks at him, and their eyes meet; the black-suited waiter appears from the kitchen, bearing a filled plate, and a bottle of red pfin.

Petworth starts to eat; the song goes on. The songeress looks over at him, and she sings, evidently, of the treachery that is in every fondness, the emptiness and brutality that hide in love, the inevitability of the loneliness beyond affection; eating the kurbii churba, which could be hotter, but can reasonably be recommended, he listens and thinks of graffiti-strewn London, of the long flight, the dark labyrinths of arrival, the neglect in the lobby, the great spaces of his hotel bedroom. The plate empty, the waiter replaces it with another; the songeress replaces her song too, singing now, it seems, of infidelities, the lies and deceits of love, the pains of self-excoriation. Picking at the sarkii banatu, rich, but possibly over-spicy for the average Western palate, sipping the pfin, which has a reasonable bouquet but is somewhat light on the tongue, he attends and thinks homeward, to his bleak wife, that dark anima, in her chair in the garden, and then of a strange bird-like face, the face of Plitplov, a face that watches and spreads unease. 'Kaf'ifii?' asks the waiter, taking away his plate; 'Da,' says Petworth, his linguistic confidence growing, 'Da.' On the podium, the folkloric songeress, with a very bright, brittle number, tossing her long skirt high up over frilly pants as she sings, her sultry expression amended, concludes her act. At the table Petworth ends his with a cup of kaf'ifii which consists of heavy grounds sunk muddily down into blackened water, and should be avoided by the visitor at all costs. The songeress throws her arms wide, dips, smiles, takes her applause, and disappears; Petworth claps, looks at his watch, sees that it is nearly eleven and time for his telephone call home, signs, with his Parker ballpoint, the bill, and goes out into the lobby.

There is ill-lit gloom in the lobby, too, much changed since he left it. The lights are mostly doused, the crowds gone. 'Change money?' whispers a listless voice from behind a dark pillar; in the red plastic chairs, just one man, big-hatted, in a grey raincoat, sits in the half-dark and stares out into the silent square beyond the windows. No trams move; the dark city moves quietly in itself, a place of dangers and treacheries, courages and cowardices, deceits and late-night arrests. Under one small lamp, the lacquered-haired girl sits alone at the desk marked R'GYSTRAYII, reading a book; she does not look up as Petworth approaches. 'Slibob, passipotti?' says Petworth. 'Ha?' says the girl. 'Petworth, passipotti,' says Petworth. 'Na,' says the girl. 'Na passipotti?' asks Petworth, surprised. 'Pervert, is still at police,' says the girl. 'When?' asks Petworth. 'In the morrow,' says the girl, 'Always in the morrow, your guide knows it.' 'She asked for it tonight,' says Petworth. 'She likes to impress you,' says the girl, 'Our police, very thorough. You have key?' 'Da,' says Petworth. 'Go to your bed, come again in the morrow,' says the girl, turning over the pages of her book. The big-hatted man has turned around to stare at Petworth; he walks over to the vacant dark cavern of the elevator, and gets into the gloomy mirrored interior. He presses the button, and the doors begin to close; then, suddenly, there is a commotion, a hand in the closing space, and the doors are tugged open again. Two people stand there. One, in a shining gold dress, is one of the dark-haired whores from the Barr'ii Tzigane; she has white make-up painted round her dark eyes, and carries a jangling key. The other is an armed man, not now armed, a soldier, in a high-necked uniform and black leather boots that come up to the knee, in cavalry fashion. The man's hand is on the girl's rump. The couple get in, laughing and teasing; they press the button, and the lift begins to ascend.

Bumping and grinding, the lift goes up the inner hole of the building. Petworth sees, from the console above the door, that it has passed his floor and is going higher, up to the top of the hotel, where he has not yet been. A musky perfume comes off the body of the girl, a leathery sweat from that of the man. Then the doors come open, and the couple get out. Petworth stands there, as the doors gape, and sees, for a moment, a view of a large room, where many men are working. It is a techno-logical room, like a recording studio; tape recorders reel, and video monitors flicker, showing blue images of hotel corridors, moving figures, rooms just like his own. Then the doors shut, Petworth descends, and steps out, when they open again, onto a corridor just like the one on the screens. In the corridor are the dull wall lights, and the elderly floormaid, who rises and watches, just as other people watch, as he goes to his mahog-any door. He unlocks the door, and goes in. The hat-rack in the anteroom looms in the half-dark like a sharp thorny tree; in the bedroom beyond, the noise of the bathroom hisses, and the lights of table-lamps leave grotesque shadows of darkness in the corners and on the walls. The room is not as it was; someone has been in. They have lit the lamps, drawn the velvet curtains, uncovered the bed to expose the duvet. His blue suitcase lies open; on the bed his pyjamas have been laid out, with careful elegance, in the shape of a flattened man, the arms and the legs splayed, as if this is someone who has been steamrollered while being searched. Mirrors glint, the lights of cars flash crazily on the ceiling, the wardrobe door is shut and will not open. Petworth stands and stares, thinking of big-hatted men in the lobby, floormaids in the corridors, ears in the walls, bugs of an unnatural kind in the roses, cameras in the glass, watchers in the roof.

Outside in the darkness, where dark things are done, there is a noise: the clocks on the government buildings, the chimes on the belfries, are sounding. It is eleven; he goes to the bed, sits down, picks up the big brass telephone, and puts it to his ear. As he does so, the telephone, with a dragging chirp, begins to ring: 'Da?' says Petworth. 'Ha,' says a sexless voice, 'You like make call for United Kindom?' 'Da,' says Petworth. 'Hold please your piece,' says the voice, 'I try to make this number.' In the interstices of the international wiring, strange things now begin to occur. Several voices come on the line, asking each other questions; ratchets begin to click, digits to whirr; connections are made and unmade; there is noise and redundancy, redundancy and noise. Then out of the static comes a voice: 'Hallo, Slaka caller, what number are you calling?' it asks, in a very British accent. The voices on the line confer; Petworth sits on the bed, and thinks of a small and fairly modern house at the end of a bus-route in Bradford, where the furniture is contemporary and the television set flickers, showing a late-night news. A dull ringing tone starts; Petworth thinks of a dark wife, tired after a domestic day, rising from a contemporary sofa and walking across to the telephone. The ringing tone continues, and into the familiar image Petworth begins to intrude a note of doubt, a sense of mystery. For his dark wife is a wife who does not go out in the evenings, a domestic wife, a woman of familiar rounds. 'I'm sorry, Slaka caller,' says the British voice, after a while, 'That number isn't

111

answering.' 'Isn't answering?' cries Petworth. 'No good,' says the sexless voice in the hotel, 'Put down please your piece.'

Mystified, Petworth puts down his piece, and looks around the dark bedroom, doubly lonely now. There is indeed something about space that brings strangeness to usual relationships, something about old hotel rooms which, just like old sad songs, administers to fear and gloom, loneliness and guilt, and forms the exact outward expression of one's anxious inner twinges. The soul empties, the familiar goes, especially in those who have not much soul to start with. He sits on the bed; the great crack in the ceiling now seems wider, the mirrors glisten everywhere, the image of the female foot in the shoe stares at him from the opposite wall. He is just about to rise from the bed when, with its dull dragging note, the telephone rings again. 'Hallo,' says Petworth, picking it up, 'Is that you?' 'Me, is me,' says a voice, 'Who is you?' 'Petworth,' says Petworth. 'Yes, Petworth,' says the voice, 'And you are alone?' 'Completely,' says Petworth. 'Excuse me,' says the voice, 'Perhaps you have there a person?' 'No, no person,' says Petworth, 'Who is this? Is it Plitplov?' There is a long pause on the line, and then the voice says: 'Perhaps it is someone like that. It is just a good old friend.' 'I see,' says Petworth. 'Of course we cannot talk now,' says the voice, Plitplov or someone like that, 'You know it is necessary to be cautious. It is not such a good situation. But I have a message from the one you mention. He is afraid you think him discourteous.' 'Not at all,' says Petworth, 'I hope his headache is better.' 'Of course it was not really a headache,' says the voice, 'He thought that occasion called for such a small ruse. You know such ladies as your guide are not always the best companies for dear old friends. They like to be such bureaucrats. That lady, she has left you?' 'Yes, she's gone home,' says Petworth. 'You had a nice drink with her?' asks the voice.

'Oh, was your friend in the bar of the hotel tonight?' asks Petworth. 'In the bar?' asks the voice, Plitplov or whomever, 'I don't believe it. He has a headache. I hope you did not give

112

that lady too much to drink. Our ladies here are not like those English ladies. I believe you have a wife who enjoys a drink and is very amusing.' 'Do I?' says Petworth. 'I have heard this,' says the voice, 'Well, our friend hopes you are comfortable and have made some nice arrangements. He hopes you have a good programme. You know he had a little finger in that pie.' 'Yes, it's excellent,' says Petworth. 'Well, I will tell him,' says the voice, 'If I see him and his head is gone away. If you are pleased, he will know there is no hard feeling.' 'No, there's no hard feeling,' says Petworth. 'I think he likes perhaps that sometime you will dinner with him at his apartment,' says the voice. 'That would be very pleasant,' says Petworth. 'Of course he does not want to raise remarkable expectations,' says the voice, 'He knows how well you like to eat, such dinners in Cambridge. Here is not so easy. His wife is a simple and confused person, and not such a cook as your marvellous Lottie.' 'He knows my wife's cooking?' asks Petworth. 'He remembers with a delight her *boeuf à la mode*,' says the voice, 'Often he speaks of it. He hopes you remembered to telephone at her, and give her his love.' 'Does he?' asks Petworth, 'Well, tell him I rang and got no reply.' 'He will think this is very strange,' says the voice, 'He knows she does not like to go out at the night. But perhaps that telephone does not march so well. Often this happens in my country.' 'Does it?' asks Petworth. 'Of course he hopes to see you again,' says the voice, 'But you know he is busy man and has many doings. He thinks your paths will cross suddenly in several places.' 'Good,' says Petworth, suddenly feeling very tired. 'I expect you are feeling very tired,' says the voice, 'I hope you sleep very nicely. And that I do not disturb you if you are with someone.' 'I'm not,' says Petworth, 'Please thank him for the message. Goodnight.'

Petworth puts down the telephone. Yes, he is tired; it has been a long day, a day of multiple chapters, of testing and troubling exertions. He briefly tries the enormous radio, which emits, for all its splendour, only one channel, in the language he does not know. He takes off his jacket, and puts it over the dressing-table mirror; to see that, all round the room, from behind the bathroom door, the walls, even the ceiling, many more mirrors are watching him as he strips down to his tartan-pattern shorts. He uses the bathroom, where more mirrors look at him; he puts out all the lights but one, a great brass Sezession tablelamp by the bedside, gets into bed, pulls the great duvet over him, douses that light too. But full darkness does not come; car lights illuminate the ceiling, the gantries of trams flash pink into the room, an explosion of neon turns the glow to green. Pipes hiss, trams clang, official clocks on government buildings clang out news of the lateness of the hour. The ceiling crack gapes; there seems to be something like a loudspeaker affixed high on the wall just above the bathroom door; and everywhere the eye in the mirror, the ear in the roses, the pain in the stomach, the doubt in the head. His feet sticking from the end of the duvet, he thinks lazily on to two weeks of life in strange and unexpected cities: Slaka and Glit, Nogod and Provd. Cold in the room, he thinks of the warm marital bed at home, where a dark wife lies, or perhaps does not: the dark wife who smokes small cigars, and whose strange doings in Cambridge now begin to mystify him, the dark wife whom Plitplov knows better than he should; then Plitplov who, grinning, chuckling, present, absent, also knows and does not know his guide, Marisja Lubijova; the Lubijova who, with cold spectacles and warm laugh, grey coat and round figure, helpfully guides and suspiciously questions.

His mind slides, and more vague, disorienting images fill it – of a man on a plane with a beetroot, another man smoking a cigarette in an airport room, two men, one in a topcoat, another with a furled umbrella, who stare after him in a corridor of space. In the darkness outside the hotel, strange unseen shouters shout, there is a faint sad sound of music from somewhere, bells ring. The bells are distant, yet seem to grow nearer, taking on a dragging, chirping note; he comes awake to realize that, by his bed, by his head, the foreign telephone is ringing. He reaches out into the dark to pick it up, put it to his ear; 'Yes?' he says, 'Da?' 'Aarrgghhh,' says a male voice down the wire, 'Aaaarrggghhhh.' 'Who's there?' asks Petworth, staring up at the frescoed ceiling, where a green light goes on and off, on and off. 'Doc doc doctor Pet Pet Petworth?' asks the voice. 'Yes, who is that?' asks Petworth. 'Aarrghhh,' says the voice, 'Ah, well. You don't actually know me, but my name's St St Steadiman. I'm the sec sec second sec secretary at the British Embassy.' 'Oh, yes, Mr Steadiman,' says Petworth. 'Just wanted to say, well well welcome to Slaka,' says Steadiman, 'Sorry I'm late. I've been ringing round all the ho ho hotels, their chaps wouldn't tell us where you're staying. Glad to find you.' 'Yes,' says Petworth. 'The Slaka,' says Steadiman, 'They're really giving you the whole tree the whole treatment. You did get a din din dinner invite from me, did you? I had to scatter them liberally round in the hope of fi fi finding you.' 'I did, thank you,' says Petworth. 'Well, my wife and I are greatly hoping to enjoy your come your come your company tomorrow evening, if you can man man manage it,' says Steadiman, 'It's not often we get a fellow cunt a fellow ...' 'No, I suppose not,' says Petworth, 'I'd be delighted.' 'Good,' says Steadiman, 'Why don't I meet you in the bar of the ho ho hotel at, what shall we say, seven seven? You'll easily spot me, I'll be wearing a suit. They're looking after you prop prop properly?' 'Very well,' says Petworth. 'Fine,' says Steadiman, 'If you do get into any diff diff snags, call me at the Embassy. If they haven't cut the fo fo phones. Or just come in. If they're not turning back all vis vis visitors. Well, till tomorrow.' 'Thank you,' says Petworth, putting down the telephone.

He lies there in the undark darkness. Outside Slaka moves, city of flowers and gipsy music, of watchers and listeners. He reaches for sleep, but his mind lies awake, swimming in tumultuous exhaustion. Noise and redundancy, redundancy and noise, pass through it, a singsong of words and images that will not fix: slibob and tinkii, passipotti and crak'akii, the steelwork is famous for the high grade of its product, we wish you pleasant tour and hope it will bring friendship between our peoples, her name is Lottie I think, you must be very tired. The chatter grows, come from the dark psychic disorientations of travel; images flutter, in accelerating disconnection. From somewhere high up, there is a view down, over vast, encrusted lunar landscapes, rough peaks, icy cavities. Now a small dark wife sits in a garden under a parasol, while an observer spies down from an upstairs window, where in a room paper flutters in a typewriter. Now a soldier comes down a long metal tube, holding a gun in his hand. There is a great glinting mirror and it cracks suddenly open; beyond there is a deep dark hole into which something is drawn. Then there is a malign father, shouting; a forgotten mistress, in a kimono, hair swinging over one eye, coming through a door into a room; an old friend who might not be a friend, lying by a river; and a HOGPo man in a hat, who sits in a technologized room somewhere over a dark city, and listens, listens, wide awake, to the sound of snores, as Petworth sleeps.

4 – MINKULT.

I

Rain and storm are beating violently against the windows when Petworth comes to consciousness again, to find himself in his great bed, in his great bedroom, in the middle of Slaka. Now his programme will begin, and a day of formal meetings and duties lies before him – a purpose that gets him from his bed, into the bathroom, and then to the window to throw open the curtains and look out on the new world beyond. The view is strange; three men on a hydraulic platform are swaying in the air a few yards away from him, staring at him in his undershorts. Below, the square, so quiet last night, is busy again, a crowded place, filled with moving umbrellas, raincoated walkers, wet-topped pink trams. The hydraulic platform rises in the air from a dull grey truck; the three men are man-handling a great neon-sign saying SCH'VEPPII, which last night had stood on the building in the corner, and are lowering it to the ground on ropes. Petworth takes his grey suit from his blue suitcase, and retires to the bathroom to put it on; clad in formality, he goes out into the corridor, where a new young floormaid sits at the desk, and descends to the lobby to find breakfast.

It is not an easy task. Breakfast is served, not in the great dining room, but in a small room at the back of the hotel, where many besuited men, as neat as himself, sit reading newspapers and awaiting service. 'Is nicht schnell here, nicht schnell,' says the bald man, reading an East German

117

newspaper, whose table he joins, none being empty, 'This is why they haf bad economy.' Petworth picks up the menu, a well-thumbed card written in several languages, and offering rich fare: sausidge and pig-bacon, sheese and eggi. A waiter comes at last, with a laden tray for the bald man; Petworth determines to set to work on the new tongue. 'Pumpi, vurtsi, urti, kaf'ifii,' he says to the waiter. 'Moy,' says the waiter, picking up the menu, shaking his head, and bearing it away. He comes back again a moment later, bearing a new menu. Petworth looks at it in mystery, for its offerings are much the same as the last. 'Ranugu up pumpu? Ku up kaf'ufou?' asks the waiter, taking out his pad. 'They make a small linguistic revolution here,' says the bald German, leaning forward, 'They change a little all the grammatiks. This alzo is vy they are nicht schnell.' 'Ah,' says Petworth, reading the new menu, 'Pumpu, verstu, irtu, kaf'ufuu.' 'Slubab,' says the waiter. 'Now the old words are to be no more used,' says the bald German. Petworth looks around. At the next table a man reads the red-masted party newspaper, *P'rtyuu Pupulatuuu*, which has the headline *Untensu Actuvu*. 'I see,' he says. 'It is a very important political matter,' says the bald man, 'Even Wanko may be replaced.' The important political matter evidently delays things greatly; it is not until just before nine o'clock, the hour at which Petworth should be meeting Marisja Lubijova in the lobby, that his breakfast arrives. There is just time to gulp a little of the large bowl of irtu, snatch a few bites of the vertsu, drink down the pumpu, and sip a little of the hot acorn-flavoured kaf'ufuu, before he rushes out to the crowded hall, where a new group of Ivanovas mills round the desk marked R'GYSTRAYUU. In a plastic transparent raincoat over her long grey coat, and shaking a folded umbrella, Marisja Lubijova is already there.

'So, you are come, Comrade Petwurt,' she says briskly, 'And you have put on your nice suit for our official day. But don't you think you need perhaps a coat for the rain?' 'I haven't had time to go and get it,' he says, 'They were very slow with breakfast.' 'Of course, you are not now in America,' says Lubijova, looking at her watch, 'And do not be long, already we are late for our sightseeings. Did you remember to call your wife?' 'She wasn't there,' says Petworth. 'So I suppose I must make a new arrangement,' says Lubijova, 'You go, I will do it. And did you get your passport?' 'I asked for it last night,' says Petworth, 'It wasn't ready.' Lubijova looks at him crossly: 'Oh, Petwurt, can't you do just one thing? Now you are not a person, is that what you want? Do you like it that you don't exist? That I can't take you to the Mun'stratuu?' 'I'll go and ask for it now,' says Petworth. 'Go upstairs now, bring your coat,' says Lubijova, 'They will give it to me, don't you think so? I think you don't try very hard. Here you must fight a bit. Go, be quick.' Petworth goes up to his room, to see from the window that the men on the hydraulic platform are raising up a new sign saying SCH'VUPPUU to replace the old sign saying SCH'VEPPII; when he comes down again to the lobby in his raincoat, Lubijova is standing outside the elevator doors, waving his passport aloft. 'Of course it comes if you make it,' she says, 'She gives it to me. Also I have arranged a new telephone call. It is for six o'clock, after your programme today is finished. Now, do we go and do it? Or perhaps first I must button up your coat for you? Petwurt, Petwurt.'

It is a chilly Lubijova who walks ahead of him out of the lobby and into the square, where a heavy nineteenth-century bourgeois realist rain is washing down the high-gabled buildings and teeming over the moving street-crowds and the clanging trams. A squad of men in oilskins are digging up the cobble-stones between the tram-tracks; Lubijova walks through them. 'This way, please,' she says sharply, 'See how the men are working. Always we are improving our city. Always the work goes on. Look where you go, you are not from the farm, I think. First I take you to a very special place. Usually for foreigners it is forbidden, but you have a special permission, you are an official visitor.' Walking ahead, Lubijova dives suddenly into a dirty-windowed eating place, where many wet people eat hot dogs in standing position. 'Not here, we go to the back,' she says, leading the way to the door of an elevator, where an old lady in a chair sells tickets. The elevator is crowded, the ascent long; suddenly the doors open, and Petworth finds himself, in the driving rain and the whistling wind, on a very wet roof, with a short wire fence around it, high above the city, which is visible below, moving remotely about its business. 'You see, this is our skyscraper,' says Lubijova, 'Of course you must not photograph. Now from here is a very good view, but we cannot really see it. I hope you do not suffer the vertige. Now, please, look on this side. Over there the power station, do you see it, through the mist, it is more than sufficient for our needs. Near there the cathedral, but it is not visible. Well, it does not matter, it is not so interesting. Now we go this side, and here you see the old town. You can see the bridge Anniversary May 15, and the festung and the capella. At night you can go there and see a sound and a light. Is that how you say it in English?'

'Well,' says Petworth, 'A son et lumière.' 'Oh, what an interesting language you have, no wonder nobody understands it,' says Lubijova, 'I think you have a very strange language and are a very strange people. Some of them cannot even get back a passport.' 'I'm sorry,' says Petworth. 'Now come to this side,' says Lubijova, 'There, with the trees, the Park of Brotherhood and Friendship with the Russian peoples. The people of Slaka love very much to walk there and enjoy the scents, especially when it does not rain. Near there, do you see a building with a red star on top? This is our Party Head-quarters, a very fine building, and behind there is our best open space, the Plazscu P'rtyuu.' 'There's been a change in the language?' asks Petworth. 'Some radical elements have pres-sured our government to make certain changes,' says Lubijova, 'They ask for a linguistic liberalization, but I do not think it is very important. So there you see it, from the best view our very beautiful city. I hope you impress. On a nice day you would stay here a long time and take much pleasure, but today it is not perhaps so nice, so I think we go down again.' On the long elevator ride down, Lubijova stands away from him in the further side of the lift; out in the open air again, she walks several steps in front of him. They take the narrow old street where Marx and Engels, Lenin, Brezhnev and Wanko bounce furiously on their wires in the driving rain; they pass by the colonnade of the Military Academy, under which disconsolate soldiers stand with portfolios under their arms; they walk beside the Palace of Culture, covered in ivy, out of which, from some basement, there comes the unexpected sound of jazz.

They turn down another street, a street of a few small shops. Most of these stores seem curiously turned in on themselves, concealing rather than revealing the goods they offer to sell. Shops at home insist on display, but these do not; they secrete this and that, showing small stacks of one thing, or a single object: light fittings, bottles of soft drink, flowers, tins of beet, a hint of meat, a notional vegetable or two. 'I hope you look,' says Marisja Lubijova, 'We know your press tells always we have very bad food shortage. Well, now you can see there is plenty of everything. Oh, look, here is a line, a queue, do you call it? I suppose you think it is for food. Do you like to join it and see?' The long line of people stands in the rain: 'Do you see how they all excite, to go into this shop?' asks Mari, 'Do you know why, you don't guess? Well, it is because our people are all very good readers, and today come out the new editions, and also in the new language. I hope your people wait so long in the rain, just to buy books!' 'I don't think so,' says Petworth. 'Of course, your newspapers tell we do not like to respect at all our writers,' says Marisja Lubijova, 'Well, now you can go home to tell them they are wrong. Oh, look, now we go in. Can you wait me, please look around, I like to buy something.' He watches Lubijova push through the jostle of people toward the counter; he turns to look at the shelf upon shelf of books, the millions of infolded words, all written in the language he does not know. Some are titled in the Cyrillic alphabet, some in the Latin, but the alphabet does not matter, for the codes will not yield, the signs refuse to become meaning.

The raincoats of the shoppers steam in the greater warmth; an assistant with a great ladder pushes Petworth aside, to climb to a distant top shelf. Petworth inspects more titles; from above, a book disturbed by the assistant tumbles down onto his head and cracks open, as if that might be a route to contact. 'Comrade Petwurt, here, come,' calls Lubijova, standing at the counter in her plastic coat, 'This is one of our new books, just out today. Do you like perhaps the cover?' Petworth takes the book, in a green paper wrapper, illustrated with a line drawing of an expressionist dark castle, which is seen through a rough shattered mirror; he looks at the title, which is *Nodu Hug*, and the name of the author, Katya Princip. He flicks the pages, the blocks of mysterious words, the units of meaning, the paragraphs, the chapters, the claim on time, the appeal to imagination. 'You know we have here a very good Writers' Union and even in the world some of our people are very famous,' says Lubijova, 'Well, here is a book by one of the best, it is Katya Princip. Of course not everyone likes her books, some people say she is not correct.' 'Not correct?' asks Petworth, 'Why?' 'Not correct because she diverts from the socialist realism, which we like, and goes to the fantastic. But she has a good imagination and often we like the fantastic here in my country, so many people appreciate her works very much. Also she writes a very strange kind of story, how can I tell you? It is like the stories we tell to children, with in it dreams, and staircases that go to nowhere, and castles, perhaps; but really those stories are not for the children at all, they are for us. No, I do not explain you very well, but please take it. I have bought for you this book.'

'For me?' says Petworth, picking up the green book, and ruffling again through the pages, 'That's very kind. But there is just one problem, I can't read it. I think you should keep it for yourself.' Lubijova, in her plastic coat, stares at him severely: 'Petwurt, really, do you like to annoy me again?' she says, 'Is this what you do always with a present that is for you? Of course I know you cannot read it, you have to have a guide. But, you see, Petwurt, perhaps you don't know it, but I am really a little bit psychic. Do you believe in that, I hope you do? And, do you know, I have an instinct; it tells me that when you go away from Slaka you will understand that book, just a bit. Also we have two weeks together, I can explain you some of it. Of course I don't read it yet myself, but I can tell you it is, what do you say, a folk-story, and some of it happens in a big forest and near a castle. *Nodu Hug*, the title, that means not to be afraid. Anyway, Petwurt, there is another reason why you must have it. I cannot tell it to you yet, but you will see.' 'Then I'll take it,' says Petworth, 'Thank you very much, Mari.' 'And don't you realize something else,' says Lubijova, laughing at him, seizing his arm, taking him toward the entrance to the store, 'That I have forgiven you your passport? Well, we cannot let all those bureaucrats upset us, I think we like to be comrades. Now, how much time have we more, an hour, almost, right, we do something else that is very nice. Turn your coat, we go round that corner, round another, and then do you know what we do? We stand again in a line; poor Petwurt, it is all lines for you today. But that line is very different and quite interesting. Now, put please the book inside your pocket, I don't want it wetted by that rain. And turn your coat, now we go.'

They go, round the corner, round another; and then, suddenly, Petworth finds himself standing on the edge of a great central square. The square glistens, vast, in the rain; there is a wide vista down to a large monument, where tangled bronze soldiers and workers collaborate in some interlocking enterprise; round the monument are stalls, the stalls of many flower sellers. People crowd round the stalls and wander the square, robed black Africans, a group of Arabs in burnouses, a gaggle of Ivanovas led by a blue Cosmoplot guide holding up high a beflowered umbrella; but the square still looks empty, so large are its spaces, so big its surrounding buildings, which are

123

square, and white, and colonnaded. 'This place, do you know it, I hope you do,' says Lubijova, 'Oh, don't you, Petwurt, really? Of course it is Plazscu P'rtyuu, where is our government, and where our people like to come to make their celebrations. Can you imagine how many peoples can pass here, with their banners? Well, you do not need to imagine, because you will see it all of course on National Culture day.' And Petworth sees that, into the steps of the buildings, great reviewing stands have been built, covered in red bunting. Indeed red is the colour of many things: of the long banners that blow out from the poles that stand high over the square, of the carnations that the flower-sellers are selling from their stalls round the monument, of the trim round the great photographs that, four storeys high, hang from the façades and stare down at them as they walk the clean white stone pavement, photographs in the style of grand or epic realism. An engrandized Marx stares across the square towards a superhuman Lenin; Brezhnev and Wanko enfold together in a vast embrace.

'I hope you impress,' says Mari Lubijova, taking his arm, 'Now we walk and I show it all to you. Over here, the Praesidium, over there with on top the red star the Party Headquarter. Over there, where the Japanese go, the Ministry of Strange Affairs, is that how you say?' 'The Foreign Ministry,' says Petworth. 'And over there,' says Lubijova, 'where is celebrate the great brotherhood of Brezhnev and Wanko, the Ministry of State Security, that is very forbidden. Really, a lot of these areas are forbidden to foreigners, so I think you don't go there, Petwurt. Also forbidden here are the cars, that is nice, except of course for the cars of the party cadres. Do you see them, the big Russian Volgas with the curtains in the back? Only the important people can ride in a car like that, I wonder if you will ride in one, Petwurt? Perhaps so, you are important person. And the stands for the parade, you will go in one of those too, on our special day.' Over the big buildings, the clocks begin to chime; they walk down the long square. 'You do not see a Ministry of Culture, that is round a corner,' says

Lubijova, 'But do you see where we are going first? Where the line waits?' And down at the bottom of the square there is indeed a long line of people – schoolchildren with flags, peasants in dark clothes, Ivanovas with plastic over their blonde hair, Vietnamese women, wearing cadre jackets – snaking across the *pavé*, and waiting, evidently, to enter a cube-like, modern, white stone building, also hung with bunting, with, standing round it, at every corner, and every entrance, stiff soldiers in shakos, a feather sticking up from the top.

'Now we join that line,' says Marisja Lubijova, 'I think you come under my umbrella, or you will catch some rheum. Don't you see the soldiers, do you like their uniforms, from our past days? They are a very special guard, but this is very special place. Now we must wait, twenty minutes, perhaps, half an hour, but you will see it is worth it. You will find out something very interesting about our people. These peasants have saved many months to make their visit here. The children at school beg their teachers always to let them make this visit. Oh, what a pity, we have forgotten something, really we should carry some flowers, we call them comrade carnation, well, never mind.' The clocks on the big buildings chime again before they reach a clefted entrance, guarded by two shako-ed soldiers. 'Oh, that is nice, now we go in,' says Lubijova, 'Now we must be quiet, but you will see what you will see. Take care, it is dark inside.' They go, in the moving line of people, down the narrow space of a chilly stone passage, with a sickly scent in the air, until the light brightens, the line splits, and there is an illuminated place with a central stone plinth. On the plinth, in a half coffin, lies the embalmed body of a dead man, dressed in modern clothes of a plain kind, sporting a big grey moustache. Skilful lights cast from above make him seem larger than life-size; the waxified face has been cast in an expression half-compassionate, half-severe. Affairs of weight have creased his brow, principle stares from his eyes. Evidently he is a man of history, since a scrolled document, a proclamation or treaty, lies on his chest; but he is also a man of the people, since a few workers' tools lie beside him, a hammer and saw, a sickle and file, and his hands are horny with use.

'Of course it is tomb,' says Lubijova, holding Petworth's arm and whispering in his ear, 'You know he is real, if dead? Do you know him from his photograph, it is Grigoric our Liberator. Don't they keep him very well? He looks just like himself!' The people all round them have stopped and are dipping their knees, putting down their carnations on the plinth; Grigoric's eyes, meanwhile, stare at the ceiling, as if he has had a vision beyond himself. Indeed, looking up, one may see it painted there: a world where large muscled men dig holes and raise buildings in energetic and momentous enterprise, where big-breasted women stack fruitful sheaves in ripe fields, and still hold onto their abundant babies. 'We love him very much, you see,' whispers Lubijova, 'He set us free to the Russians after the war, and planned our socialist economy. You see he was worker, his father made saddles for the horses in Plit. But also he studied at Berlin and Muskva, and so we say he was intellectual as well. Then he was brave in our uprisings, so also a soldier. So we like him very much. Here we love our dead, and we think they love us. Do you do the same for your great men?' 'No, we don't,' says Petworth. 'Well, perhaps you don't have any like that,' says Lubijova, as they move forward with the people through another narrow stone corridor, to where the light of day bursts, and they are out again in the wet and windswept square.

'So, Petwurt,' says Lubijova, stopping and looking at him gaily, 'Did you like it? I think now you have had many pleasures. You have seen our city, and you have seen our great leader. Of course there are many more sight-seeings you must do, but you have so many days. Now, what is time? Oh, we were long there, we must go straight away to the Mun'stratuu. Now, put on please your very official behaviour, I hope you have some. Let me see you, your suit is nice, but your tie is not neat, put it up please. And now do you have your passport? I hope so, they do not let you in there without it.' Petworth feels in his pockets, grows desperate: 'No, I don't,' he says. 'Petwurt, no, is it gone?' cries Lubijova, 'I hope you don't think somebody steals it? In my country nobody steals.' 'It's not there,' says Petworth. 'No,' says Lubijova, laughing at him, 'Petwurt, it is here. I kept it all the time, just to be safe. Now, we are in a hurry. So do you run?' She turns on her heel and begins to run, away from the scented tomb and across the wide space of the paved square, beneath the flapping red banners. Her hat bounces, her bag swings; she stops, looks back at him, shouts 'Come,' and runs on again. In his best suit and raincoat, Petworth clumsily lifts his feet and pursues his guide, running beneath the great buildings and the high photographs, toward his next appointment.

II

The Mun'stratuu Kulturu Komitet'uuu are not to be found in Plazscu P'rtyou; it lies, perhaps appropriately, just round the corner, in Stalungrydsumytu, a small dark street with high old buildings. A khaki soldier sits outside it, in a box with a telephone in, and inspects their papers; a blue militiaman in a cage inspects them again, and points them up a wooden staircase. 'They know me here,' says Lubijova, leading Petworth through a mess of dusty and ill-painted corridors, where men and women wander carrying files. Then she stops at a door, on which there is a sign saying UPRATTU L. TANKIC, knocks, and goes inside. In the office there sits on a typist's chair a full-bodied young lady with auburn hair and a tight blue dress; she rests her elbows, as if exhausted, on an old black typewriter. 'Prifussoru Pitworthu?' she asks, getting up and going into an inner room. 'Vantu,' shouts a male voice. 'We go in,' says Lubijova, leading him into a small room with many high cupboards, a big metal desk, and behind the desk a small bald round man in a black suit, smoking a cigar with a plastic mouthpiece. The man rises, embraces Lubijova, and puts out his hand to Petworth. 'My English, bad,' he says, 'But we have beautiful interpreter. Very tough lady, picked special for you.' 'So I translate,' says Lubijova. 'Make us sound very good,' says the bald man, who has a humorous glint in his eye, 'Please.' He points to a set of plastic black armchairs surrounding a small coffee table; then, still standing by his desk, he begins a little speech.

'Says you are here, says he is pleased,' explains Lubijova, 'Says his name is Tankic, he is high official here, Uprattu. Says the Minister of Culture wished himself to greet you, but he must attend a meeting of the Praesidium on a certain matter. Says before he departs, the Minister has asked to him, Tankic, to convey warm amity and fraternal felicitations to your own Minister of Culture and to all your government. Also he tells Tankic to make your visit very happy. Also he wishes you pleasant tour and hopes it brings friendships between our peoples. Now I think you say something, Petwurt.' 'Please tell him how glad I am to be here, and how grateful I am for the excellent arrangements made for me. I look forward to my programme, and I know I bring the good wishes of Her Majesty's Government, who also wish this tour to be a great success.' Tankic beams, nods, and lifts a book from his desk. 'Says he wishes to present you with a book describing our five-year-plan and the collective achievements of our people, signed by the Minister himself,' says Lubijova, 'Do you have a book, Petwurt?' 'No,' says Petworth. 'Then thank him very nicely and I will translate,' says Lubijova. This is done; Tankic beams, chuckles, nods his head, rubs his hands, and sits down opposite Petworth, tapping him on the knee. 'Asks how you like our Slakan rain,' explains Lubijova, 'Says we have imported it from Britain especially for you, in exchange for some Slakan sunshine.' Tankic nods his head very emphatically, and then laughs out loud; Petworth laughs too, and says: 'Tell him that Britain has two exports we are only too glad to make. Rain is one; I'm the other.' When this is translated, Tankic laughs uproariously and hits Petworth on the knee. 'Says you must

128

find some more such exports,' says Lubijova, 'Then perhaps you would start to make a real economic progress.'

The tight-dressed lady now stands over them, beaming and giggling. 'Take some coffee, Prifusorru?' she asks. Tankic says something: 'Asks if you think his secretary speaks the good English,' explains Lubijova, 'She has typed your programme. If you say yes, says perhaps he pays her more money.' The secretary blushes red; 'She deserves a rise immediately,' says Petworth. Tankic laughs and slaps Petworth's knee again. 'Says definitely you are a friend of the people,' says Lubijova, 'Always wanting to improve their economical conditions.' 'You like such coffee?' asks the secretary, pouring a rich syrupy liquid from a copper receptacle into the small cup in front of Petworth. 'Ah, Turkish, excellent,' says Petworth. 'Na, na, na, na,' says Tankic, shaking a finger. 'Says we do not call coffee after our oppressors,' says Lubijova, 'Here we call it comrade coffee.' 'I'm sorry,' says Petworth. 'Asks, your programme, do you like it, or do you ask many changes? He says his secretary can go to the typewriter and change it, instead of standing there looking at your handsome face.' 'It's fine,' says Petworth. 'Explains he has worked very hard on it, because officials must always have much paperwork to do,' says Lubijova, 'Otherwise they might do something important.' Tankic laughs, and Petworth laughs; then Tankic points at Lubijova, who goes red. 'Asks if you are pleased with the guide he has provided you, to take care all your wants.' Tankic leans forward and taps Lubijova on the knee: 'Says of course these are official wants only.' 'Real tough lady,' says Tankic in English, laughing. 'Tell him I like the tough ones,' says Petworth. 'Says good,'says Lubijova, 'Says he thinks you are the sort of man who will drink a little brandy with him.'

The tight-dressed lady goes to one of the cupboards and produces a bottle and four glasses; Tankic says something which makes her laugh very loudly. 'Says he does not smoke, drink, gamble with cards or play at all with women, except when you come,' says Lubijova, 'This is why he hopes you

129

come very often.' The lady puts the glasses on the table; Tankic takes the bottle and begins to fill the glasses with a bright clear liquid. 'Says it is special from a farm he knows,' says Lubijova, 'Now he makes a toast. Remember with the eyes, Petwurt, I taught you. Says: a toast to many more toasts together.' Petworth, raising his glass, tries to remember Lubijova's lesson: 'Na, na, na,' says Tankic. 'Oh, Petwurt,' says Lubijova, 'He says you do it wrong. Says in our country when we do a thing, we always follow afterwards a criticism session, so we can do things better. He remarks you let the brandy touch the tongue and the throat, which wastes much time that could be devoted to the good of the people. Now he regrets he must fill your glass again, to see if you make improvement.' And over the next half hour, in the office of the Uprattu Tankic, Petworth improves and improves. There is much laughter in the room; Tankic chuckles and grins; other heads from other offices peer in. Then Tankic rises and claps Petworth on the arm: 'Says he must take you to another place, to give you some lessons in Slakan food,' explains Lubijova, 'It is an official lunch given in your honour, he hopes you accept.' 'Delighted,' says Petworth, rising, a little uncertainly, from the black plastic chair. Tankic puts on a belted black overcoat, and a black Homburg hat; then he leads the way into the corridor, shouting boisterously at functionaries sitting at their desks behind half-open doors.

Down the stairs and out into the street they go, past the militiaman in the cage, the soldier in the box. In front of the building, a crop-headed driver in a grey shirt and black trousers stands in the rain, holding open the door of a large Russian Volga, a great black car with a toothy front grille. 'Oh, Petwurt, you go in one after all,' cries Lubijova, from the front seat, turning round to look at where Petworth sits in the middle again, between the tightly dressed lady and Tankic. 'Where are the curtains?' asks Petworth, looking round. Tankic laughs and claps Petworth boisterously on the shoulder. 'Says do you think he would let you ride with his beautiful secretary in a car with curtains?' explains Lubijova. The secretary wriggles and laughs too, a rich perfume spilling from between her breasts. 'Tells the people who wait at the restaurant to meet you. Professor Rom Rum, of the National Academy of Arts and Sciences, who makes an important research into literary science from a hermeneutic viewpoint. Perhaps already you know him by his work?' 'I'm afraid not,' says Petworth. 'And someone you know already, Katya Princip.' 'I know her?' asks Petworth. 'Petwurt, Petwurt, you are terrible, sometimes you make me annoy. Don't you remember please that book I just gave to you?' 'Yes, of course,' says Petworth. 'Oh, dear, you are terrible,' cries Tankic, mimicking, laughing, 'Very tough lady, this, ha? Like a wife. I pick her special for you.' 'Sometimes he is very bad,' says Lubijova. 'But I also think quite nice,' says the lady in the tight dress, smiling at him. The car is passing along the modern boulevard, past MUG and WICWOK; Petworth suddenly notices that, lined up along the curbsides, there are thick rows of children, waving small green flags at them as they pass. He points them out to Tankic, who laughs. 'Says not for you,' explains Lubijova, 'A sheikh of Arabia comes here today. Says when you bring us something useful, not culture but oil, you also can have the children with little flags.'

But now the stiff-necked driver turns the wheel, and they leave the boulevard, turning up a narrow, rising street, lined with high old houses, toward the ancient part of the town. 'Here now old Slaka,' says Lubijova, 'Notice please the buildings of Baroque and Renaissance. Now you see how Slaka is so fine.' 'You come before?' asks the tight-dressed lady, wriggling against him. 'No, my first visit,' says Petworth. 'A church and a rectorate,' says Lubijova. 'Many pretty girls,' says the lady. 'Oh, don't look at those, please,' says Tankic, laughing, 'Think of production.' 'Now the festung, builded by Bishop Vlam,' says Lubijova, 'Where is made the sound and the light.' 'Vlam, very successful,' says Tankic, 'Much power, many ladies. But no more, under socialism.' 'Oh, no?' cries the tight-dressed lady, 'I think so!' 'A famous old square,' says Lubijova.

131

The car stops in the famous old square, which is filled with trees, and lies under the crenellated wall of the castle; there is a vista down across the river, to gardens and white-painted, creeper-clad houses on the further bank. 'Here very nice restaurant,' says Tankic, pointing to an old timber-framed building in the corner, with tables outside it, now wet with rain, 'No gipsy, no violin, only talk, very good.' The driver opens the rear door of the big Volga, and they step out into the square. Elevating a large flowery umbrella, the tight-dressed lady puts her arm through Petworth's, and leads him under the trees toward the restaurant; heavy drops of rain explode on the thin fabric over them. 'Please,' says Tankic, ushering him through a door where a sign says РЕСТОРАН ЛРОЛЛ, 'Nice, yes? Many official come here.'

And it is pleasant indeed in the Restaurant Propp; there are wine barrels in the corners, old swords on the wall, and a great vine grows through and over the diners who sit there at white-clothed tables, served by waiters in black waistcoats and white aprons. Some open-mouthed carp, four silver trout, gape at them from a bubbling fishtank. 'Not here, more,' says Tankic, leading the way toward a curtained alcove; when the curtain is drawn there is a small room, a table set for six, a waiting waiter, and two other waiters too, the early guests, standing there, holding small drinks. One is a small middle-aged man, in a neat dark suit and a white shirt, who wears his topcoat hung over his shoulders; he stares at Petworth, who stares back. 'Lyft'drumu!' cries the man, 'Flughavn!' 'Feder! Stylo!' says Petworth. 'Scrypt'stuku!' says the man, laughing. 'You meet before?' asks Lubijova. 'It's the man from the airport who borrowed my pen!' says Petworth. 'And Plitplov thinks he steals it?' says Lubijova. 'Oh, yes, Plitplov, you know him?' asks the other guest, a fine, handsome lady, who wears a loose batik dress, cream sheepskin waistcoat, high glove-leather brown boots, and has white sunglasses pushed up into her blonde hair, 'That silly man who writes those essays in the newspaper?' 'Trollop,' says the middle-aged man. 'Yes, he writes on Trollope,' says Petworth. 'It is awful,' says the lady. 'Weren't you at the airport too?' asks Petworth, looking at her. 'Oh, did you notice me?' asks the lady, who looks like a very elegant shepherd, 'You know your silver pen was for me? Well, it is a magical thing, to lend a pen.' 'Our writer Katya Princip, our Academician, Professor Rum,' says Tankic, 'Meet please our English guest of honour, Dr Petworth.'

III

And so it is that Petworth comes to the Restaurant Propp beneath the castle in Slaka, residence once of Bishop-Krakator 'Wencher' Vlam (1678–1738, if my hastily scribbled notes are correct), and meets there the brilliant, batik-clad magical realist novelist Katya Princip, who takes him familiarly by the arm, leads him out of the group, and moves him toward the corner of the room. 'Come now and talk to me,' she says, 'Not about that Plitplov, you don't know him, do you; no, please, explain me something. Why am I here? Why do I get invite to an official lunch?' 'I'm afraid I've no idea,' says Petworth, 'Of course I'm delighted you did.' 'I am not invite before,' says Katya Princip, 'You know, I am not so well, with this regime. Usually it is only the reliable ones, like Professor Rum, who come to such things. So of course I wonder, have I done something bad, and don't know it? Is my new book so terrible? Do they think I am good?' 'Your new book,' says Petworth, 'I have it.' 'Oh, really?' cries Katya Princip, staring at him with grey eyes, 'Then perhaps that is it. Perhaps you are famous admirer of my writings? Perhaps I am chosen just for you? But you have our language? It is not translated in English.' 'I don't yet,' says Petworth, 'I mean to try.' 'Yes, I see,' says Katya Princip, 'You don't be my admirer yet, but one day you will be. Now I understand everything. You see, nothing in this world is accident. Especially here in Slaka.' 'Could you sign it for me?' asks Petworth. 'If you have a pen,' says Katya Princip,

'But of course you have a pen.' 'Oh, she signs your book?' says Lubijova, coming up. 'Oh, don't you know, this is my admirer,' says Katya Princip, 'That is why I am here.' 'Comrade Tankic likes you to come to the table,' says Lubijova. 'Oh, we are naughty, we talk too much,' says Princip, 'Everyone thinks we are rude. Well, I leave you now, I hope we meet again.' 'She's very nice,' says Petworth. 'Well, perhaps you must be a little cautious with this lady,' says Mari Lubijova, leading him over to the table, 'Sometimes she makes a little trouble, and not everyone likes her work.' 'Here, Comrade Petworth, between our fine Slakan roses,' says Tankic, gesturing him to the seat facing him; Petworth sits down.

'Oh, you sit with me, is nice,' says the tight-dressed lady, giggling, placed to Petworth's left. 'Oh, we meet again, what a surprise, how good,' says Katya Princip, coming to Petworth's right. 'I'm afraid I don't know your name,' says Petworth, to the tight-dressed lady. 'Oh, it is Vera,' says the lady, 'It means truth.' 'No, it means faith,' says Katya Princip, 'Pravda means truth. Oh, Mr Petwit, you must be very important man. Look, they draw the curtain to hide you. I expect you are at least a Shah or a Minister.' 'Expert,' says Tankic, pointing at Petworth with his fork. 'Oh, expert,' says Princip, 'And what do you expert? I am sorry I do not know.' 'The teaching of English,' says Petworth, 'That's all.' 'Really, well, you must show us your skill on Professor Rum,' says Katya Princip, 'His English is terrible. We like it perfect by the end of the meal.' 'Yes, my English, poco, I am all mistake,' says Professor Rum, who has tucked his napkin into the neck of his white shirt. 'Don't mind, Comrade Rum,' says Katya Princip, 'We will translate you. If we like what you say. My English, not so little, not so big, just middle. You are lucky Mr Petwit, you speak a language everyone understand. Except for Professor Rum.' 'Not everyone,' says Petworth. 'But think of us!' says Katya Princip, 'We are just a little country, a tiny flyshit on the great map of the world. And we speak just a silly little language, and no one understands. Not even us.' 'He tries to learn it,' says Lubijova, who sits opposite Vera, 'He likes to read your book.' 'Oh, don't bother,' says Princip, 'My book is so good you can understand it in any language. And now we make a language reform, so what you learn this week is no good next.' 'Now we must change all our signs, it is very bad,' says Vera. 'No, very good,' says Katya Princip.

Then the waistcoated waiter leans across Petworth's shoulder, and fills his glass with a clear spirituous liquid. 'Rot'vitti?' he asks. 'Now you must not say rot'vitti, rot'vuttu,' says Vera. 'But in any case is not rot'vuttu,' says Princip, 'Is lubuduss, made of the squish of a plum.' 'I think kicrak,' says Lubijova, 'From the mush of a pear.' 'No, is plum,' says Katya Princip, 'I am writer, I know everything.' 'Oh, everything?' says Vera. 'Yes, everything,' says Princip, 'Example: I do not come before to official lunch, I am not such good citizen, but I know Comrade Tankic will rise now and tell of our great cultural achievements. And then, Comrade Petwurt, you will reply, and tell us of your milk production.' 'My milk production?' says Petworth. 'Of course, we concern very much,' says Princip, 'Why do you think we come so far, through Slaka in the rain?' And the prophecy seems correct, for Tankic has risen already, and is tapping his glass with his knife; he begins a fluent, beaming speech. 'Says Comrades,' explains Lubijova, when he pauses, 'I am pleased to represent here our Minister of Culture, who regrets he is elsewhere, to welcome our excellent visitor Comrade Petwurt.' 'Our Minister of Culture,' Princip whispers in Petworth's ear, 'A soldier who has read a book. Better than the last one: a soldier who had not read a book.' 'Says we are proud to welcome you to our country of many achievements, economic and also cultural. Since the feudal and bourgeois times, we have made a great leap forward.' 'Who hasn't?' murmurs Princip. 'Our peoples support the modernization programmes everywhere in train,' says Lubijova, 'The productions of our agro-industries rise thirty times since socialism. Per capita floor space is ten square metres.' 'Now we no longer sit on top of each other,' whispers Princip.

'Our National Academy of Arts and Sciences makes notable wissenschafts, represented by Professor Rum. Our Writers' Union claims over a thousand fine members, represented here by Comrade Princip.' 'Your nice friend,' whispers Princip. 'Comrade Petwurt, you will see many great achievements in your tour,' says Lubijova, 'We hope you like them much and tell them in your country. You will see many beauties of our heritage, but let us make toast to the very best, we know you agree it. Welcome, and please drink to our finest treasure: the beautiful ladies, for the first time.'

Tankic sits down, grinning at Petworth. 'A quite good speech, a very bad toast,' says Katya Princip, 'It is to me, so I cannot drink.' 'Comrade Petworth, is your turn,' says Vera. 'Please, your milk production,' says Princip. 'Oh, me?' says Petworth, but hands from either side are pushing him erect; he finds himself looking round the table. 'Friends,' he says. 'Comrades,' says Princip. 'Comrades,' says Petworth. For some reason, the room seems to be swirling and creaking a little, and words, which are his business, will not come easily. But, words being his business, it occurs to him to comment, sociolinguistically, a word that, somehow, is not very easy to say today, on the great differences between the speechmaking habits of different nations: Germans will speak soulfully of Kant and Beethoven, Americans colloquially of space and territory, Norwegians poetically of mountains and fish, Russians proudly of industry and sport, while the British will speak only about their weather, and then to condemn it. An illustration comes to mind, perhaps not the best, Petworth realizes after a moment, as he reports a tale of what different women of different nations are supposed to say after love-making – 'What, finished so soon?' says the Frenchwoman, 'My sadness has almost gone away,' says the Scandinavian, 'Great, what did you say your name was?' says the American, 'You have made a great contribution,' says the Russian, 'Okay, now let's eat,' says the German, and 'Feeling better, darling?' says the Englishwoman. No, it is not of the best; Lubijova, scribbling furious notes for her translation, stops, staring up at him over her glass; 'It is yoke?' asks Tankic, fuming to her. It seems wise to conclude the occasion, to raise the glass, to propose a toast, and what better than to language? 'To language,' he says, 'The words that bring us all here, and bring us closer together.'

'Well, it is not so good a speech,' says Katya Princip, squeezing his arm as he sits down, 'I am ignorant about your milk production much as I was before. But I like very much your toast. You see, I can drink it.' 'Comrade Petwurt,' says Lubijova, leaning over the table, 'You did not leave time for me to interpret you. Also you make yokes, and those are not so easy.' 'Really, no need to translate,' says Katya Princip, 'Everyone understands enough, except Professor Rum, and I think he has heard speeches before. Oh, look, here is Professor Rum, he likes to say something to you, what do you like to say, Professor Rum?' 'This is naughty lady,' says Tankic, grinning at Petworth across the table. 'Oh, he asks about the politics of your speech,' explains Katya Princip, 'He likes to know whether in our language revolution here you are supporting the forces of stability, or of reform.' 'I know nothing about the situation,' says Petworth, 'There were no politics.' 'I told him that already,' says Katya Princip, 'He doesn't understand it. Well, I think while you are here you will learn some. We make here a fine change.' 'A very bad change,' says Tankic. 'Oh, dear, I am sorry,' says Princip, 'Already you learn there is more than one opinion in this world. Well, I am bad, I talk too much. But then you know our saying? The more talk, the more country.' And there is more talk; the chatter flows round the table, and the glasses fill and refill. Across from Petworth, Tankic is rising again, and tapping his glass: 'Cam'radayet,' he says. 'Says he understands our excellent visitor likes yokes,' explains Lubijova, 'He is pleased, because also in Slaka we like yokes very much.' 'Of course,' whispers Princip to Petworth, 'Many of them are in office.' 'He tells our visitor, you will go on your tour to Glit, so here a yoke of Glit, where the yokes are about peasants. One day a man meets on the road a Glit

137

peasant who is crying over the corpus of his dead donkey. "I am sorry is dead your mule," says the man. "It is much worse than you think," says the peasant, "He was not an ordinary mule. Since a week, he had learned to live without eating." So he makes another toast: to all here, who have not learned to live without eating. Also to the beautiful ladies, this time sincerely.' 'And to the politicians, who find for us all our food,' says Princip, raising her glass, 'May their efforts one day be rewarded.'

And then the waiter comes, and pours a rich red soup into their dishes: 'I hope you like, *kapus'nuc*,' says Vera. 'Soup of the cabbage,' says Lubijova. 'We call it, Comrade Cabbage,' says Tankic. 'Because it is red,' says Princip. Wine is poured into their glasses: 'It is very typical,' says Vera, 'We call it pfin.' 'They say we export always the best wine, and keep the worse,' says Lubijova, 'Now you see it is not true.' 'No, we drink the best, and the people drink the worse,' says Katya Princip, 'So works the planned economy.' 'Our state vineyards, co-operative, very advanced,' says Tankic, across the table. 'Once they were nunneries,' says Vera. 'I think monasteries,' says Lubijova. 'From the klosters,' says Tankic. 'Where live the religious,' says Vera. 'If a monk, always a bottle,' says Tankic, 'Now no more, under socialism.' 'No, now if an apparatchik, always a bottle,' says Princip. 'Nothing wrong with a bottle, I hope?' says Tankic. 'Of course, I also like,' says Princip, 'Mais plus ça change, plus c'est la même chose.' A certain sharpness is in the air; Petworth, drinking soup, attempts diplomacy, as he likes to. 'So you speak French too,' he says, 'How many languages?' 'Oh, my dear,' says Princip, turning to him, and reaching out to ruffle the hairs on the back of his neck, 'When I am with you, then I speak everything.' 'Our writers, very good translators,' says Tankic. 'Oh, yes,' says Princip, 'As you hear in the speech, we have many writers here. They work for the state and the future, especially of course the state. For this is needed many skills. Example: sometimes I am a writer, sometimes I drive a tram.' 'Really?' says Petworth, 'That's amazing.' 'Yes,' says Princip, 'Here, if they do not like what you write, they let you drive a tram. But never, I notice, the other way round.' 'We have very good Writers' Union,' says Tankic. 'And always they will look after you very well,' says Princip, 'And make sure that you do not write things that are silly and not correct. And if you do, well, they are very kind, and you can go to a dacha on Lake Katuruu. And there all the best writers will come, and sleep with you, and tell you how to write in a way that is correct. Oh, look, Professor Rum says something else, what is, Professor Rum?' 'A very naughty lady,' says Tankic, his eyes rather less twinkling. 'Oh, he tells that Maxim Gorky founded modern writing,' says Princip, 'Then he died, and that was great mistake. Do you agree?'

And so, in the Restaurant Propp, in the older part of Slaka, under Vlam's great castle, the official meal of welcome unfolds. Certain bitternesses are in the air, trading uneasily through Petworth's head as he struggles to catch the prevailing discourse, the flow of interlingua, English as a Second Language for Social Occasions (ESLSO). A new course comes: 'You know this, ruspi?' asks Vera, pointing with her knife. 'I'm not sure, what is it?' asks Petworth. 'Ruspi is a swimmer,' says Tankic. 'Is a fish,' says Princip. 'With two pencils in its nose,' says Lubijova. 'Two pencils?' asks Petworth. 'Yes, so,' says Katya Princip, putting two fingers beneath her nose, and jutting them out, 'What do you call those pencils in English?' 'Feder?' cries Professor Rum, 'Stylo? Pen?' 'No, you do not at all understand, Comrade Rum,' says Princip impatiently, 'And our guest is liking to tell us that language brings all together. But really it is like sex. You think it brings you together, but only it shows how lonely you truly are.' 'Sex is not so lonely,' says Vera. 'Do you try at all our sex in Slaka?' asks Katya Princip, 'In Slaka, sex is just politics with the clothes off.' 'Well, perhaps everywhere,' says Petworth. 'And do you try also our beer?' asks Vera, 'It is called, oluu.' 'Not yet,' says Petworth. 'Well, he tries everything else,' says Lubijova. 'Professor Rum says, in England your ideas are bad, but your beer always very good,' says Katya Princip, 'Of course here, you will find, it is entirely the opposite.' 'But he must try some,' says Vera. 'Of course,' says Katya Princip, 'I hope we are friends now, I take you to a nice place afterward.' 'Well, he has a very full programme,' says Lubijova, 'Also perhaps he is very tired.' 'I think not too full, not too tired, to drink one beer with me,' says Katya Princip, 'Of course he must go to the cafés where our most interesting people go. Then, my friend, you can try our beer and also our thinking. Often the beer runs short, but the thinking, always in full production.'

The waiter comes again, taking away the fish course, and bringing instead a meat dish which bubbles away in strange sauces. 'Lakuku,' says Vera, pointing, 'The veal of a cow cooked as not in any other country.' 'The vegetable,' says Lubijova, 'A special grass that grows only under the sheeps on a mountain.' Across the table Tankic is rising, with a refilled glass: 'Says he likes to make another toast,' says Lubijova, 'To the beautiful ladies, for the first time, this time very sincerely.' 'Really, this man,' says Katya Princip, 'I think he does not like me to drink. Perhaps he knows that when I am drunk I talk only about my lovers.' 'What about your lovers?' asks Vera, giggling. 'Oh, do you like to know?' asks Princip, 'Well, I have had many lovely lovers, such nice lovers, because, you see, I love love.' 'You are lucky,' says Vera. 'Not always,' says Princip, 'So, Mr Petwit, what do you do here? Do you make lectures?' 'Yes,' says Petworth, 'Tomorrow, at the university.' 'Oh, I would like to come there,' says Katya Princip. 'It is for the students,' says Lubijova. 'See, she does not like me to come there,' says Princip, 'Do you like me to come there?' 'I'd be delighted,' says Petworth. 'Then perhaps I do it,' says Katya Princip, 'Here we have a saying: a good friend is someone who visits you when you are in prison. But a *really* good friend is someone who comes to hear your lectures. Well, I hope now I am your really good friend, so perhaps you will see me there. But you must speak for me very slowly, if you do. I am not so good with the English. Do you do it?' 'Of course,' says

Petworth. 'I like you,' says Katya Princip, 'Yes, I think perhaps you will see me there, listening to you.'

Across the table, Tankic is on his feet again, with a full glass: 'Says, to the beautiful ladies, for the first time, this time truly and entirely sincerely.' 'How can we be beautiful, if we cannot drink?' asks Princip. 'Of course,' says Vera, 'The more that drink the men, the more are the ladies beautiful.' 'Oh, Professor Rum likes to ask you a question,' says Princip, 'He asks, where do you keep your dissident writers?' 'Comrade Tankic asks you something,' says Lubijova, 'He asks, how is your British disease?' 'He wonders, do you keep them perhaps in a jail in Northern Ireland?' 'He asks about the economics of your liberal Lord Keynes, are they dead now in your system?' 'Professor Rum says he has been often to London, on his scientific travels, and seen many beggars there, is that true?' 'Many beggars, where?' asks Petworth, eating his grass. 'He tells they play for money in all the stations of the metro,' says Katya Princip. 'Oh, they're not beggars,' says Petworth, 'They're American tourists financing their vacations.' 'He does not believe you,' says Princip, 'He says this is what your press likes you to think, but is not the reality. He says do you not think that here under Thatcher is marked the collapse of the capitalist system?' 'Soon you join us,' says Comrade Tankic, leaning over the table, laughing. 'It's in trouble,' says Petworth, 'But I don't think it's collapsing.' 'Oh, Mr Petwit, now you have upset Professor Rum!' says Katya Princip, 'He thinks you deny the immanent reality of the historical process. He suspects you are a bourgeois relativist. I tell him it cannot possibly be true.' 'I'm afraid I don't know much about politics or economics,' says Petworth, 'It's really not my field.' 'Oh, Mr Petwit, you don't know politics, you don't have economics, how do you exist?' cries Princip, 'I'm afraid you are not a character in the world historical sense.' 'Your heart's good, your system, bad,' says Tankic, leaning across the table, laughing. 'So who could put you in a story?' says Princip, 'Poor Petwit, I am sorry. For you there is no story at all.'

141

The curtains to the alcove are now thrown open, and through them comes the waiter; impressively, he is bearing high a vast white dessert, an elaborate concoction from which bright blue flames are rising. 'Oh, look,' cries Vera, 'It is *vish'nou*!' 'Oh, this is very nice,' says Lubijova, 'Do you have in your country?' 'I don't think so,' says Petworth, 'What's in it?' 'Outside is an ice cream, inside, nurdu,' says Vera, 'You know nurdu?' 'I can't say it in English,' says Lubijova, 'A very nice fruit that is not an orange.' 'And not a lemon,' says Vera. 'A melon?' asks Petworth. 'A little bit like, but not really,' says Lubijova, 'Do you know that name, Comrade Princip?' 'No, not the name,' says Katya Princip, 'But I know a story all about.' 'Oh, tell us,' says Vera. 'It is a bit long,' says Princip, 'Do you really like to hear it, Mr Petwit?' 'Of course,' says Petworth. 'Well, really for a story you should give me a precious stone, but I don't think you have one,' says Princip, 'Perhaps if I tell it you give me one little wish instead. Do you agree?' 'Yes,' says Petworth. 'So, once upon a certain time, and you know all stories start so, there was a king who had three sons, and the youngest is called Stupid,' says Katya Princip. 'That is his name?' asks Vera, 'Stupid?' 'In your story call him what you like,' says Princip firmly, 'but in mine he is called Stupid. And one day the king tells Stupid he must travel to another land and make a peace with the king of it, because these two kings have fighted each other. Fighted?' 'Fought,' says Petworth. 'Good, you help,' says Princip, 'So Stupid goes to that other court, and there he sees the king's daughter, a very beautiful princess, and you know what happens, because it always does. Stupid falls there in love.' 'That is why he is called Stupid?' asks Vera. 'He is called Stupid because I like to call him Stupid,' says Princip, 'Do I go on?'

'Please,' says Petworth. 'Her father the king, a rough man with a big red beard, tells: Stupid, no, you cannot marry her, because already she is promised to marry another else, so go away. Well, of course, poor Stupid, he is sad, a long, long face right down to here. And he walks out into the forest and there he meets an old woman who is special, she is a makku, we say, do you know?' 'A witch,' says Petworth. 'That is the word, a witch,' says Princip, 'Perhaps you know this story already?' 'No,' says Petworth. 'Well, of course you know some like it,' says Princip, 'But perhaps not my special story of poor Stupid. So, that witch tells to Stupid, please, come walk with me in the forest. Well, he goes, the branches catch at his hairs, the animals make howl, he does not know where he goes, you know how it is in forests. And then suddenly they are both falling, down a dark, dark hole, a long far way. And then, bouff!, they are at the bottom, with sore behinds. And there in front is a new land, with great trees and sunshine and gardens, and on top of a hill a castle, with some high towers. Well, Stupid looks up at the castle and there, in the very highest window, on highest tower, he thinks he sees, looking out, his very beautiful princess. In the sky is the shining sun, in front of them some water. Some frogs sit there on the water-plants, and the witch, who can talk to them, asks them all about that castle. And they tell, be careful, it belongs to a great big bad man, bigger than anybody, what do you call him?' 'A giant?' asks Petworth.

'You are very good, really you should tell this story, it is a giant,' says Katya Princip, patting his arm, 'A giant who every day takes a prisoner, a very beautiful girl, and he kills her at night when goes down the sun. Well, Stupid does not like this news, and sees also that the sun begins to go down, down, down behind the trees. And so of course he approaches to the castle and tries to go in there, to rescue his princess. But the gate is shut, and on every window are many bars. He looks up again at the sun, it slips nearer and nearer the ground. He looks up at the high window, and there, beside the lady, who cries, he sees that, what do you call, giant, and there in his hand is a big axe that is made specially just for great giants like him. The girl leans, and tries to shout, but over her face the giant puts his big hand, and he laughs down the tower at Stupid. Well, Stupid shakes at the gate, he pushes at the

143

windows, what would you do, but he finds no ways to get inside. What can he do next?' 'He could ask for help the witch,' says Vera. 'My dear, you are right,' says Princip, 'He turns to that witch, a good witch, a bad witch, he does not know. He does not know anything, he is Stupid. So the witch tells again, come, walk with me, and she takes him to a beautiful garden next the castle, in it many trees and plants. The sun is going now, the castle rises high, and no way at all to go in. But the witch takes Stupid over to a big round fruit that is on the ground. The sun has made it a bright yellow, and inside is fat and good to eat, how do you call it, Petwit?' 'A marrow,' says Petworth. 'No, not marrow, but like,' says Princip, 'Inside is more sweet. A fruit that is in all the stories.' 'Yes, of course,' says Petworth, 'A pumpkin.' 'That is it, pumpkin,' says Katya Princip, 'And now you know what vish'nou is made of. Now you know what you eat. Try it and tell me you like it.'

'Yes,' says Petworth, 'But what happened to the prince?' 'To Stupid?' asks Princip, 'Oh, now it is no matter. Don't you find out what is your dessert?' 'I'd also like to find out how the story ends,' says Petworth. 'But you know how it ends,' says Princip. 'That is the end, on your plate. I made it to make you remember a name.' 'But now we all are thinking, what has happened to Stupid?' says Vera. 'Why? How does it matter?' says Princip, 'You know what happens to Stupid, all stories are the same, you know the end already.' 'Please tell,' says Vera. 'Oh, of course the witch is a good witch, Stupid goes into the castle and he kills the giant, the princess goes home with him, the king her father with the big red beard tells he is very sorry, and they marry and live happy ever after, under socialism, and make many children who all work hard for the state.' 'But no more adventures for Stupid?' asks Lubijova. 'Of course some adventures, but the adventures are always the same, and they do not change the story,' says Princip, 'What matters is: it is a useful story, Maxim Gorky would please. Petwit knows now what meal he eats, it is pumpkin,' 'We never heard what the pumpkin did, in the story,' says Petworth. 'Oh, so many questions, I wonder why?' says Princip, 'The pumpkin of course did what pumpkins like to do in the stories. It turned to something else, perhaps a ladder, perhaps a coach. Perhaps someone climbed the ladder, perhaps someone rode the coach. But it is no matter. You are in Slaka, you make your meal, you eat your fruit, and you know it is pumpkin.' 'You see now what kind of a book Comrade Princip likes to write,' says Lubijova. 'Not really,' says Princip, 'My books are a bit magical also, but more complete. And I never tell them at official lunches. Of course, Mr Petwit, if one day our paths are crossing somewhere, if you come back again here to Slaka, well, then I might really tell you what happened to that prince and that pumpkin. You see, what I tell now is not true. There were some more adventures. The witch was not such a good witch, the giant did not die like that. The girl in the tower was not as she appeared, the king with the red beard was not such a good king. So, poor Stupid.'

'And the pumpkin?' asks Vera. 'No, the pumpkin did not really turn into a ladder or a coach. Poor Stupid ate it, and came in the power of the witch, and some very strange things happened to him.' 'Won't you tell?' asks Lubijova. 'Please, it is late,' says Princip, 'Also I have talked so much to our guest that, don't you see, his vish'nou gets cold. Finish it quickly, please, Mr Petwit, or it is not nice.' Tankic leans across the table and says something to Petworth, laughing. 'Says a bureaucrat always has a bureau, and he must go to his,' says Lubijova, 'He says he knows you are a good man because you like to drink with him. So he makes you one last toast. To good tour, good lectures, good times and also one more thing. To the beautiful ladies, for the first time, this time completely and more than ever sincerely.' The glasses go up again; Tankic beams, half kind and half malicious. 'So, Mr Petworth,' says Tankic, putting on his shortie raincoat and his black Homburg hat, 'Take care for bad witches.' 'I will,' says Petworth. 'Oh, Comrade Princip,' says Vera, squeezing Petworth's arm, 'You didn't ask your wish of him!' 'Oh, yes, my wish,' says Katya Princip, combing her hair at a mirror, 'I had forgotten it. It was just a little wish and you probably do not have time for it. My wish was only, Mr Petwit, please come take walk with me.' 'To the forest?' says Vera. 'Not the forest, I am not bad witch,' says Katya Princip, laughing, 'Just to a café. I want to show you our beer, our thinking, and something else interesting. Do you have just a little time?' 'Comrade Lubijova can go with you,' says Vera, 'Then you do not get lost.' 'Do we do it?' asks Princip. There is a small pulsing in Petworth's head, the effect of a long day of toasts. The lunch has been good, the company pleasing, and it seems too soon to end it. 'Do you think so, Marisja?' he asks. 'If you want it,' says Lubijova. 'Good, we go,' says Katya Princip, holding out Petworth's coat to him, leading him through the dining-room beyond, now quite empty except for the gaping fish, and out of the Restaurant Propp.

IV

And now it is later, and the sun is going down, and a very good-humoured, very confused Petworth is walking through a vast busy market place. The rain still falls, the crowds are wet, the people push; the stalls are lamp lit, and on them strange twisted vegetables, great beets and garlics, release a warm odour into the air. All round are high old gabled houses; by the curbside, an organ-grinder in a bent old felt hat, and white moustache fringed with nicotine, turns a handle on a hurdy-gurdy where a wet, jacketed monkey chatters. Peasants with sere old faces move by in shawls to keep off the rain; in the centre of the square is an ancient market hall, topped with a high ornate tower with on it a decorated old clock. 'Isn't it nice, don't you like it?' asks Katya Princip, in her sheepskin waistcoat, holding his arm, 'Really my favourite place in Slaka. Don't you like the shapes of these vegetables? It is the private produce those peasants grow in their yards, to make a little money.' Ahead of them, Marisja Lubijova walks with Professor Rum, whose topcoat is back over his shoulders: 'Which café do you like?' asks Lubijova, turning to stare back at them. 'Oh, dear, she does not enjoy this,' says Princip, 'Café Grimm, on the other side. Yes, it is nice, Mr Petwit. I hope it makes no trouble for you.' 'Trouble?' asks Petworth, 'Why?' 'I was wicked there, they do not ask me again, to an official lunch,' says Princip, 'Of course they cannot blame you, but if you are clever, you should refuse to come with me.' 'But they wanted me to come,' says Petworth. 'Oh, yes?' says Princip, laughing, 'Didn't you see their faces, Tankic and his mistress? This is why they sent your nice lady guide with you.' 'His mistress?' asks Petworth. 'Of course his mistress,' says Princip, 'Why else does she go to such a lunch? There is a saying here: in my country some people advance on their knees, others on their backs. I think that is one that advances on her back.' 'This one, Grimm?' asks Lubijova, turning, 'Do we go inside?' 'No, we sit outside, even though it rains,' says Princip, 'You see, we have a thing to show you, Mr Petwit.'

And now it is a little later still, and Petworth is sitting in a metal chair in the rain outside a café in the market place of Slaka. The metal chairs are all affixed to the ground, arranged in straight rows, looking outward. The crowds press in front of them; they sit in their row, with Katya Princip to one side of Petworth, Marisja Lubijova to the other, and Professor Rum, ruminative, beyond her on the end of the line. 'You see, nobody serves us,' says Lubijova, 'They do not serve here because it rains.' 'Do you like to go inside and see if they bring some beer to us?' asks Princip. 'All right, I do it,' says Lubijova, going into the crowded inner café. 'She does not please with you, that one,' says Princip, 'She sees you in bad company. She does not like to leave you.' 'She admires your novels,' says Petworth, 'She bought me your book.' 'Not all who admire the novels admire the novelist,' says Princip, 'And not all who admire the novelist admire the novels. Let us ask Professor

Rum.' Princip moves to Petworth's other side, and begins a conversation; Petworth stares at the red banners that dangle over the square on high poles. 'He explains he is of the party of socialist realism,' says Princip, 'He thinks he will not like my new book at all. In it no characters who are people. The central figure is a cake with two horns.' Lubijova comes out of the interior of the café and stands before Petworth: 'I am sorry, it is no use,' she says, 'They have finished all their supply of beer.' 'Then we get something else,' says Princip, 'Tea with a tort. I go and arrange it.' 'Comrade Petwurt, take care please with this lady,' says Marisja, sitting down beside him, 'She does foolish things and she gets you into trouble.' 'Realismus,' says the Academician Rum, stirring from thought at the end of the row, 'You tell?' 'He asks me to explain you that the problem of realismus is to combinate the reality inherent in the historical process with the sufficient subjective perception, do you agree?' 'Well, yes,' says Petworth.

'And here we are,' says Princip, returning with a tray on which stand four tall steaming glasses of water. In the water are small iron bombs, which emit a seeping brownness that twists into strange hieroglyphs. 'Now take your drink please and look at the market hall, up at the top, because it is almost time for this thing.' And high up on the bell-tower, something is indeed happening. Below the clock face, decorated with necromancer's symbols, two wooden doors are opening, very jerkily. From inside the doors, on tracks, come two stiff wooden peasants, each one carrying a cudgel. The peasants come forward, bow down to the crowd, then turn to face each other. They slide a little closer, and as they do so their cudgels rise into the air. The clock above them begins to strike; at each clang of the bell, they belabour each other. 'Do you count them,' says Princip, 'One, two, three, four, five, six.' The crowds have stopped, and everyone is looking up. Petworth then notices that affixed to the top of the tower are crowd-control television cameras, looking back down. 'Don't you please I bring you?' asks Katya Princip, 'Now you see my wish.

You see, I like things just a little bit magical. Perhaps you do too.' 'I do,' says Petworth. 'And every day at six when the men come out I come here,' says Princip, 'So this is where everyone finds me. If you ever like to do it.' 'Oh, Petwurt, Petwurt,' cries Lubijova, 'Your wife!' 'My wife?' cries Petworth. 'On the telephone,' says Lubijova, 'I arranged you to call her from the hotel at six o'clock.' 'Oh, do you have a wife?' asks Princip, 'You don't have a ring.' 'His wife waits a call from him,' says Lubijova, 'Well, now it is too late. Now we make all the arrangements over again, oh, Petwurt, Petwurt, and they will not be pleased with you.' 'Six o'clock?' says Petworth, 'But we've only just finished lunch.' 'It was a long, long lunch,' says Lubijova, 'And don't forget, tomorrow you must make a conference at the university. I think he goes to his hotel.' 'I think so too,' says Petworth, dimly recalling another social engagement, which it might not be entirely wise to talk about.

'Come, I take you,' says Lubijova, standing up in front of him. 'Which hotel?' asks Princip. 'Slaka, in Wang'luku,' says Lubijova. 'My dear, let me take him, I go by there,' says Princip, 'My apartment is right by that corner. I go there anyway.' 'I think I come too,' says Marisja Lubijova. 'Really, no need,' says Princip, 'He does not have to have always two beautiful ladies.' 'Do you know your arrangements, Comrade Petwurt?' asks Lubijova anxiously, 'Do you remember your programme? I shall come to the same place in the hotel, the same time. But will you have eaten your breakfast?' 'I can manage,' says Petworth. 'Well,' says Lubijova, doubtfully, 'Perhaps.' 'Of course,' says Princip, seizing Petworth's arm. Professor Rum rises, adjusts his topcoat, and puts out his hand to Petworth. 'He says he is pleased to meet you and he looks forward to hearing you when you make conference,' says Lubijova, 'Even though he does not understand English and he thinks you are a pragmatist.' 'Then I'll see you tomorrow,' says Petworth to Lubijova, 'And thank you so much for the tour and the book.' 'The book, perhaps it was not such a good idea,' says Lubijova, 'But I wanted to make you nice present.'

'You did,' says Petworth. 'We go this way, to the tram,' says Princip, 'Do you go yet on a tram?' 'Not yet,' says Petworth. 'Oh, Petwurt, Petwurt,' cries Lubijova, hurrying after them as they walk, 'Your passport, I think you take it. Remember, you do not exist without it. Yes, I see you tomorrow.' 'Oh, she is cross, that one,' says Princip, looking after her as she goes off through the market in her mohair hat, 'Or perhaps it is jealous, you know she likes you. Yes, of course. You are not so macho as our men, and that makes you attractive. Why do you think I like so much to go with you?' 'I'm pleased you do,' says Petworth, as they cross the market, past the sere-faced peasants standing behind the stalls, the flowers, the twisted vegetables. 'Now here we wait the tram,' says Princip, 'Oh, hold please my arm, I think you took too many toasts. And when that tram comes, push, push, push. We are not so polite here, like the British.'

They stand in the crowd until the high-prowed pink tram comes; the sign on its front, over the uniformed woman driver, says WANG'LUKU. 'Push, push, go inside, I have two tickets,' says Princip, 'If you do it well, you get seat, and one beside for me.' He does it well, and finds two seats; the tram grinds off. 'So, Mr Petwit, I am glad you are my admirer,' says Katya Princip, sitting down beside him, 'You know I am a little bit yours, too. Yes, I think I come to your lecture tomorrow. If you speak it very slowly.' 'I will,' says Petworth. 'Isn't it nice, on a tram?' says Princip, putting her arm through his, 'I told you, once I drove one. When I could not write.' 'But you can write now,' says Petworth. 'Yes, I have some protection,' says Princip, 'It is best always to have some protection. But I am not reliable, you know. I have friends in America who make to me some telephone calls. I go abroad perhaps too many times, and meet wrong people. I am not polite to those apparatchiks. So often they like to watch me. That is why I am not such good friend for you, really. And you not a very good friend for me. That is a pity.' 'A great pity,' says Petworth, staring down as they rattle over the Bridge of Anniversary May 15. 'Oh, look, look, we go over the river,' says Princip, 'Do you see all those fishermen down there, fishing even in the rain? Do you know how we call them? We say they are the men from HOGPo.' 'Why?' asks Petworth. 'There are so many fish down there,' says Princip, 'Someone has to find out what they are thinking. And so, Mr Petwit, you have a wife. Is she a nice one?' 'A good woman,' says Petworth. 'That is what we say,' says Princip, 'Every man needs a good woman, and when he has found her he needs a bad woman also. Well, you are nice, Mr Petwit, you drink too much and smoke too much and you are not character in the world historical sense, and all that makes you attractive. But perhaps I don't after all come to your lecture. We are both really not cautious enough, and here this is dangerous.' 'You think we shouldn't meet again,' says Petworth. 'What would we do it for?' asks Princip, 'So I can tell you the real story of Stupid?'

From a hazed memory, Petworth now remembers something. 'When you were at the airport, with Professor Rum,' he says. 'Oh, the airport, where you saw me wave to you,' says Princip, 'I had come back from Provd, there was meeting of the Writers' Union.' 'Who was the man, the other man, who waved after the taxi?' 'Oh, this man with the umbrella?' asks Princip, 'We did not know him. He was foreign, from somewhere else. He did not speak Slakan so well. You see, Mr Petwit, here there is so much following. You are a nice man, in a nice place we would like each other. But I don't think so in Slaka. Look, we are almost at Wang'luku. Get up, comrade, push, push.' Above the tram, Marx and Engels, Wanko and Grigoric, bob in the narrow street. Then they are in the square, busy tonight with people, crowded round the newspaper seller, buying from the man with the balloons. 'So, I have brought you home,' says Katya Princip, in her sheepskin waistcoat and batik dress, looking at him with grey-green sad eyes, 'I have really liked to meet you. But I cannot be your good witch, I cannot be your bad witch, it would be so nice and very silly. Did you like to meet me?' 'Very much,' says Petworth. 'Well, if you don't have me, you have my book,' says Princip, 'And if you open it very carefully, and learn the words very slowly, and look for the hidden places, the corners that are secret, then in a certain way you can have me. Perhaps, now you know me you will have me much more like that than if we decided to be silly and go and make some love. Do you know the title, what it means? It means not to be afraid.' 'Then perhaps we shouldn't be,' says Petworth. 'Yes, you like to like me, I like to like you,' says Princip, 'And in a nice world it would all be very nice. But it is not a nice world and everyone must take care for themselves. Now I think you go in your hotel.'

'Then come in for a minute,' says Petworth. 'You don't understand, they will take notice there, they watch everyone,' says Princip, touching his lips with her finger, 'Oh, Mr Petwit, I have told you. You are really not a character in the world historical sense. You come from a little island with water all round. When we were oppressed and occupied and when we fought and died, and there were mad mullahs and pogroms against the Jews, what did you have? Queen Victoria and industrial revolution and Alfred the Lord Tennyson. We sent Karl Marx to explain you everything, but you didn't notice. What did you do with him, put him in Highgate cemetery, some would say the best place, I know. You never had history, just some customs. Now, go in there. Think of your nice Mrs Petwit, all the little Petwits if you have some. Perhaps in your room you make a little toast for me. To the beautiful lady, this time really meaning it. So, enjoy our country, please, and make a good lecture. I like to be there, but I will not, because I like you, I really like you.' She stands looking at him, in her white dress and sheepskin coat; then she kisses his cheek, turns, and is gone into the crowd. Petworth turns too, stepping in through the glass doors, past the limping doormen. In the lobby, a crowd of oriental gentlemen stands round the desk; there is noise and emptiness, people and personlessness. He goes to the desk to change his identay'ii for his key; 'Pervert, don't you know what time is, six and a half,' says the lacquered-haired girl, tapping her watch crossly, 'Do you know you have missed your telephone? Well, is too late now.' He goes up in the great lift, past the white floormaid, and into his dark room, that empty place for his filled spirit. Brandy tastes like nausea in his throat; an unfamiliar pulse beats at the back of his head; there is post-surgical pain in his feelings. He takes off his official suit, knowing that he has missed something, or that something is missing. Ten minutes later, naked in the vast bathroom, under the groaning, creaking shower, hard water hitting a head filled with the sediment of his governmental lunch, hand twisting taps that will not quite come to balance, so that now the water turns his white body scalding hot, now freezing cold, his face staring upward into the painful flood, while the split peach of his buttocks and the limp profitless dangle of his thighs flicker at him from the opposite, misting mirrored wall, a gloomy nude, his long day by no means over, he tries to call himself back to duty, sociability, affability, to find a face that will meet the face of Mr Steadiman.

5 – CD/GB.

I

The clocks on the nearby government buildings, the chimes in the belfries round about, are all ringing seven as Petworth descends the rough stairs to the cellar bar of the Hotel Slaka, looking for Mr Steadiman. His hair is wet from his hasty shower, his head heavy from the day's hospitality; he knows himself for a man of sorrows, who, in one day, has met and found, loved and lost. Raising the curtain to the Barr'uu Tzigane, he expects the gloomy cavern to match his mood. But something has changed in the underground place; yesterday's drabness has turned into something almost resembling joy. Behind the caravan bar is a laughing gipsy barman, while the whores who sit, teasing and giggling, in a line along the bar in front of him, drinking specialist drinks, are brighter, more glittering, and far more numerous. They all turn to look through silver eye make-up at Petworth as he comes in; in the lap of one, a new one, with hennaed red hair and a golden dress, a small beribboned lapdog barks brightly at his entrance. At the red-checked tables there is much busyness and noise; laughter and jollity sound as Zaïrean timber talks to Ukrainian grain, Indian cloth to Polish leather. Bright-sad music is in the smoky air; among the tables, with their gleaming table lamps, two small gipsies in frilly sleeves pass, fiddling furiously. It is a frivolous place, almost too frivolous for a man not hunting frivolity. But diplomatic matters attend him, the duties of his visit; he steps inside and walks slowly among the tables, staring

154

from side to side, looking for the Second Secretary from the British Embassy.

Evidently the task will not be easy. Mr Steadiman, to identify himself, has promised to wear a suit; but a suit is precisely what all the many single men who sit at the tables – staring, waiting, looking at the girls, gazing dubiously down into small drinks – have elected, on this evening, to wear. Steadiman, no doubt, has no desire to draw special attention to himself; and yet, as Petworth looks carefully around, going from table to table, it seems to him that none of the men who sit there quite looks like a British Second Secretary. This suited man wears a black plastic hat; that one smokes a plastic-ended cigar. This one works steadfastly on notes, a pocket calculator clicking away in his hand; that one has his big bullet head thrust deep down into the pages of *P'rtyuu Populatuuu*. That one is Chinese; these two are black Africans. Steadiman, presumably, has not arrived, or obscured himself so well that he will make himself known. A table comes vacant in one of the dark alcoves; Petworth sits down at it, facing the curtained doorway. After a moment, looking rather surly, a red-checked waitress halts beside him; Petworth orders a Sch'veppuu. He sits, and looks carefully round the room; only the pretty whores at the bar look back at him, and one, the new one with the henna hair and the lapdog, mouths a kiss at him; Petworth ignores it. The gipsies play, the men at their tables sit and work, from time to time the door curtain rises and a man comes in – a turbanned man, a black man, a bespectacled man, a man in a see-through fold-up raincoat – but none of them look like a Steadiman. Meanwhile, his drink, like Steadiman himself, fails to come. Staring at the whores, jogging their pretty legs, in silver boots and high-heeled shoes, up and down, Petworth broods on blonde hair, a batik dress, a brief happy tram-ride, a bleak separation, on the sadness and solitude behind the public spaces of society and exchange.

The clocks on the nearby government buildings, on the belfries around, chime seven-thirty, and still Steadiman has not come. Petworth is just thinking of returning to his room, or of attempting a taxi, when the door curtain lifts once more. A man stands there, looking expectantly round the noisy room: a tall man, fresh-faced, forty-ish, thin, wearing a suit, carrying a rolled umbrella. He steps into the room, looking – carefully at the whores along the bar, evidently seeking someone; and Petworth knows that this man has been somewhere in his story before. The man steps onward, between the tables, and Petworth suddenly recalls where he has seen this face, this suit, this umbrella, this look; this is the man who jostled him in the entrance to the arrivals hall at Slaka airport, as Lubijova led him toward his taxi; this is the umbrella that waved after the taxi, when, looking back, Petworth saw Professor Rum, Katya Princip, and a third figure, a man with a sack, this man, chasing his arrival. The man is now moving from table to table, a crisp, confident expression on his face, speaking to the people sitting there: the man with the black plastic hat, the man with the plastic-ended cigar. His quest is clearly unsuccessful; he turns now to the man with the pocket calculator, then the man behind *P'rtyuu Populatuuu*. Petworth now realizes suddenly that it is he who is being looked for; at the same time he understands at once who his follower is. He rises from his seat and goes toward the man, who, an expression of waning confidence on his features, is now approaching the solitary Chinese. 'Excuse me,' Petworth says, coming up to the man, who, rejected by the Chinese, has now turned to the two black Africans, 'Would you happen to be Mr Steadiman?'

'Aaaarrggghhh,' says the man, turning; the two gipsies now come on either side of him, and begin bowing their fiddles at him in musical frenzy. 'Not today, thank you,' says the man to the gipsies, 'Who are you?' 'My name's Petworth,' says Petworth, 'I thought you might be looking for me.' 'Pet Pet Petworth?' says the man, his fresh features taking on an expression of cunning, 'And you're looking for a chap called Ster Ster Steadiman?' 'Yes,' says Petworth. 'You're alone?' asks the man. 'Yes,' says Petworth. 'And no one followed you here?'

asks the man. 'Only you,' says Petworth. 'And you think I might be this chap whatsisname you're looking for?' says the man, who has a public-school English accent. 'Yes,' says Petworth. 'Look, do let's sit down,' says the man. 'I've already got a table,' says Petworth. 'Where is it?' asks the man. 'Over there in the alcove,' says Petworth. 'Show me,' says the man, 'Is this it?' 'Yes,' says Petworth. 'Very good, old chap,' says the man, after a moment, sitting down, 'Do take a pew.' 'Thank you,' says Petworth. The man looks around, and then lifts up the table-lamp and looks curiously underneath it. 'We should be alright here,' he says, 'Do you have a pass pass passport?' 'Yes,' says Petworth. 'May I see it?' says the man lifting up the table cloth and looking underneath it. 'Yes,' says Petworth. 'Aaarrggghh,' says the man, taking the passport, and looking at it, 'Very good. And what was the name of the contact you were looking for?' 'Steadiman,' says Petworth. 'Well, believe it or not,' says the man, 'That's me, actually. Yes, I'm St St Steadiman. Well well welcome to Slaka.' 'Thank you,' says Petworth. 'Clever of you to spot me,' says Steadiman, 'I like to keep a low pro pro profile. I suppose it was the suit.' 'Yes,' says Petworth.

And indeed, close to, it is clear that this suit is not like other suits; the other male garments here and there about the room are only pale approximations to the suit Steadiman wears, which is suit itself. It is pin-striped, its lapels hand-stitched and exact; the jacket falls open to reveal a neat waistcoat, the bottom button left statutorily undone; the finely creased trousers drape carefully over clocked silk socks and finely cleaned shoes. The shirt underneath is wide-striped, and bespeaks an address in Jermyn Street; on the collar is a scatter of blood spots, that necessary testament to fine wet shaving. The tie is an English tie, indicating its character as a badge of membership, of some club or regiment or school, without uttering the vulgarity of being actually recognizable. And the face above, staring frankly at Petworth, and then with sus-picious cunning round the rest of the room, well, that is clearly made from British genes; fine, long-chinned, it has that hopeful, boyish expression, touched with a small adult pain, that makes all Englishmen feel they have once sobbed collectively together in the dorm of some universal prep school after lights out, even if, like Petworth, they never went to one. Yes, Steadiman is, quite certainly and unmistakably, Steadiman, the Second Secretary at the Embassy. 'Awfully sorry,' he says 'Multos apologiosas about being late. I had to go out to the air and pick up the dip, out to the airport and pick up the diplomatic pouch. Of course the Heathrow flight was three hours late again. I wonder if those chaps who are always on strike ever think they might be putting our international relations in utter jep jep jeopardy. I think it's time for drinkies.'

Steadiman suddenly raises his right arm high in the air, and leaves it there. 'Were you out at the airport yesterday?' asks Petworth. 'Ah,' says Steadiman, 'Aaarrgghh. Why do you ask? Think you spotted me there, do you?' 'I did actually, yes,' says Petworth, 'I saw you waving after my taxi.' 'Oh, did you?' says Steadiman, looking a little crestfallen, 'Yes, I had to go to the air and pick up the dip, so I thought I'd do a little careful checking to make sure you'd made a safe land land landfall. We like to keep an eye on our high-level visitors, you know; but their Min Min Ministraty doesn't like us po po poaching on their pa pa patch. Naturally one's a little discreet.' 'Naturally,' says Petworth. 'But they are looking after you nicely?' asks Steadiman, 'Giving you a goo goo good time?' 'Very good,' says Petworth. 'And did they give you an official lunch today?' asks Steadiman. 'They did,' says Petworth. 'Tell me,' says Steadiman, looking carefully round the room, 'Who was the host? Was it the min the min the Min . . .' 'No, it wasn't the Minister,' says Petworth, 'It was a man called Tankic.' 'Ah, yes, Tankic,' says Steadiman, 'My wife's met him. Bald, humorous sort of chap.' 'That's it,' says Petworth. 'Yes, well, they gave you their number three,' says Steadiman, 'Not bad. Very clever operator, Tankic. Big in the party, they say, and undoubtedly destined for high high higher things.

Ruthless as hell, of course. As they put it here, he'd sell his mother to the butcher to improve the food production target. Where did he take you?' 'The Restaurant Propp,' says Petworth. 'Really?' says Steadiman, 'Very good. They're treating you well. I wonder what they're up to. What happened to our drink?' 'I ordered one three-quarters of an hour ago,' says Petworth, 'It never came.' 'Oh, they'll come for me,' says Steadiman, confidently, clicking the fingers on his raised right arm, 'Over here, my dear. Two thirsty gentlemen waiting.' Evidently the confidence is justified; the red-checked waitress, smiling pleasantly, comes over to the table. 'See what I mean?' says Steadiman, beaming up at her cherubically, a faint baby-fuzz on his cheekbones, 'They always come, I don't know why. Hello, my dear. Now then, what would you say to a nice cock a nice cock . . .?' 'Not a cocktail for me, thanks,' says Petworth. 'Something a bit softer, then?' asks Steadiman, continuing to beam up at the waitress. 'I'd just like the Sch'veppuu I ordered earlier,' says Petworth.

'Ah,' says Steadiman, 'Aaarrggghhh. The Sch'veppy you ordered earlier. Let me just explain that to her. Heh, froliki . . .' 'Da?' says the waitress, attentive. 'Mi amicatog,' says Steadiman. 'Ah, do, tou amucutak,' says the waitress, encouragingly. 'Da, mi amicatog op darigayet ei Sch'veppy,' says Steadiman. 'Da, durg'atap oc Sch'veppuu,' says the waitress. 'That's it, well, if you could just bring it,' says Steadiman. 'Ah, da, da,' says the waitress. 'I think she's got it,' says Steadiman, 'Ec op ig ei ginnitoniki, da?' 'Da,' says the girl, 'Oc gunnutonukku.' 'That's it,' says Steadiman, 'Ec froliki, metto pikani, da?' 'Mettu pekanu,' says the girl. 'Nice girl,' says Steadiman, looking after her appreciatively as she goes away, 'Good bust good bust good bustling manner. Of course she's flat she's flat she's flattered if you try to speak the lingo. The trouble is they're changing it, you've probably heard. Hence the small diff diff difficulties.' 'Yes, I gathered that,' says Petworth. 'I find that typically foreign,' says Steadiman, 'It's just like the French parking system. You learn to park on one side of the street and then, just because it's the ver ver vernal equinox or something, they switch it over to the other.' 'Well, there have been languages that changed with the seasons,' says Petworth, 'And others that changed according to sex.' 'Acc acc according to sex?' says Steadiman. 'Where men and women have different words for the same things,' says Petworth. 'Ridiculous,' says Steadiman, 'Of course, you're a bit of an expert on these things, I believe. Isn't lin lin lingo your line?' 'Linguistics, yes,' says Petworth. 'I suppose you know lots of languages,' says Steadiman, 'Shouldn't bother too much with this one, though. You're only here for two weeks, and you'll never need to use it again. I've been here three years, and only just mastered it. Then they change it. Thank God for Eng Eng English, at least that stays the same.'

'Well, not exactly,' says Petworth, 'Actually it's changing quite rapidly.' 'Not in Sevenoaks,' says Steadiman, adjusting his tie, 'In any case, this change is quite diff diff different, purely political.' 'Really,' says Petworth. 'Of course,' says Steadiman, 'It's a bunch of lib lib liberals and diss diss dissidents putting pressure on the regime. So they've given ground on the easiest thing, the lan lan language.' 'Hardly the easiest thing,' says Petworth, 'Change the language and you change everything.' 'Oh, they know what they're doing,' says Steadiman, 'They draw the radicals out of the woodwork, then put them away and everything goes back to normal. It'll all be the same again in a couple of months, you'll see. One ought to sympathize, but one's quite grateful really. Change plays hell with dip dip diplomacy. Anyway, un un understand and be un un un understood, that's always been my motto.' 'So it won't come to anything,' says Petworth. 'It's a hard regime,' says Steadiman, 'But they do know how to run a country. Ah, here come our drinks. I told you she'd look after us.' And the red-checked waitress is standing smiling above them, putting their two drinks onto the table, along with a bowl of cocktail delicacies. 'Slibob, my dear,' says Steadiman, beaming and putting some money in a dish, 'Por vo.' 'Slubob,' says the waitress, putting the money away, and smiling at Steadiman. 'Nice people here,' says Steadiman, watching her leave, 'Healthy and charming. And the chaps here have the most marvellous nuts.' 'Do they?' asks Petworth. 'Oh, yes,' says Steadiman, holding out the bowl of cocktail bits, 'Try some. They're a local speciality.' 'I see,' says Petworth, 'Thank you.' 'And they've certainly put you in an ex ex excellent ho ho hotel,' says Steadiman, looking appreciatively round the bar, 'Couldn't have done better.' 'Yes, it's quite pleasant,' says Petworth.

'Well, first-rate, I'd say,' says Steadiman, looking around again, 'You can always tell a good ho ho hotel here by the quality of the tarts. You ought to see the old bags at the Orbis, where we put our visitors. Tell me, what do they charge here?' 'I don't really know,' says Petworth, 'The Mun'stratuu's paying the bill.' 'Not the room, the hew hew whores,' says Steadiman, 'How much are they?' 'I haven't asked,' says Petworth, 'I'm only here two weeks.' 'No need,' says Steadiman, looking at the exotic row of girls by the caravan bar, swinging their legs languorously, 'You can always tell by their feet.' 'Their feet?' asks Petworth. 'They always chalk their price on the so so soles of their shoes,' says Steadiman, 'Have a look.' Petworth looks at the swinging legs along the bar, and sees that Marx was right; beneath each leathered shining superstructure there is an economic infra-structure, for each decorated boot, each shining fashion shoe, bears a waving chalked hieroglyph. 'I didn't bring my specs,' says Steadiman, 'But take for instance the blonde in the middle, the one with the enormous nip enormous nip enormous nip of whisky. How much is she?' 'It looks like forty,' says Petworth, looking. The girl smiles; 'Forty, really, amazing,' says Steadiman. 'Unless it's her shoe size,' says Petworth. 'No, that's her price,' says Steadiman, 'Very good for a girl like that, in a place like this. Think what you'd pay in Chelsea.' 'Really, is it?' asks Petworth, 'I wouldn't know. No one's told me the rate of exchange.' 'Ah, the cambio,' says Steadiman, 'The wechsel. No one's explained it to you?' 'No,' says Petworth. 'Oh, well,' says Steadiman, 'You have to understand you have now entered a loo entered a loo entered a lunatic economy. For all their socialist rationalization, they've ended up with about five different rates of exchange.' 'Five?' asks Petworth.

'It's utter chaos,' says Steadiman, sipping his drink, 'One never knows the value of anything. There's a dip dip diplomatic rate, the one we get, the worst, of course. Then there's a bis bis business rate, a congress rate, and a tourist rate. Then there's the unofficial rate, that's these chaps who stop you on the street and ask to buy your trousers. They'll offer you up to twenty times more than the banks. Strictly illegal, of course, mustn't touch it with a bar bar barge-pole.' 'It sounds very confusing,' says Petworth. 'It is,' says Steadiman sourly, staring across at the girls along the bar, 'What it means is you could be paying anything between the price of a round of drinks and the cost of a three-piece suite for exactly the same ba ba bang. You can get anything you like for a few dollars. Of course, these girls, mustn't touch them with a bar bar bargepole. You know they make their money by whip whip whipping.' 'Do they?' says Petworth. 'Whip whip whipping straight round to the security police with any information they can get. Or they arrange for fo fo photographs to be taken, to go into the file until they prove useful. We call it the turn of the screw.' 'I see,' says Petworth, looking at the teasing, tossing, multivalent girls, who are looking across at them. 'Fraid so,' says Steadiman, looking gloomily down into his drink, 'Actually, the answer, as so often, is to turn to private enterprise. Plenty of it about, they're a prac prac practical people, the Slakans. Or you could try the girls in some of the smaller nightclubs downtown.' 'Well, I'm not anxious,' says Petworth. 'But even that's risky. They tell me some of those strip strip strippers have the rank of colonel in the army.'

The girls at the bar have all turned round now, and are staring at them with interest; Steadiman, raising his glass, regards them morosely. 'I'm afraid cha cha chastity's the only sensible answer,' he says, 'If you can manage it. Of course, you're only here two weeks. I've been here for three years. You know, it's funny. Before you're po po posted, the effo the effo give you a brief brief briefing, very detailed and explicit. Microphones and moles, unreliable staff and drugged cigarettes. And they show you these films, all very frank, of dips being comped, diplomats being compromised by beautiful women, sitting up there on the bed, naked except for a gold chain round the waist. For the first year here, you're ter ter terribly cautious. You stay out of shady corners, you won't get into a car without the company of a chap chap chaperone. In the second year you relax a bit, and, by God, nothing happens. By the third year, you're wondering when the devil it's going to be your turn. You go to the embassy parties, all the French and the Swedes and the Americans and the Ger Ger Germans, and wonder which lucky sod is getting it. And why no one's after you. Is your info info information so worthless? Are you going to the wrong parties? Have you got bad breath? Doesn't Britain count any more?' 'I see,' says Petworth. 'Well,' says Steadiman, putting some money in the saucer on the table, 'I suppose we'd better wend our way. We have some people coming in. And my wife has just been die die dying all day to meet you.' Picking up his umbrella, Steadiman rises, fine in his suit; the whores at the bar watch and giggle; Steadiman casts them a sad glance, and leads the way, through the curtain, up the stairs, out of the lobby, into the night-time square outside.

In the square, blank and empty of most of its people, a sharp fine rain falls over them, blown by an iced wind straight from the Urals. 'Ah, nice night,' says Steadiman, erecting his umbrella and looking around, 'Thought it might be nice to take a stroll. I've parked my car several streets away. Share my um.' Steadiman raises his umbrella over them both, and seizes Petworth firmly by the arm. The icy wind digs deep into his lungs; Marx and Lenin, Lenin and Marx, creak noisily over them as they turn down the narrow street leading out of the square. 'Yes, I think we just go down here,' says Steadiman, glancing behind him, and then steering Petworth down a blank-looking alley. 'It doesn't seem to go anywhere,' says Petworth. 'Oh, yes,' says Steadiman. 'It looks like a dead end,' says Petworth, as they reach, indeed, a dead end, blocked by a small, closed shop, with one tin of beets in the window, and a small sign over the doorway, which flashes and says PLUC. 'Now if you'd just mind stepping into this door door doorway,' says Steadiman, suddenly taking Petworth by the arm and pulling him into the shuttered entrance of the shop. 'Why?' asks Petworth. 'We can't be seen,' says Steadiman, folding up his umbrella and clutching Petworth by the arm, 'Now, I'd like you to show me your it.' 'My it?' asks Petworth. 'Your it, your it, you must have an it,' says Steadiman, 'The Ministraty must have given you one, well, I'd like to see it.' 'The it?' says Petworth, 'Do you mean my itinerary?' 'That's it,' says Steadiman. 'Very well,' says Petworth, profferring the grey sheet of paper; Steadiman unfolds it and, like one trying to read a novel with the aid of the Eddystone lighthouse, he holds it out under the flashing neon sign.

'Why are you doing this?' asks Petworth. 'Entirely in your own in in interest, old chap,' says Steadiman, 'It's my job to keep an eye on you over the next two weeks, and their Ministraty plays its cards very close to its chest. I'll soon take it in, if this light would just stop flashing, I'm blessed with a fo fo photographic memory.' 'It says I'm going to Glit, Nogod and Provd,' says Petworth. 'Oh,' says Steadiman, 'Does it? Very interesting. You know western dip dip diplomats aren't allowed in Nogod and Provd?' 'Really,' says Petworth. 'You are making a report when you get home?' asks Steadiman. 'On academic matters, yes,' says Petworth. 'That would include soldiers in classrooms, tanks in quads, that sort of thing?' asks Steadiman. 'If it affected the teaching of linguistics,' says Petworth. 'Ex ex excellent,' says Steadiman, 'Provd especially is a centre of linguistic unrest. So if they should shut the place down . . .' 'Of course I'd mention it,' says Petworth, 'Hardly worth sending visiting lecturers there, is it?' 'Splendid,' says

Steadiman, 'Perhaps we'd better retrace our steps. Could look odd if anyone saw us like this. My car's by the hotel. Excuse the little ruse, but I wanted a chat. And in this country the street's the only place where you can hold a rat hold a rat hold a rational conversation.' 'I suppose so,' says Petworth. 'Car's dangerous, of course,' says Steadiman, 'At least, it has to go in every two weeks for what they call an off off official service, so I assume there's a bug in it. And of course they have devices in the apartment, and the embassy. We really should be talking in the middle of a newly ploughed field, but that can be a bit difficult in the mid mid middle of a city.'

'What about my hotel room?' asks Petworth, 'Will that be bugged?' 'Oh, I should think so, in a hotel of that standard,' says Steadiman, 'Of course one just can't take it too seriously. You know the story about the dip dip diplomat in Moscow who searched his hotel room and found a small metal plate under the carpet?' 'No, what happened?' asks Petworth. 'He took out his penknife and unscrewed it,' says Steadiman, 'And the chandelier fell down in the ballroom underneath. One just has to live with it. Otherwise in in intelligent conversation would become im im impossible.' 'This isn't the way we came,' says Petworth. 'One just tries to live a normal life,' says Steadiman, 'But it's bound to have some si si psychological effect. I find the worst thing is not being able to quarrel with one's wife. Sir sir surveillance are always looking for signs of marital disharmony. It's very hard, Budgie and I are very fond of a qua qua quarrel.' 'We're going a different way,' says Petworth. 'Sometimes we take a weekend in the West, book a hotel room, and just go at it ham ham hammer and tongs. We come back quite refreshed. That's odd. This isn't the way we came.' 'No,' says Petworth, stopping in front of the high blank wall that stands in front of them, 'That was my impression.' 'Never mind, small city, easy to get the hang of,' says Steadiman, hooking the handle of his umbrella over the top of the wall, and using it to climb up it, 'If we can just get over here we're back in the main street. Give me a push up, will you?'

'There you go,' says Petworth. 'Yes,' says Steadiman, standing up on top of the wall, and looking all round, 'We're right by the hotel. My car's just over there, actually. Grab hold of the end of my um and I'll haul you up. How's that? All right?' 'Fine,' says Petworth, as he heaves himself onto the top of the wall with his elbows. 'Good, ready to jump?' says Steadiman, holding his umbrella in the air, 'One doesn't want to attract too much attention.'

Several passers-by – a soldier in khaki, three old women in headscarves – inspect them curiously as they pick themselves up off the ground in the street where, high above, Marx and Lenin, Lenin and Marx, creak on their wires. 'This way,' says Steadiman, erecting his umbrella, and striding out confidently, his fresh face shining, 'Yes, you know, I quite enjoy having some cul cul cultural work to do. After spending most of my time looking after Brits in prison. I don't get much on the cul cul culture side. We get the odd writer out, poets mostly. One hand up skirts and the other on the bott bott bottle. Not always the best of visitors, one usually ends up collecting them quite pissed from dubious apartments all over the city. I much prefer your sko sko scholars, definitely a better class of person. Ah, look, here's my car. You see I fly the flag.' Like Steadiman himself, standing there in his suit, the car that rests under the leaking linden trees in a dog-fouled corner of the square evokes an immediate shock of recognition; Petworth knows that it too has been in his story before. Inspected closely, the dark brown Ford Cortina that rests listlessly half on the road and half over the pavement presents a somewhat defeated appearance. Mud covers its body, tree-squit covers its roof; its tyres seem unequally inflated, and there is something astigmatically wrong about the gaze of its headlights, while the exhaust hangs loosely down into the road next to the diplomatic plates. 'Remember, bugged,' says Steadiman, pointing at it, and then approaching it cautiously, as if it were mined, 'Don't say anything till I switch on the radio.' Putting down his umbrella, Steadiman unlocks the driver's door, and gets in; a moment later, a hundred military voices begin to sing an anthem through the speakers, and he beckons Petworth in.

'Yes, drove it all the way out from London,' says Steadiman, switching on the headlights, one of which illuminates the trees above them, the other the ground beneath, 'The moment we crossed the frun frun frontier the headlights fell out. Plop into the road. And there isn't a screw screw screwdriver in Slaka to fit them. But sell sell Sellotape's all right, except when it rains.' The rain lashes the windscreen; Steadiman starts with a jerk, and the car bumps down onto the cobbles of the street. A pink tram clangs at them: 'Away we go,' says Steadiman, 'Just a twenty-minute drive. We all have to live out in the dip dip diplomatic quarter, where they can keep their eyes on us.' 'There's someone in the road,' says Petworth, as a dark figure appears briefly in front of them, and then leaps desperately for the curb. 'Look, would you mind belting up?' says Steadiman, turning toward him, 'It's illegal to travel in a car without a belt. I'm not surprised. The pedestrians have no traffic sense, and they have the most ridiculous rules.' 'Have they?' asks Petworth. 'Yes, like having to stop for cars coming in from the right,' Steadiman says, failing to stop for a car coming in from the right, which honks at him, 'And they're rude. No wonder so many of our chaps end up in prison. Got the hang of the city yet?' 'A little,' says Petworth. 'I'll just point out a few of the more obvious landmarks. That,' says Steadiman, pointing to the Sportsdrome, 'is Party Headquarters, and that' he adds, pointing to the Military Academy 'is the State Publishing House. It's not really a diff diff difficult city to get hold of. I say, that's funny, isn't it? They've put a bar bar barrier up right across the road.'

And their tentative headlights have indeed managed to illuminate a red and white pole that is set firmly across their path. Beside the pole are set two military boxes; from each comes a khaki soldier, bearing a Kalashnikov automatic sub-machine gun. Vast arc-lights suddenly come on, and there is shouting: 'I don't think we can go this way,' says Steadiman.

Beyond the pole, Petworth can see a vast area of public space, with swinging banners and a white *pavé*, and many official buildings: 'It's Plazscu P'rtyuu,' Petworth says, 'I believe it's closed to traffic.' 'Is it?' says Steadiman, 'That means we're a bit off course.' The two soldiers stand on either side of the car, pointing their guns in the windows: 'Pardonnez moi,' shouts Steadiman through the window, putting the vehicle into reverse. It goes backward at high speed, hitting a bollard and, apparently, a pedestrian who has been walking behind them, for a high-ranking officer carrying a portfolio begins to hammer violently with his fists on the roof. 'Sorry,' says Steadiman, out of the window, 'These people simply have no idea how to cross a road.' The soldiers are shouting; Steadiman drives off, burning tyre; 'If you go left here, you'll come out onto the main boulevard,' says Petworth. 'Oh, yes, I was explaining the city to you. That's the Sportsdrome over there,' says Steadiman, pointing to the Party Headquarters, and, pointing to the Palace of Culture 'that's the pal pal Palace of cul cul Culture. Is this a red light or a green one?' 'A red one,' says Petworth, holding onto his seat. 'Ah, is it?' says Steadiman, 'Aaarrgghhh. Well, this is the right road, we'll soon be home. Actually my wife's absolutely dying to meet you.' 'It's nice of you to have me,' says Petworth.

In the car, the military music booms; in front of the shops on the main boulevard, the glistening umbrellas go; a bleak line waits outside a cinema, to see a film called *Yips*. Pink trams clatter past, carrying home the workers from the factories, and the tired HOGPo men, finished with their day's work with the nation's biggest employers. 'Nice to have a cul cul cultural visitor again,' says Steadiman, driving down the middle of the street, his wheels apparently caught in the tramtracks, 'Actually you probably don't realize this, but I'm responsible for all the traffic accidents here.' 'So I believe,' says Petworth. 'Tell me,' says Steadiman, 'Tell me, you should know, what's a good book to take to an Englishman in prison? I thought pru pru Proust. Long, isn't it?' 'It rather depends on the man's tastes,' says Petworth, 'Does he like experimental modernism?' 'I'm not sure,' says Steadiman, 'He's a lo lo lorry driver.' 'Probably not Proust,' says Petworth, 'Perhaps *The Forsyte Saga*.' The urban centre has fallen behind them, the trams have gone; they are ascending a hill between residential houses. 'Nice quiet part of town this,' says Steadiman, gesturing vaguely beyond the dirty windscreen, 'How about a game of Scrabble?' 'What, now?' asks Petworth. 'Of course not now,' says Steadiman, 'I'm driving now. No, I meant for the chap in jail.' 'It takes two to play Scrabble,' says Petworth. 'Yes,' says Steadiman, after a moment's thought, 'I suppose that does rather rue rue rule it out. Ran over a peasant, you know.' 'You did?' asks Petworth. 'No, of course not,' says Steadiman, 'He did. That's why they put him in jail. Funny lot, these peasants here. If they see a large mechanical object coming fast toward them, their nat nat natural instinct is to walk straight in front of it. Actually the nat nat natural instinct of all the drivers here is to speed up and get them. But fo fo foreigners aren't allowed to play. Well, here we are, old chap. Home. That's our apartment block, over there.'

They have stopped; to one side is a dark park, spreading off into grotesque shadows; across the street is a row of solid grey apartments, with ornate torsos supporting the balconies. Bullet holes have added new navels to old; a small white box with a soldier sitting in it stands outside every entrance. 'Dip dip diplomatic protection,' says Steadiman, 'Now just hang on one minute.' Steadiman gets out of the car and goes in front of it; his face peers in at Petworth as he reaches out over the windows and detaches the windscreen wipers. When he comes back to open the passenger door, the two wiper arms are sticking from the top pocket of his suit, and waving in front of his face. 'We always remove them here,' he says, raising his umbrella and ushering Petworth across the street, 'Of course off off officially there's no crime, under so so socialism. On the other hand, people do frequently appropriate the goods of others for their own use. Quite why they go for why why wipers I can't imagine, since most of them can't afford cars. Wave to the soldier.' The soldier in the white box peers out at them as Steadiman pushes open the glass and iron entrance to the building; inside it is quite dark. 'One moment while I find the light,' Steadiman says, still holding his umbrella aloft, and pressing a switch that illuminates a cavernous hallway with raw old walls and, in the centre, an ancient caged elevator, 'Now, quick, rush for the lift. I'm afraid this is one of those timed lights that only lasts for a moment and then—' Utter darkness falls: 'Feel your way in,' says Steadiman in the blackness, 'Another light comes on when we shut the door.' The light in the cage comes on, illuminating a dirty floor, and walls covered with graffiti; slowly, the lift begins to ascend the windy shaft.

'Oh,' says Steadiman, as, midway between floors, the lift halts suddenly, and the light goes out, 'This sometimes happens. All we have to do is reel reel relax until someone comes and lets us out. Usually it's not long.' In the shaft, a gale howls, blowing the stale smell of past meals at them; a child screams somewhere behind unseen closed doors. In the darkness, picquant with aftershave, Steadiman begins to discuss the earlier novels of Margaret Drabble. A long time passes, and then footsteps sound somewhere in the unlit, hollow stairwell. 'Slibob, cam'radakii,' Steadiman calls out, 'Pongi! Pongi!' This has effect, for two eyes may just be seen, peering down at them from an invisible landing; there is the sound of a button being pressed and pressed again. The light begins to flicker, the lift to strain and jerk; unsteadily it rises, to halt just below the level of a landing. 'There we are. Now then, we can either stay here and see if it makes it to the top,' says Steadman, 'Or walk up in the dark.' 'I'd rather walk,' says Petworth. 'Why not?' says Steadiman, opening the gates of the cage, 'Can you see in the dark?' 'Few people can,' says Petworth. 'Just follow the sound of my foot foot footsteps, then,' says Steadiman, 'I'm used to all this.'

So, in total darkness, stumbling, tripping, going endlessly

round and round, Petworth begins to climb, in ascending gyres, the spiral of the great stairwell, as it twists and turns, onward and upward, much like life itself. The smell of foreign foods, the quack of incomprehensible radios, comes from unseen doors; the walls are rough and damp; the footsteps of his guide patter somewhere ahead, until, suddenly, they stop, and Petworth walks into a mass, big, black, hard-soft. It is Steadiman's back. 'Almost there,' says the back, 'I just stopped to war war warn you of one thing before we go into the apartment. It's bugged, you know.' 'Yes,' says Petworth. 'There's also Magda, the maid,' says Steadiman, 'We have to hire her from the dip dip diplomatic servants' office. She says she doesn't speak English, but that's bound to mean she does. And of course she whips whips . . .' A door in front of them opens suddenly, casting bright light over their huddled figures; in the doorway a great dour maid, in black dress, white apron, white gloves, stares chastisingly down on them. Her hair is tugged back in a bun from her great face; one arm is bent, as if already awaiting the receipt of coats. 'Ah,' says Steadiman, handing her his umbrella and the windscreen wipers, 'Slibob, Magda.' 'Slubob,' says Petworth, handing her his coat; Magda grunts and stares at him suspiciously. Beyond Magda is light and a high flutter of sound, the light laughter of amused people, the sound of a party; blinking in the light, Petworth calls up his small talk, his working chatter of Derrida and Saussure, of Hobson's Choice and Sod's Law.

There, beyond, is a spacious diplomatic apartment, decorated, as diplomatic apartments so often are, with the relics of many previous postings. Iranian saddlebags, Mexican dance-masks, African rugs hang on the walls; the room is filled with chairs from Sweden, or Denmark, or Habitat, Indian coffee tables, Kurdish camel-drivers' trunks. Table-lamps are lit; there is a great window opening up, as diplomatic apartments so often do, onto a fine view of the dark park, and, beyond it, the city with its flashing spurts of neon. But in the room the professors do not come and go, talking of T. S. Eliot; indeed it

171

is almost empty. It is from a small black box on an Indian coffee-table that the party chatter comes: 'Cass cass cassette,' says Steadiman. But there is a fine-looking hostess standing there, in something ethnic; indeed she too, as diplomatic wives so often are, is decorated with the relics of many previous postings. Arab filigree earrings hang from her ears, Navajo pawn bracelets from her wrists; she wears a wrap-around Hawaiian muu-mau. She steps forward, tall, stately, dark, fragrant with *Ma Griffe*; she seizes Petworth by his hand, and holds it. 'You must be Mr Petworth,' she cries, 'Do come in. I can't tell you how nice it is to have a new face. Yours, of course, not mine. I've had this one for years.' 'Good evening,' says Petworth. 'Hello, hello,' says the lady, 'Oh, my dear, I can't tell you how one yearns for a visitor, the sight of someone even remotely interesting. And you are remotely interesting, aren't you? You look like a nice, healthy, vigorous sort of person to me. 'This is my wife Budge Budge Budgie,' says Steadiman, giving the lady a small peck, 'I think I told you she's been dying all day to meet you.'

II

'Yes, I have, I have, my dear Mr Petworth,' says Budgie Steadiman, putting her arm through Petworth's and leading him toward a settee, 'And now come and tell me what you think of Slaka.' 'What time are we expecting the other guests, darling?' asks Steadiman, standing in the corner. 'Eight-thirty,' says Budgie, 'You know I wanted a little time to myself with Mr Petworth. You see, Mr Petworth, I wanted to find out if you were as charming as I'd hoped.' 'I'm afraid it's not very likely,' says Petworth. 'Oh, are you modest?' asks Budgie Steadiman, 'Please, first impressions are quite in your favour. Now, come and sit down here with me on the sofa, and we'll go on to second ones. Felix will get you a drink.' 'Perhaps you'd care for a pee,' says Steadiman, 'Care for a pee a peach

172

brandy?' 'It's not to be missed,' says Budgie. 'I seem to have had rather a lot of that today,' says Petworth, 'They entertained me to an official lunch.' 'Oh, those things,' says Budgie, 'Sudden death.' 'Well, how about a sort of piss a sort of Piesporter?' asks Steadiman, who has opened the Kurdish camel-driver's trunks, to display an exotic quantity of diplomatic liquor. 'It's a nice dry white wine they make here,' says Budgie, 'I do recommend it for loosening the inhibitions.' 'Very well, I'll try that,' says Petworth. 'Excuse me a moment,' says Steadiman, holding up a bottle, 'I'll just have to go to the kitchen and ask Magda for a screw.' 'Of course, you do that, darling,' says Budgie Steadiman, throwing out her hand in a careless gesture, so that it lands by some chance on Petworth's knee, 'And meanwhile dear Mr Petworth can tell me everything there is to know about his fascinating day.' 'It wasn't enormously fascinating,' says Petworth, 'I had a very large lunch and I saw Grigoric's tomb.' 'Well, of course,' says Budgie, 'They always do. I'm afraid I never did understand the pleasure it's supposed to give. But then I never liked Madame Tussaud's either.'

Budgie Steadiman's loose muu-muu dress seems to be growing progressively looser; she smiles at Petworth warmly. 'Well, tell me what you think of Slaka,' she says, 'Tell me what you have made of it.' 'It seems very pleasant,' says Petworth. 'Slaka, city of art and music, bugs and spies,' says Budgie, 'I suppose discretion has been urged on you? You've been warned that walls have ears, windows have eyes, that the maid flashes signals to the security police with her stockings?' 'So I gather,' says Petworth. 'Yes, the golden rule of Slaka is, whatever you do, do it out of sight. And what do you like to do, Mr Petworth, what are your sports?' 'No sports, really,' says Petworth. 'Oh, do be frank,' says Budgie, putting her hand on his, 'I am. You may have noticed I lack what's called a discreet temperament. I am one of those in whom the heart leads the head. Really I'm not a Slaka sort of person at all.' 'It must be difficult,' says Petworth. 'Felix, dear, Magda can do drinks,' calls Budgie Steadiman over her shoulder, 'Why don't you have a quick shower and wash off the beastly grime of the day? I can entertain Mr Petworth. Yes, Mr Petworth, yes, a difficult life. How shrewd you are, I can see you're simpatico. I am, as I say, a feckless, wild, windswept spirit. Imagine, then, some-one like me, shut up in Slaka, watched and inspected, photo-graphed and recorded, like a Julie Christie with political significance. The voyeur in me responds, the hungry, struggling soul resists.' 'It must be very trying,' says Petworth. 'Trying is hardly the word,' says Budgie, 'I lead a tragically confined existence, Mr Petworth. I am in effect a prisoner here.' 'Oh, surely not,' says Petworth.

'Indeed, Mr Petworth,' says Budgie, seizing him firmly by the femur, 'Police cars follow me to the tennis club. Agents pursue me to the butcher-shop. Microphones are trained on me now. When we make love, we have to play Wagner, and I doubt if he is enough. Tell me, are you fond of Wagner at all, Mr Petworth?' 'Yes, very fond,' says Petworth. 'I knew it,' says Budgie, 'You like a little Wagner, do you? Well, perhaps if our evening goes well, I shall play you some. Opera, opera, Mr Petworth, that is very much to my taste. People travelling round masked in coaches, singing away, I've always felt I belonged in that world. That is how I see myself. Dancing in gauzy veils with men of destiny. You see how I aspire. And what about you, Mr Petworth? Are you a man of destiny?' 'I hardly think so,' says Petworth. 'Oh, I think so,' says Budgie, 'Governments have chosen you, you're a man of affairs, of secrets. Perhaps there is a power in you you do not even know you possess. I believe there is a power in most of us we never fully tap, don't you?' 'I suppose so,' says Petworth, as a hand gently feels the hair on the back of his neck. 'Please, don't think so humbly of yourself,' says Budgie, 'I never have. You have a very nice neck. A dull thought, I'm afraid, but sexual attraction is always expressed as cliché.' 'Yes, indeed,' says Petworth, looking round, 'Felix is having his shower,' says Budgie, 'We are quite alone, except for the policemen. And think how dull life would be for them if one didn't light the occasional flame. One feels almost a duty to be a little interesting.' 'I'm sure you are,' says Petworth.

'Indeed, I am,' says Budgie Steadiman, staring at him, 'Do you know how long I have been here? Three years, three imprisoned years. As you might gather, this is not a posting I desired, not at all. I've always seen myself in one of the world's great cities. Dancing, laughing, wearing a diamond in my navel. Do you know what they say? That if Felix hadn't stammered, we'd have had Tokyo?' 'I'm sure there are worse postings than Slaka,' says Petworth. 'Oh, yes,' says Budgie, 'Perhaps an oil rig in the North Sea? Assistant Language Officer, Accounts, Bangladesh? Yes, they always say there's someone worse off than you are, but I've never found it a great consolation.' 'But Slaka must have its compensations,' says Petworth. 'What do they call you?' asks Budgie, 'What is your first name?' 'Angus,' says Petworth. 'Really, like the steak?' says Budgie, 'Well, Angus, I don't think you quite understand what I'm telling you, as one kindred soul to another. I'm telling you, Angus, I am a lonely woman, a very lonely woman.' 'Yes, I understand,' says Petworth. 'And I think I understand you,' says Budgie, putting her hand into Petworth's trouser pocket, 'Do you know how I see you? As a man disappointed in love. You have that gloomy, self-engrossed look, am I right? Have I struck the truth?' Petworth recalls his day, sees the image of Katya Princip: 'well,' he says, 'More or less.' 'How much we share in common,' says Budgie, 'Loneliness, and the need for reassurance. I have a migraine, Angus, would you mind stroking the back of my neck? No, not there, a little lower; don't worry about the dress. Oh, Felix, I thought you'd gone to have a shower.' 'They've cut off the wart cut off the water again,' says Steadiman, standing there in his fine suit, looking down on them. 'I was just explaining to Angus what a confined life we lead,'says Budgie Steadiman.

Steadiman sits down in a Danish armchair opposite and looks at them: 'It's not so bad,' he says, 'One can hardly expect it to be as lively as Washington or Moscow.' 'Or Belgrade or Chittagong or Wagga Wagga,' says Budgie. 'I enjoy it,' says Steadiman, 'One doesn't have to mind the earthquakes, and there are only certain days when you can get food, but there's an excellent pee peach brandy, yes, I like it very much.' 'Beneath that boyish charm, Felix is dullingly sober,' says Budgie, 'Little wonder my mother, an intelligent woman, warned me not to marry. She said it could well inhibit the taste for wandering into other people's bedrooms, and it has.' 'Yes, Budgie,' says Steadiman, 'Can you just try now? Magda's coming in with the drinks.' A moment later a large tray stands before Petworth's face, on it two large fizzing gins and tonic, and a glass of white wine, equally large and equally fizzing. 'Plis, comrade,' says Magda, standing staring down at him, as if his face might be worth remembering. 'Slubob,' says Petworth. 'Yes, indeed,' says Steadiman with great warmth, taking his drink, 'We love it here. There are some nice resorts and some excellent . . .' 'Countryside,' says Budgie. 'I was going to say that,' says Steadiman. 'Marvellous lakes and beaches,' says Budgie. 'Splendid horseback riding,' says Steadiman, 'Large woods for sportsmen.' 'Magda's supposed not to understand a thing,' says Budgie, after her big black back has disappeared round a corner, 'But she always starts dropping drinks when we complain about anything here. I suppose you're awfully busy, Angus, I do wish we could take you to the lake. You can take all your clothes off there.' 'Budgie, you are really not supposed to take your clothes off at the lake,' says Steadiman, 'This is a very puritanical country. I'm sure it's reported.' 'I don't find them so puritanical,' says Budgie, 'Look at my tan, Angus. And just think, I'm like that all over underneath.' 'Very nice,' says Petworth.

'Budgie,' says Steadiman, standing up, 'You did actually invite some other guests, didn't you?' 'Oh, yes,' says Budgie, 'But we did have quite a lot of refusals. There's a party for the Sheikh and it's the first night of the opera.' 'However, some people did consent to visit us?' says Steadiman. 'The Ambassador sent his apologies,' says Budgie, 'He very much wanted to meet you, but he doesn't like to go out at night now. He says he's being followed everywhere by a man with a raincoat and a cigar.' 'Very probably he is,' says Steadiman. 'Yes, but he thought that when he was still in the Ministry of Education in London,' says Budgie. 'What about the Wynn-Joneses?' asks Steadiman, 'He's our first sec.' 'They're awfully sorry, but they're asked to the Sheikh's reception,' says Budgie. 'And the Couttses?' asks Steadiman, 'He's the thir thir third sec.' 'You know how they love music,' says Budgie, 'They've gone to this strange new opera.' 'So did anyone say yes?' asks Steadiman, 'I did send out the car all over the town with invitations.' 'Miss Peel and Mr Blenheim,' says Budgie. 'The confidential sec and the information officer,' says Steadiman. 'And then of course we invited a number of the locals.' 'The trouble is,' says Steadiman, 'one never knows whether any of them would take the risk of coming. They're really supposed to report it. Or whether if they did the g g guard would let them in. It could be a small g g gathering.' 'But that's awfully good for getting to know each other,' says Budgie, 'And then, of course, there's the surprise.' 'Oh, yes,' says Steadiman, 'Yes.' Even now, the doorbell rings, and Magda, who has evidently been hovering in an alcove just behind them, emerges in her white gloves and walks across the room to open it. 'You see?' says Budgie, squeezing Petworth's hand quite tightly, 'They're all coming.'

There are murmurs at the door; someone hands in a coat and a pair of windscreen-wipers. Then the visitor stands in the doorway, in a dark suit, and under it a neat white roll-necked sweater, holding in one hand a male handbag, in the other a few red carnations. 'Good evening,' he says, his bird-like eyes gleaming, 'Plitplov.' 'Flowers, how gallant, I love them,' says Budgie Steadiman. 'Oh, please, my dear Mrs Steadiman,' says Plitplov, bending neatly and giving Budgie's ringed fingers a fine kiss, 'You are most charming to invite me. We have met a time or two before, I think. Here is the sad thing, I bring you an apology. Professor Marcovic likes to come, but he does not

177

like to be photographed at the door. Of course you know I have taken a certain not small risk to come here.' 'Well done, old chap,' says Steadiman, 'Now come over and meet our guess guess guest of honour, Dr Petworth.' 'Oh, yes, your English visitor, Dr Petworth, I believe I have read some books of him,' says Plitplov, standing at the doorway and looking around the room in all directions, as if any one of the people not standing there might be the distinguished visitor, 'So despite the strikes in London he still manages to arrive?' With some effort, Steadiman steers him face to face with Petworth; the dark eyes gleam. 'Ah, then you are the well-known Dr Petworth,' says Plitplov, 'You see we have heard of you. My name is Plitplov. Please allow me to welcome you to Slaka.' 'Delighted to meet you,' says Petworth. 'You've not met before?' asks Steadiman. 'You have been in Slaka before, Dr Petworth?' asks Plitplov, inspecting him up and down, 'I don't think so. No, then it cannot be possible. Tell me, please, is it true you make some lectures now in my country?'

'I thought you already knew,' says Steadiman, 'He's speaking to the universe speaking to the university tomorrow morning,' says Steadiman. 'Really, at what time?' asks Plitplov, 'How very interesting.' 'Eleven,' says Petworth. 'At eleven, what a pity,' says Plitplov, taking out a small diary and opening it at what seems to be an entirely blank page, 'There are many meetings and it will not be easy to be there. But you will accept me if I can change things? And understood also if I do not manage it? I expect you teach in a university, you know how busy is the life, I think.' In her white gloves, Madga now appears before them all, offering a silver tray filled now with many drinks, enough for some much vaster scale of party. 'I think I try something just a little Western,' says Plitplov, bending over to inspect them very carefully, 'Vusku, da?' 'Da, cam'radaki,' says Magda. 'I am told whisky is the drink of all Western intellectuals,' says Plitplov, taking one, 'Perhaps there is something in it that is very good for the brains. Therefore I need it very much. A toast to your tour here, please,

Dr Petworth. I hope you go to many places.' 'A few,' says Petworth, 'Glit, Nogod, Provd.' 'All are good,' says Plitplov. 'I thought you might have had an organ organ organizing role in all this,' says Steadiman. 'Oh, I?' cries Plitplov, with an air of great surprise, 'No, of course it was Marcovic.' 'I've never actually met him,' says Steadiman. 'Perhaps you know him, Dr Petworth?' asks Plitplov, 'Perhaps you met him at a conference? Perhaps he is a dear old friend of yours? Perhaps he knows your wife, if you have one?' 'No,' says Petworth, 'I've never met him.' 'Well, he tells me he looks forward very much to meeting you and having good critical talks,' says Plitplov, 'I expect you know the fine book he makes on Defoe.'

'You are actually at the universe university, aren't you, Dr Plitplov?' asks Steadiman. 'The answer is a bit yes and a bit no,' says Plitplov, 'I have certain important connections there, but also I do other things. Of course our system is different from yours, and very boring to explain. In any case we now make certain reforms that make it not useful. What is your field, Dr Petworth? Some people say it is language. That must be a very interesting matter.' 'It is,' says Petworth, 'Particularly in Slaka at the moment.' 'Oh, you hear about our changes,' says Plitplov, 'Some of them are very good and some of them are very bad. My opinions are in the middle.' Out in the hall, the doorbell rings. 'Ah,' says Budgie, squeezing Petworth's hand again, 'Someone else!' Magda has appeared with great rapidity, and gone to the door; the Steadimen, a handsome couple, rise and follow. 'Always with the pretty ladies,' says Plitplov, turning his sharp dark eyes on Petworth, 'I remember that. And this one likes you. But we must all be cautious. Everywhere are some ears.' Meanwhile in the doorway two new guests are handing their coats to Magda. One of them is a lady peasant in a mittel-European dirndl, with a sharp face, bunned hair and a very English accent; the other is a grey-headed man with a silver moustache, a foulard neckerchief tucked into his shirt, white jacket and dark trousers. Some misfortune has evidently attended their arrival; tears course

179

down the nose of the lady peasant. 'Sorry we're late,' says the man, giving Budgie a small peck on the cheek, 'A slight contretemps.' 'I've been stuck in your lift for half an hour,' says the lady, 'People kept passing but no one would answer. Luckily Mr Blenheim came by and, gallant man that he is, managed to get me out.'

'Well, come on in and meet everyone,' says Budgie. 'Perhaps you were shouting,' says Plitplov, graciously stepping forward. 'Yes, I was bawling my head off, actually,' says the lady. 'I heard some shoutings when I came upstairs,' says Plitplov, 'But I thought to myself, perhaps this is a marriage, I do not interfere. In my country one always takes a care not to interfere.' 'So I've noticed,' says the lady peasant. 'But accept please my apologies,' says Plitplov, taking the lady's fingers and kissing them, 'I am Plitplov.' 'This is Miss Peel and Mr Blenheim, both from the em em Embassy,' says Steadiman. 'Wasn't there a guest of honour or something?' asks Miss Peel. 'Here he is, our darling Dr Petworth,' says Budgie, plucking Petworth forward by the hand. 'Ah, got here, good,' says Miss Peel, 'Enjoying it, hope so.' 'Hullo, old chap,' says Mr Blenheim, 'Welcome to the madhouse.' 'Now, how about the big event?' asks Miss Peel, 'Have they come? Did they arrive?' 'Yes,' says Budgie, 'But let's keep it a secret.' 'Oh, marvellous,' says Blenheim. 'Oh, is there secret tonight?' asks Plitplov, 'Everywhere secrets.' 'An extremely nice secret,' says Miss Peel. 'And do we perhaps find it out?' asks Plitplov. 'You do, later on,' says Budgie, 'Which is why I must just disappear for a minute. Please amuse yourselves. And keep yourself pure for me, Angus.' 'Another of Budgie's marvellous evenings,' says Miss Peel, 'That's how she lures us here.' 'And with Mr Petworth, of course,' says Mr Blenheim. 'Cam'radaket,' says Magda, appearing with her tray. 'Orange juice, please,' says Miss Peel. 'Da,' says Magda, handing it to her. 'Doesn't she do marvellously, considering she can't speak any English?' says Miss Peel, turning to Petworth, 'Well, isn't it lucky you came tonight? You wouldn't have wanted to miss one of Budgie's secrets.'

III

And so there, in foreign parts, in distant Slaka, under another ideology, where the big maid is omnipresent and the walls undoubtedly have ears, the far-flung British exiles start their party. Wind and rain blow outside, and a big, almost green moon has been pasted, by whomever is responsible for providing such detail, over the dark roofs of Slaka; a dome and a tower or two stick up into its green orb. Below is the city, revealing itself in an occasional flash of COMFLUG and MUG, a place of watchers and listeners, threats and fears. The party, it is true, is sadly depleted, by the conflicting claims of the sheikh and the opera, and the silver tray the big maid holds out to them displays far more good things to drink than the small gathering they make can ever possibly consume. A certain civil caution hovers in the air, as you might expect when the nations meet across complicated political and social barriers; in any case conversation is never easy for the British, who are never keen to express themselves to strangers or, for that matter, anyone, even themselves. But a certain mood of relaxation now begins to emerge, as Steadiman, in his suit, goes over to the record player and puts something on, a nostalgic number called 'Try a Little Tenderness,' and people turn and talk to people. The tray of drinks comes back and forth, back and forth, and a small sociability begins to grow, a set of glimpses of a world somewhere that links them somehow all together. 'See the test matches?' asks Blenheim affably of Petworth, lighting up his pipe. 'Oh, do you smoke one of these?' cries Plitplov, taking out his vast carved smoking bowl, and waving it, 'I also.' 'I'm afraid I don't follow it,' says Petworth. 'Cricket? You talk perhaps of cricket, your national game? The men in the white

181

clothes like doctors?' asks Plitplov. 'They say a man who is tired of cricket is tired of life,' says Blenheim. 'I don't think Mr Petworth is tired of life,' says Miss Peel. 'Tired of, tired by,' murmurs Plitplov. 'No, I can take it and I can leave it alone,' says Petworth. 'I expect you know my friend Sir Laurence Olivier,' says Miss Peel. 'Not personally,' says Petworth. 'Then you don't know him at all,' cries Miss Peel. Made doubly ignorant, Petworth also knows, with a true British instinct, that he has also now been made welcome; in their own way, the British have begun to enjoy themselves.

Outside the treacherous dark city turns on itself; inside a certain version of the good life begins to flower. Now Miss Peel begins to talk about someone or other's Papageno, and Steadiman chatters about Princess Margaret's visit to some island somewhere or other to which he was at some time posted; Mr Blenheim talks of the All Blacks, and even Plitplov, refusing exclusion, becomes entertaining, magically producing nuts from his ears. 'I hear all the plays in London now are about sex and have naked people in them,' says Miss Peel, 'It sounds dreadfully dull. I've never been fond of realism.' 'The work of your Edward Bond is very famous,' says Plitplov. 'Who?' asks Blenheim. 'He writes *Saved*, also a Lear,' says Plitplov. 'Never heard of him,' says Blenheim. 'He's rather of the left,' says Miss Peel, 'They rather fancy him here.' 'I think nobody in Britain wants to work now any more,' says Plitplov, 'They tell it is too boring for them. Here our people like very much to work. Often our workers ask the managers to do more work for no money because they are liking it so much.' 'Really?' says Miss Peel, 'Amazing.' 'You'll gather our indus industrial reputation isn't too high here just now,' says Steadiman. 'We're not an easy race to explain to the world,' says Blenheim, puffing comfortably on his pipe. 'But perhaps this is your job?' asks Plitplov, 'Perhaps this is why your government is sending you here to Slaka?' 'Ah,' says Blenheim, chuckling, 'You're asking me what I do. What's my bag? It's the diplomatic one, actually.' 'I think you like to be cautious,' says

Plitplov, 'But doesn't your economy collapse? Won't you one day be socialist economy, like us?' 'I don't think so,' says Blenheim, 'Not our cup of tea, really.'

'Ah, here you are, all enjoying yourselves hugely,' cries Budgie Steadiman, emerging in a small apron from the inner intestines of the apartment, 'Our little sensation is going very well. Angus, give me a wee sip of your drinkie. I hope they're all entertaining you. Has anyone bothered to show you our quite outstanding view?' The outstanding view to which Budgie leads him is mostly of darkness, for Slaka at night is not as brightly lit as most Western cities. But the big moon glows, with a dome and a tower or two sticking up into its great orb; lights twinkle somewhere down below, and the red star flashes on the top of Party Headquarters. Down below in the street, under faint trees, a few, a very few, cars and a few muffled human figures move. 'I never cooked terribly well,' says Budgie, interlacing her fingers with Petworth's, 'We always used to advise our guests to eat first before they came to our dinner parties. But I'm quite a vigorous hostess. Of course I had an excellent upbringing. You don't think I'm too grande dame for one of my tender years?' 'Not at all,' says Petworth. 'Bless you, Angus,' says Budgie, 'You know, I think we're two of a kind. Two lonely, tense, star-crossed people. In this world, like knows like. I feel a curious deep intimacy growing up between us.' 'Cam'radaku,' says a voice; the big bulk of Magda is somehow squeezing itself in between them. 'Angus, excuse me,' says Budgie, 'I'm afraid I must try my pidgin. Da, Magda?' 'Squassu, squassu,' says Magda. 'I'm afraid that means our tête-à-tête must be deferred a little, not, I hope, for long,' says Budgie, 'Magda tells me the soup is ready. Attention, please, everybody. Magda bids us to the table!'

And so the small party moves, across from the Mexican masks and the Iranian donkey bags to the dining table just round the corner, set with silver from Paris and place mats from Korea. Before the settings stand little folded place cards, written in a foreign hand; to the right of the hostess is one that says 'Doktor Pumwum.' 'Yes, come beside me,' says Budgie, squeezing Petworth's leg under the table, 'And you're on my other side, Dr Plitplov.' 'Do we get nearer now to the secret?' asks Plitplov, sitting down and shaking out his napkin, 'Is it perhaps a something to eat?' 'Cunning man,' says Budgie, slapping his wrist, 'Remember, pleasure deferred is pleasure increased. That has always been my motto, so long as I haven't had to wait too long. As the great Mae West once said, I like a man who takes his time.' 'This is a philosopher?' asks Plitplov. 'No, she's a film star, in our part of the world,' says Budgie, 'Have you been to our part of the world, Dr Plitplov? Have they let you out to take a look?' 'I have been several times,' says Plitplov, 'In London and some other cities. I have good recollections of Tottenham Court Road.' 'I'm not surprised,' says Budgie, 'How that imprints itself on the memory. They must think well of you here, if they let you out.' 'I have not committed bad offences,' says Plitplov, 'But of course we are quite liberal now, in many ways. You see how we invite here your fine speakers, like Dr Petworth.' 'A quite outstanding choice,' says Budgie. 'Of course, I think so,' says Plitplov, 'We expect to learn many fine things from him and improve our self-criticisms, Do you read perhaps his good books?' 'Well, no,' says Budgie, 'I think I'll wait for the film.'

Magda appears, with a soup tureen and a ladle; Steadiman tours the table with a bottle of white wine. 'And do you perhaps have some children?' asks Plitplov. 'We did have some somewhere, two or three,' says Budgie, 'Where are our children now, Felix?' 'Ow ow Oundle,' says Steadiman, pouring wine. 'Please?' says Plitplov. 'At an English public school,' says Budgie, 'Which of course means a private school. You probably know, the better class of Briton likes to send his children away to school until they're old and intelligent enough to come home again. Then they're too old and intelligent to want to. Angus, do you have children? Little Petworths crying in their cots?' 'No, I don't,' says Petworth. 'But there is a Mrs Petworth, is there?' asks Budgie, 'Matrimony has not passed you by?' 'Yes, there is,' says Petworth. 'I hope she is very charming,' says Plitplov. 'Indeed,' says Petworth. 'Yet you didn't bring her with you to Slaka,' says Budgie, 'Was that thoughtfulness or neglect?' 'She's not entirely well,' says Petworth. Plitplov looks across the table at him: 'I hope you have telephoned her,' he says. 'Mr Plitplov, I seem to remember we sent you to the Cambridge summer school once,' says Miss Peel, leaning along the table. 'Who, I?' cries Plitplov. 'Do you know it at all, Mr Petworth?' asks Miss Peel. 'Yes, I do, actually,' says Petworth, 'I've given the odd lecture there.' 'We've managed to send a few people over on scholarships,' says Miss Peel, 'Rather difficult, the authorities always want to substitute others. It must have been three years ago when we sent you, Mr Plitplov.' 'To Cambridge?' asks Plitplov. 'Yes, to Cambridge,' says Miss Peel.

Magda has come again, to collect up the soup plates; Steadiman has risen, to fill their glasses again. 'It won't be long now for the secret,' cries Budgie, 'Oxford was my university, I read history with A. J. P. Taylor. I was very famous there, for my breasts.' 'Of course,' says Plitplov, gallantly, 'This is to be expected.' 'Alas, they're not what they were,' says Budgie, 'Time and tide, wear and tear, take their toll even of the most perfect monuments.' 'Of course not, they are quite outstanding, one immediately remarks it,' says Plitplov, 'Don't you say so, Dr Petworth?' 'You're very kind,' says Budgie, 'Notable, perhaps, but not outstanding. Good but not excellent. Not of the first rank, but worthy of a visit.' 'So did you go to Cambridge?' asks Miss Peel. 'To beautiful Cambridge?' says Plitplov, 'perhaps I was there. But you understand my confusions. In my country, if you study English, you must study also the Russian. This is how we keep a balance. So now I am in Moscow, now perhaps in Cambridge. Here I read Gorky, there I read Trollope. Here I see Bolshoi, there I see Covent Garden. In Moscow I study the Marxist aesthetics, and in Cambridge, if it was Cambridge . . .' 'You study Marxist aesthetics also,' says Budgie Steadiman. 'And for the travelling scholar it is hard to keep such things apart, don't you say so, Dr Petworth?' says Plitplov. 'It can all become a blur,' says Petworth. 'Cambridge and Moscow? Really?' says Miss Peel, 'I wouldn't have thought they were terribly easy to confuse.' 'Of course one remembers certain differences,' says Plitplov. 'Like what?' asks Mr Blenheim. 'In Russia the smell is of food and cats,' says Plitplov, 'In England of drink and dogs.' 'I see you're a man of subtle cultural discriminations,' says Budgie. 'Can I just be clear?' says Miss Peel, 'Did you or did you not go to Cambridge? I'm sure we sponsored you.' 'Then I am very grateful,' says Plitplov. 'Good,' says Miss Peel, 'Now then, Dr Petworth, when did you lecture there? Where you there three years ago?'

'Just a moment, just a moment!' cries Budgie, 'Here comes the secret! The sensation of the evening!' In her big black dress, Magda is now advancing on them from the kitchen; high in her hands she holds a large silver covered dish. 'It is here, in here, your secret?' asks Plitplov, staring at it curiously. 'Put it down on the table, Magda,' says Budgie, 'Thank you very much. Well, shall we ask our honoured guest if he'd unveil it? I'm a great believer in putting our visitors to good use. If you please, Angus.' As the faces round the table watch, Petworth reaches and lifts the cover of the dish: to disclose, beneath it, a quantity of meaty, brown, skin-covered objects, not unlike cooked turds, assembled in neat rows. 'Oh, don't they look marvellous,' cries Miss Peel. 'Bella, multa bella,' cries Mr Blenheim. Only Plitplov looks sceptical; he leans forward a little, to inspect. 'Do you know them?' asks Budgie. 'Of course,' says Plitplov, unbelieving, 'This is a sausage.' 'Yes, but a *British* sausage,' says Budgie. 'A Marks and Spencer sausage,' says Miss Peel. 'The secret is a sausage?' says Plitplov. 'You must have gone to an enormous amount of trouble,' says Miss Peel. 'Actually,' says Budgie, 'they came over yesterday in the diplomatic bag. They must have been on the same plane as you, Angus.' 'Let's empty our glug glug glasses,' says Felix Steadiman, 'I think we really ought to switch to the red.' 'This party is all for a sausage?' asks Plitplov. 'The party is to celebrate Angus's arrival,' says Budgie, squeezing Petworth's leg under the table, 'But we wanted to give everyone a treat.' 'I will tell you a secret myself,' says Plitplov, 'Even in Slaka, where we are so backward, we have invented the sausage.' 'Ah, but not like these sausages,' says Miss Peel.

So, as the big orb of the moon shines curiously in through the window, and in the Slakan night the signs saying MUG and COMFLUG flash furiously on and off, the British exiles raise their knives and forks and devote themselves to the delicacy. The sausages are served, as well they might be, with an attempt at mashed potatoes, a bottle of red tomato sauce, and a red wine that Steadiman takes round the table, saying: 'They have some quite out outstanding wines here you can't get at home. Unfortunately this isn't one of them.' The candlelight flickers; only Plitplov appears bemused. 'How do I explain such a people to my students?' he says, 'In the middle of history, in these strange times, when everywhere there are diplomatical dangers, you come all here to celebrate the sausage. Is this what is called phlegm?' 'Just tell them the British know how to make a good sausage,' says Blenheim. 'I'm afraid it's not such a treat for you, Angus,' says Budgie, 'You probably have them all the time,' 'Yes,' says Petworth, 'But they are quite delicious.' 'Always he is diplomatic,' says Plitplov, 'This was noticed, even in . . .' 'In Cambridge?' asks Miss Peel, 'You did meet there?' 'These things are very hard to know,' says Plitplov, 'So many lectures, so many faces. How do you recall?' 'What about you, Dr Petworth?' asks Miss Peel, 'Do you recall Dr Plitplov?' 'We may have talked once, in a public house,' says Petworth. 'Oh, I don't think it,' says Plitplov, 'I do not like to go into those places.' 'What did you lecture on, Dr Petworth?' asks Miss Peel. 'I believe it was on Chomskyan linguistics,' says Petworth, 'A rather specialist affair.' 'It doesn't ring any bells, Dr Plitplov?' asks Miss Peel, 'The lecture made no imprint on you at all?'

'I think I do now recall it,' says Plitplov, 'An excellent

piece, now I remember. Such a strange coincidence, that our paths cross again.' 'Yes, isn't it,' says Miss Peel. 'Of course you will not at all remember me,' says Plitplov, 'I was just one of so many listening to your words with admiration.' 'I believe I do, actually,' says Petworth, 'Weren't you working on Trollope?' 'Oh, my small chef d'oeuvre,' says Plitplov, 'Do you recollect it?' 'Trollope,' says Budgie, 'Wasn't he some kind of postman?' 'Your great novelist,' says Plitplov, 'More famous than a sausage.' 'I think you know each other perfectly well,' says Miss Peel, 'I don't see any need for concealment.' 'Well,' says Plitplov, as if stirred to act, suddenly looking at Petworth with his bird-like eyes, 'Perhaps I do not wish to embarrass your guest.' 'How could you possibly embarrass him?' asks Budgie, 'He doesn't look at all embarrassed.' 'Oh, I think we don't discuss such a thing,' says Plitplov, 'In front of the nice people enjoying their sausages. I think you make a saying in your country: let the sleeping dogs lie?' 'I can't imagine what you're talking about,' says Petworth. 'It is just I recall a little problem between us that has made me very discreet.' 'How utterly fascinating,' says Budgie, 'What little problem?' 'No, I go too far,' says Plitplov, 'Really I should not mention it. Your wife would not please with me.' 'My wife?' says Petworth. 'Her name is Lottie,' says Plitplov. 'I know her name is Lottie,' says Petworth. 'A very amusing lady,' says Plitplov, 'She smokes the little cigars. She came to Cambridge and we made some very good walks together, also sometimes the shoppings. Well, on these occasions sometimes certain confidences are made that should not be repeated. Now you see why I make a little concealment.'

'You went for walks with my wife?' asks Petworth. 'Oh, you do not know this?' asks Plitplov, 'I am wrong to mention it, then. Really I do not mean it. But so many glasses of whisky, and now this nice sausage, I am not so cautious as I should be.' 'This is fascinating,' says Budgie. 'What kind of confidences?' asks Petworth. 'I think I displayed her just a friendship that was necessary,' says Plitplov, 'Often the ladies need a

188

person to talk to about their troubles.' 'This is true,' says Budgie. 'What troubles?' asks Petworth. 'Oh, you are angry, please do not blame me,' says Plitplov, 'You see how hard I try to conceal what has happened there from these people. You know I am your good friend. Only if your wife is still with you, and you are happy again, please to remember I had just a little finger in that pie.' 'She wanted to leave him?' asks Budgie, 'Oh, Angus, now we begin to see the secret of your gloom.' 'This is nonsense,' says Petworth. 'She did not ever explain you?' asks Plitplov, 'Well, it is natural. We cannot always tell our distresses to those who come closest to them. That is why a stranger is sometimes a good friend. Such a person may see what the involved ones do not: that a person is sad, feels a neglect, has a distress.' 'And you performed this generous service for my wife?' asks Petworth. 'I was there when a certain help was needed,' says Plitplov, 'You must remember, you are a famous scholar, everyone is admiring you. You are giving notable lectures on the Chomskyan linguistics and all are spellbound. But for her life is not the same. She comes, but no one regards her. She walks alone in the streets. There are fulfilments she does not enjoy. It is natural she talks to someone who can listen, even if that is a stranger from a faraway country where you cannot get even an English sausage.'

'I recognize all those feelings,' says Budgie Steadiman. 'What exactly did you do with my wife?' asks Petworth. 'Please, it was just a little friendship,' says Plitplov, 'All the time I am speaking very well of you. I tell her a fine scholar is a very valuable man, who needs very special understandings. I point out to her the high spots of your work. Not every woman appreciates these achievements. I explain of course you are attractive to other women, of course your students fall a little sometimes in love with you, and you are flattered. But this does not mean always that love is ended. Now you understand perhaps why I am curious about her condition. When one has been of such an assistance, one feels a devotion. Of course my respect is for both of you. You know you helped me very well with my book. I have made due acknowledgement in the preface, which I will like to show you. But now you see why I do not like to mention such acquaintances. It is better if such things are just a little secret. Like a sausage.' 'I think in matters of sex discretion is sometimes advisable,' says Budgie Steadiman, 'I'm afraid we live in an age of excessive sexual confession. There are people nowadays who only go to bed with you to tell you long stories about all the other people they've had, who, and when, and how often, where and why and which way up. Personally I find it quite distasteful. One gets quite enough of that sort of thing at the hairdresser.' 'Please, Dr Petworth, remember,' says Plitplov, his eyes glinting sharply across the table, 'I am always your good friend. I like to make a nice toast to you for your tour, and hope it will be always a success. Also I try to get to your lecture, because I hope our paths cross somewhere again.' 'How very nice,' says Budgie.

But now Magda is with them again, putting on the table a cakey, flakey dessert. 'Perhaps you could tell Dr Petworth a bit about these places he will visit,' says Felix Steadiman from the other end of the table. 'I will make some advices if I can,' says Plitplov, 'But of course I do not know the places you visit.' 'Glit, Nogod and Provd,' says Petworth. 'Oh, really?' says Plitplov, 'Well, these are cities out in the country. You will have nice times there, I know.' 'But what are they like?' asks Steadiman. 'They are towns, like all towns,' says Plitplov, 'I do not know them so well. But I think you have a guide-interpreter. She of course will tell you where you are. You know: in my country we have a saying.' 'I bet you do,' says Mr Blenheim. 'You cannot build a city with words only,' says Plitplov, 'Also: the future will come, whether we speak of it or not. I am afraid my poor words would spoil these places for you.' 'But who will he meet?' asks Budgie. 'In Glit is Professor Vlic,' says Plitplov, 'He has good assistants who will ask advanced Marxist questions. In Nogod, not so good perhaps, the professor is a lady, Personip. In Provd is not university, so

I think you attend congress, perhaps in a place that was once hunting lodge for the emperors. But I think you can explain all this, Mr Steadiman.' 'Well, no,' says Steadiman, 'These places are in the yellow areas.' 'What is yellow areas?' asks Plitplov 'The areas marked yellow on the diplomatic map,' says Steadiman, 'Where we're not allowed to go.' Plitplov's face whitens: 'Then you should not ask me,' he says, 'Now I am indiscreet again. Tonight I say too many things.'

And Madga stands over them, taking away the last plates; under the table, Petworth feels Budgie Steadiman's hands playing rhythmically across his knees. Across the table is the sharp, glinting face of Plitplov, half malicious, half worried. The troubling conversation runs through his mind, fuddled and gloomy with the day's drink. Down vague, complicated passages, he tries to think back to his wife, that dark anima; sitting at a table with candles in Slaka, he tries to recover Cambridge, the brown river, the punts, the greenfly, but it seems very far away. The glinting face opposite him looks across, in an expression that could be apologetic, or victorious; he has a moment's glimpse of that face as it comes, late one night, to the room he and his wife have shared somewhere high in the Cambridge college, bearing, civilly, some carved wooden object, which may have been an egg-holder or a pipe-stand, doubtless carved by some peasant in these Slakan woods, and talking on into the night long after Petworth has retired exhausted to sleep. But is there more? He remembers the long hours in which his wife wandered, tries to recall whether Plitplov was present or absent at those same times; it is too far away. He looks around at the table of exiles, and wonders why he is here; he recalls a domestic conversation: 'He asked me if you had great sexual energy; I told him so so.' A sense of being implicated, complicated, in someone else's plots comes over him, but he is too tired to understand them, too will-less, too lonely, too personless, not enough the noun, too much the object. 'Some brandy,' says Steadiman, coming up with a bottle. 'No, thank you,' says Petworth, putting a debilitated hand over his glass. 'I see you make an excellent choice among our spiritous liquors,' says Plitplov, smiling, 'Just a small. But you enjoy it, I think, your diplomatic life here?'

'Talking of secrets,' says Budgie Steadiman, putting her hand back on Petworth's knee, 'A story that illustrates the odd difficulties of the way we live here. About those yellow areas. You know whenever we leave Slaka, we're checked to find out where we're going. We have to report at the control points on every route out of the city. One Friday night we left in the car to go skiing for the weekend. The roads were dark, we had to go through the thick forest, and we must have missed our turn. We came to a small town and checked on the map, and it was in one of the yellow areas. Felix tried get the car turned round, but there was a dance going on in the street, and the dancers came all round us, gipsies playing their violins through the window, you know. We couldn't move, so I made Felix get out and we joined in the dance.' 'I wanted to go, you remember,' says Felix. 'But I like dances,' says Budgie, 'You know I have a wild and foreign nature. Well, we danced, then we were taken to a house to get warm, and these peasants all started pouring brandy down us, and I sang some songs. Well, we went back to the car, and a huge tent had been built on top of it.' 'Who did it?' asks Miss Peel. 'The militia,' says Budgie, 'They weren't allowed to move it, you see, because we had diplomatic plates, but they weren't going to let us move it either.' 'So what did you do?' asks Miss Peel. 'Oh, we slept in it all night,' says Budgie, 'Then in the morning Felix said the only way to get out was to go to the militia and explain. Well, they held us there for two days. We asked them why; they said we had seen things we were not allowed to see. But, I said to the colonel at the barracks, all we saw was a dance. Yes, said the colonel, but to see it is not permitted. So I told him not to be silly and they put us in the car and we drove between two army trucks all the way back to Slaka. Then the Ambassador put on his raincoat and went and apologized and the incident was closed.'

'But you should not go there,' says Plitplov, 'You should not know that place.' 'You mean it's a secret dance?' asks Budgie. 'Your secret is a sausage,' says Plitplov, 'Why not ours a dance?' 'You know these things ex ex excite you, Budgie,' says Steadiman at the other end of the table. 'Excite me?' cries Budgie, 'Who knows what excites me? Who in thirty-five years has ever succeeded in unlocking that particular door?' 'I think it's getting late,' says Miss Peel. In a big black coat, carrying a plastic bag, Magda appears gloomily beside the table. 'Yes, time to take Magda home,' says Steadiman, rising, and going to look for his windscreen wipers. 'Dr Plitplov,' says Budgie, seizing her visitor by the arm, 'Do you perhaps understand, just a little, why in this country, in this world, I feel a confined soul?' 'Of course,' says Plitplov, 'But really you must not depress.' 'Depress?' cries Budgie, 'I think I'm awfully gay.' 'Time for bye-byes, I think,' says Mr Blenheim, stretching his arms, 'Look, I'll see Miss Peel safely down the stairs and take her back to her apartment.' 'I think I make also a quiet excuse me,' says Plitplov, 'My wife probably has a headache. Also I have said perhaps some things I do not mean.' 'Not at all,' says Budgie, 'I thought you remarkably good value.' 'Yes, well, my friend,' says Plitplov, rising and shaking hands with Petworth, 'I hope so much we stay good colleagues. You know I do not like to distress you. But, as you say, a man has to keep his end up. I hope please one day you come for a dinner to me. Of course I cannot promise you such a sausage. And remember always, when you call your wife, to give her the love of Plitplov.' 'Going?' asks Budgie, 'Everyone going?' 'Mrs Steadiman,' says Plitplov, kissing her hand, 'A most interesting evening, and my compliments to your menu. You know I have taken many risks to come, and perhaps it was worth it.' 'I must get back too,' says Petworth, 'Can I call a taxi?' 'Of course I would take you,' says Plitplov, 'But I do not like to go in your direction.'

'No, Angus, you stay here and help me with the washing up,' says Budgie. 'Oh, really, you should not do it,' says

Plitplov, putting on his coat, 'You are the wife of a diplomat.' 'How nice of you to offer,' says Budgie. 'Oh, I do not offer, I am guest,' says Plitplov, 'But you have a maid to do it.' 'I like a maid to leave early,' says Budgie, 'A hostess needs a little privacy for her indiscretions. Angus, you're not too proud to help me? And Felix will take you back when he returns from dropping Magda.' 'Bye, Mr Petworth,' cries Miss Peel from the door, 'Told you it would be a stunning evening.' 'Take care, old chap,' cries Blenheim. Then Petworth looks round at a diplomatic room suddenly empty; drained glasses shine on the table, the Mexican dance-masks stare blankly off the wall. 'Could you just take a few of those things into the kitchen?' says Budgie, 'I must just discard a few jewels and make myself more comfortable.' In the kitchen, it seems churlish not to put on rubber gloves and wash a dish or two in the sink; it is in this domesticated condition that Budgie finds him when she comes in a few moments later, clad in a very diaphanous nightdress. 'A sorry tale that funny little man tells,' she says, 'I hope it hasn't distressed you.' 'I don't understand what he's up to,' says Petworth, scouring a saucepan. 'When two people are together in agony, Angus,' says Budgie, drawing him away from the sink, 'There is only one solution. You are not a young man, Angus. You have a certain sophistication and expertise. This is the centre of the house. I always think it's harder for telescopic sights to see in here. Do you prefer the kitchen table or the floor?'

'It doesn't seem a terribly good idea,' says Petworth.

'You're worried about Felix?' asks Budgie, 'Felix and I have an arrangement. He lets me get away with murder.' 'It's not really that,' says Petworth. 'You're worried I don't have protection,' says Budgie, 'Believe me, I don't just have protection, I have diplomatic immunity.' 'No, it's not that,' says Petworth. 'You have other interests,' says Budgie, 'That does not concern me in the slightest.' 'It seems rather dangerous,' says Petworth. 'Of course, it's dangerous,' says Budgie, 'But England expects, my dear. One is not a guest of honour for nothing.' 'I'll call for a taxi,' says Petworth. 'You will not call for a taxi,' says Budgie, 'You'll stay here and fly the flag. I'm just going out to put on a little music, you did say you liked Wagner, didn't you? You look like a man of taste. I imagine you have quite an eye for specialist lingerie. Let me show you some.' Petworth stands in the kitchen: a booming noise begins in the back of the apartment as the noises of Wagner, that metaphysical romper, sounds on the record player, and on, doubtless, the tapes and the film, the screens and the consoles, that whirl and flicker in some technologized office nearby, where the HOGPo men sit, reducing Petworth, that virtuous subject, into sign or object, transient image. Luckily there is just time to finish the saucepan before, along the corridor, he hears the bedroom door open.

IV

'Actually,' says Steadiman, as he drives the brown Ford Cortina back through the urban darkness toward the centre and the Hotel Slaka, 'I'm afraid it's terribly easy to get the wrong impression of Budgie. She finds life here rather diff diff difficult, and she reacts to it. Also, you know, she has an aristocratic background, her father was a duke, actually, and she expects service from everyone. I think she rather expected it from you.' 'Yes,' says Petworth, through his split lip, 'I see what you mean.' 'People often get a wrong impression of dip dip diplomatic life,' Steadiman explains in the dark, 'It can be awe awe awfully confining. That's what she revolts against. Besides, she's always liked to extra-mural a bit, I understand that. And if we were in Paris, or Athens, or Washington, I can't say I'd terribly mind. That's the trouble with Slaka, it's rather diff diff different. I do hope that wrist isn't sprained.' 'Oh, no,' says Petworth, 'I don't think so, just bruised.' 'Yes, well, terr terr terribly sorry,' says Steadiman, 'One hardly wants to wound one's most distinguished visitors. I must be a bit bit fit fit fitter than I thaw thaw thought. Yes, Budgie's really a sort of tease, you know. I think what she enjoys best is just tan tan tantalizing all these little secret police squits who spend all their working hours listening in on us, beastly, isn't it? I suppose she just doesn't like to think how unutterably boring their nasty little lives must be, so she tries to brighten them up a bit. At least, that's how I explain her conduct. So there's nothing sort of personal about you.' 'Oh, isn't there?' says Petworth, holding his wrist, 'Well, yes, I see.' 'I'm awe awe awfully sorry about the suit,' says Steadiman, driving into the rain, 'I hope you've brought another one. Never mind, there should be a sort of tailor person somewhere in the hotel.' 'I expect so,' says Petworth, 'It's just a little hard to explain.' 'Tell them it was a football match,' says Steadiman, 'Nowadays I find that more or less explains everything.'

The rain pours down in front of them; it is not, as it turns out, a good night in Slaka. 'I really didn't mean . . .' murmurs Petworth. 'No, no, of course you didn't,' says Steadiman, 'I do understand. You know the trouble with Budgie? She just doesn't recognize the realities of the game she's playing. And with half of myself I don't blame her. The only trouble is, that stuff is terr terr terribly terr terr terribly dangerous.' 'Is it?' asks Petworth, nursing his wounded arm. 'You know dip dip diplomacy,' says Steadiman, 'Well, it's like life, isn't it? Everybody trading this for that. The trouble with these chaps here is they play some very nasty games indeed. A dip dip diplomat is just a chap on the football field, trying to protect his own goal and hoping to score once in a while. But of course there are some corrupt types who try to get at the players.' 'I see,' says Petworth. 'And this is what Budgie doesn't understand,' says Steadiman, 'This stuff could be the end of my dip dip diplomatic career.' 'Surely not,' says Petworth. 'Oh, yes,' says Steadiman, 'You see, it's not what you do that's important. It's the way it looks. When they write it down, or record it, or photograph it, or put it into the Smolensk com com computer, or wherever all this stuff is put together. Of course that's how life is played now, in front of the screens. Collate, file, store, re-arrange, produce at the opportune moment.' 'And with me too?' asks Petworth. 'Well, of course,' says Steadiman, 'You've travelled a lot, you have a position, you don't seem very discreet, I should think they've got a hell of a lot on you by now, all there in the computer. Lip still bleeding?' 'No, I think it's all right now,' says Petworth. 'Please don't think it was per per personal,' says Steadiman.

Yes, it has been a difficult departure, from the diplomatic apartment, with its Danish chairs, its Kurdish trunks, its Afghan wall-rugs, somewhere five floors up over Slaka. Indeed the details, still, are not quite clear in Petworth's admittedly not quite clear head. 'Don't you love red lingerie?' Budgie Steadiman, he recalls, has said, standing there in the kitchen in some, of admirable quality, while the coffee maker bubbles and Tannhäuser rages somewhere nearby, 'Actually I bought it in the Reeperbahn in Hamburg. Look what it does.' 'Budgie, I really think it's time Mr Petworth was returning to his ho ho hotel,' Steadiman has then said, coming into the kitchen in his coat, dropping windscreen wipers on the floor to grip Petworth rather firmly by one wrist, 'He looks pretty tired and ready for bed.' 'Oh, he doesn't want to go, Felix,' Budgie has said, 'Can't you see he's sad and lonely? And I too am sad and lonely. I want him to try on uniforms. I want him to stay here with me.' 'Come on, Budgie, let go of him, there's a go go good girl,' Steadiman has said, taking Petworth round the head in an expert arm-lock, 'The ho ho hotel will probably alert the po po police if he's not in his room tonight. We don't want him in trouble.' 'Loneliness and the need for reassurance,' Budgie has said, holding fast to the waistband of Petworth's trousers, 'Don't you understand, Felix, that is the meaning of life.' 'Budgie does *not* understand the meaning of life,' Steadiman has said, wrenching Petworth free with a ripping of material, and dragging him into the living room, 'She only thinks she does. Mr Petworth would like to go home.' 'He wants to spend the night with me,' Budgie has said, falling sobbing into a chair. 'Don't you, Angus?' 'Well, I do,' Petworth has said, diplomatic in the diplomatic living room, 'But I'd better go.' 'He's a very polite man and he doesn't want to hurt your feelings,' Steadiman has said, 'But he's go go going.'

And so it is that Petworth now sits, with throbbing arm, hurt lip and torn trousers, the zip quite gone, in the brown Cortina as it drives speedily and erratically toward Slaka. Driving rain and road mud smear over the windscreen, eliminating all visibility – for, in the rush of his departure, out of the flat, down, down, down the long staircase, into the car, Steadiman has failed to bring the wipers with him. 'Well, look, I do apologize,' says Petworth. 'Not at all, old chap,' says Steadiman, 'You gave her a good evening, che che cheered her up no end. I should have warned you, really, she does that. I should apologize to you. I don't usually use violence on my guests of honour.' 'It could be serious for you?' asks Petworth. 'Oh, God, for heaven's sake,' says Steadiman, looking into the mirror, 'There's a tail on us.' 'Why?' asks Petworth. 'Oh, they follow us everywhere,' says Steadiman, 'HOGPo is the biggest employer in the country. That's how they manage to have no unemployment. Everyone's followed by somebody else. I just hope I don't hit anyone. See anything ahead?' 'There's someone now,' cries Petworth, as a khaki figure leaps for the curb. 'I hate to think what the sentence would be, after all the stuff we've put away tonight,' says Steadiman, 'Pru pru Proust wouldn't be half long enough.' 'I really shouldn't have had so much myself,' says Petworth, 'Two parties in one day.' 'Never mind, good fun, enjoyed it,' says Steadiman, 'Thank God, they've turned off.' A sign on a building in front of them flashes through the mud, saying SCH'VEPPUU. 'This is your square, isn't it?' asks Steadiman, 'Wang'likii? I'll just park and make sure you get in all right.' It is lucky that Petworth has his topcoat to cover his one best suit, split now right down to the crotch; they walk together toward the entrance of the Hotel Slaka. 'Marvellous evening,' says Petworth. 'Yes,' says Steadiman, 'Let's do it again. Call me when you get back to Slaka next week. I'd like to hear your news. Oh, damn, look, the hotel's all locked up.'

Peering through the glass doors of the hotel, they see it is dark, dark, dark in the lobby; but then it is late, late, perhaps three in the morning. One faint light shines over the registration desk, but nobody in blue uniform sits at this hour beneath Marx and Wanko. 'They seem to have lock lock locked you out,' says Steadiman, 'Can you see a bell?' 'No,' says Petworth, tapping on the glass door. No one walks, no trams grind, in the great square; the rain beats on the gravel. After a long wait, and much tapping, a door inside does open, casting a beam of light; a limping figure comes toward the doors, looks out at them, and then turns away in a gesture of dismissal. 'Don't you have an ident'ayii?' asks Steadiman. Petworth takes out his hotel passport, spreads it against the glass, and taps again. The doorman turns, puts on spectacles, stares; then, slowly and grudgingly, he takes out a key and unlocks the door. 'Give him a tip,' says Steadiman, 'And don't forget. If you feel in need of a bit of ass, a bit of assistance call me, any time.' 'I will, thank you very much,' says Petworth, 'It's reassuring to have someone to turn to. Many thanks.' He watches a moment through the glass as Steadiman walks off, in quite the wrong direction from his car, while the aggrieved doorman inspects the ident'ayii. Petworth takes out a handful of vloskan; the doorman nods, stares, and then limps away to the desk, to come back with Petworth's key, and disappear inside his door.

The lobby is dark, but somewhere in the darkness there is a faint murmur: 'Change money?' says a voice. 'Na,' says Petworth, groping toward the elevator, to find it switched off. Groping, he finds a back staircase, long and dark, like the staircase at Steadiman's apartment, like life itself, in a sense; he ascends, up and round, round and up. In his corridor, at her desk, under a little light, the floormaid sleeps, to wake in surprise as Petworth unlocks his door. Inside the great room the lamps are lit, the cracks in the ceiling wide, the pyjamas spread. Loneliness and fear, guilt and betrayal, spread from the room into Petworth, from Petworth to the little house in Bradford, his old domestic space. In the great mirrored bathroom Petworth takes off his torn and ruined trousers; under the duvet he tries to sleep. The voices begin to sound again: she is a very tough lady, chosen special for you; this is a forbidden area, you do not go there; the witch was not a good witch; this is not the posting I would have desired. In the night there are dark and winding staircases, going up and down, round and up; a wind blows; a car follows; a maid in gloves waits by a dead man's tomb. Two men talk under a sign that flashes and says PLUC. A soldier with a gun appears and holds it toward a car. There is a glimpse of Katya Princip, falling falling down a hole, to the middle of a forest, where people dance and gipsies play violins. There is a pain in the wrist, a taste of blood in the mouth, and around the wall secrets hanging, like sausages, in strings.

6 – LECT.

I

Petworth wakes in the morning, under the great duvet, in the great room, to find himself in a world that has changed its weather. A bright sun glints through the cracks in the dusty curtains; a warm wind dries off the gravel under the people and the trams in the Plazscu Wang'luku, down below his window; flashes of sunny light twist and turn the knobs and domes of the great government buildings. No one is taking down the sign saying SCH'VEPPUU, and in the breakfast room the menu is the same as yesterday's, and so, despite the fact that he makes a quite different order, is the breakfast. In the lobby, at the appointed time, it is a more summery Marisja Lubijova who stands there; she wears a flowered dress and a tam o'shanter hat that falls to one side over her dark hair and tense white face. Only her manner does not fit the illuminated brightness; it contains – Petworth has every reason to expect it – a note of saddened rebuke. A man, he knows, in a difficult world, a place of false leads and harmful traps, doors that will not open and toilets that will not flush, needs a guide, severe yet competent, warning yet enlarging, to bring shape to the shapeless, names to the unnamed, definition to the undefined. Yes, a bruised man, he is pleased to see her, neat in the lobby; but evidently she is less pleased to see him. 'Oh, today you are on time,' she says abruptly, 'You amaze, Comrade Petwurt. Your breakfast, did you eat it?' 'I did,' says Petworth. 'And your evening, you enjoy it?' 'It was very quiet,' says Petworth,

'I just ate and went to bed.' 'All by yourself?' asks Lubijova, 'You didn't do it with a lady writer?' 'Oh, no,' says Petworth, 'She just left me here and went home. I don't suppose I shall see her again.' 'Of course,' says Lubijova, 'She comes today to your lecture,' 'Well, no,' says Petworth, 'She changed her mind.'

'Oh, poor Comrade Petwurt,' says Lubijova, looking brighter, 'What a shame for you. I have good intuitions, I am a little bit psychic, I think yesterday you were very pleased with Comrade Princip. Oh, Petwurt, look at you, you spent a quiet evening, I don't think so. You have bruised all your face, at the mouth.' 'Ah,' says Petworth, 'Ah. Yes, I walked into a door I didn't see.' 'At the hotel?' cries Lubijova, 'You should complain to them. It hurts? A doctor comes here, I think we go to the desk and ask he looks at you.' 'Oh, no,' says Petworth, 'It's just a small bruise.' 'A door in your room?' asks Lubijova, 'You don't go out and make some fights?' 'No,' says Petworth. 'Oh, Petwurt, I don't know if I believe you,' says Lubijova, 'You have met a lady writer and now you tell me some stories. Do you think you can lecture very well, your mouth is important.' 'Oh, yes,' says Petworth. 'And your telephone to your wife, did you lose it?' asks Lubijova. 'Yes,' says Petworth. 'You see, you drink so much, and you must go somewhere with a lady writer,' says Lubijova, 'Then you cannot do the things you must do. Always you are a trouble, hah? Well, I go to the desk and arrange again. When do we fix it? In the morning you make lecture, you have free afternoon, and then tonight we go, do you remember it, to the oper, that will be very nice. Do we say before the oper?' 'Yes,' says Petworth, 'That's fine.' 'Sit down please and I fix,' says Lubijova, 'Then it is time to go to the university.' Petworth sits down in one of the red plasticated armchairs; along the row, the big-hatted man who sat here two days ago, still wearing his raincoat despite the shining sun, looks up. Petworth glances rapidly through the text of his lecture, on 'The English Language as a Medium of International Communication,' to ensure that all the pages survive; they do, in all the novel neatness imposed on them by the lady in DONAY'II, so long, it seems, ago.

'So, Comrade Petwurt,' says Lubijova, coming back, 'You ate and then you went to bed last night, did you? I don't think so.' 'Pardon?' says Petworth, getting up. 'They tell at the desk you came in at three in the morning,' says Lubijova, 'Your clothes are torn and you do not walk straight.' 'Oh, yes,' says Petworth, 'I did go for a walk.' 'Where do you walk, at this time?' asks Lubijova, 'Well, no matter, it is not my business. Your telephone is arranged: six o'clock. They do not please that you do not come last night. Also the porters like to take a little sleep and not have to wait for the official guests who are here for a purpose. Now I think we take the tram to the university. It is not far but perhaps too far to walk, especially if you do not have so much sleep. Your lecture, do you have it? I must check on everything. I try to be good guide but you must help me. You were well when I find you at the airport. I hope when you turn back home to England and you are tired and your clothes are torn and your face is hurted and there are perhaps other troubles as well they do not blame me because I do not watch after you. I try, Petwurt, I try.' 'You do,' says Petworth, as they walk out of the door of the hotel, 'You're a fine guide, really.' 'And I don't like it you do not tell me the truth,' says Lubijova, 'I don't know what to believe of you, Petwurt, I don't really. You understand I do not want you to have some troubles here. But I think you don't know life here and its difficulties. I believe you don't mean harm, Comrade Petwurt, but you will find some. Petwurt, not on that tram, please, this one goes the wrong direction. Wait here with me and be good.'

They stand in the square, in the sunlight; the people move, and the newspaper man sells newspapers, the balloon man balloons. A tram comes with a sign on the front saying KREP'ATATOK: 'Now we go on,' says Lubijova. They bounce, standing, as the tram rattles them through the city, along the fine wide boulevard, past the statue of Lip Hrovdat, who shines on his horse in the brightening sun. 'Here we get off for the university,' says Lubijova, 'Watch always for Hrovdat, then you tell you arrive.' Young people with briefcases stream across the crossing with them, toward a large classical facade of stained stone, where pigeons strut back and forth over the portico; more sober-looking young people sit taking the sun on the steps. Caryatids support the roof of the entrance, statues of the muses; 'They say they move when a virgin passes in,' says Lubijova, 'But you see they are quite still. Now we go along many corridors here. You are lucky I know the way. That is because I made my studies in filologie here.' 'Is it a good department?' asks Petworth, following Lubijova past a porter's box filled with many faces and up a wide dark staircase. 'Of course,' cries Lubijova, 'You see what a good student they produce. The professor is Marcovic, very old, very famous. Perhaps you will not meet him. Often he does not come because so many of the faculty work against him. Of course he himself worked against the professor before.' They turn into a long dark corridor where faint figures scurry past; posters flap on noticeboards on the wall. 'Oh, look what these students do now,' says Lubijova, 'When I came, the authorities would not permit.' 'What do they do?' asks Petworth. 'Here are posters to ask for more language reform,' says Lubijova, 'As if the party has not been kind enough. They will not get a reform, they will get the police and some prison.' 'I see,' says Petworth.

The corridor is dirty and has bare board floors; offices with glass doors stand open along it. 'Now here Germanic languages and filologies,' says Lubijova, 'Of course it is always hard to find somebody. They are all so busy working somewhere. Look, I try here.' She knocks on a door and opens it; Petworth waits in the corridor, where a few students pass, looking at him with suspicion. 'Oh, is here, Prifessori Petworthi?' cries a voice, and a sturdy short middle-aged lady emerges into the corridor, wearing heavy spectacles suspended around her neck on a chain, as if otherwise someone might steal them, 'Prifessori Petworthi, welcomi. I have been reading your booki, what an interesting thingi. Of course it is not my sorti of worki.' 'No?' says Petworth, 'What's your field?' 'Goldi and silveri imagery of the *Faerie Queeni*,' says the lady, 'I am afraidi Professori Marcovic sends apologies, very sorry. He is not so well, is his stomachi. I step instead into the breachi, my name is Mrs Goko.' 'Delighted,' says Petworth. 'Come pleasi into my office,' says Mrs Goko, 'Here some coffee, and also some of my assistanti, waiting to meet you. All are doing most interesting scientific enterprisi, and they welcome your criticisms and suggestions.' Petworth steps out of the dark corridor into a dark room, shelved with old wooden shelves holding books, some in the Cyrillic alphabet, some in the Latin, some even British paperbacks. In the middle is a desk, in the corner a coffee table, with a coffee machine on it, and some cups, and around it a worn settee and some easy, all too easy, chairs. On the chairs sit three young ladies and one young man, who wears Tonton Macoute sunglasses, and a camera round his neck. The three young ladies rise civilly and look at Petworth with sceptical curiosity; the young man takes the lens hood off the camera and takes a photograph. 'Here has come Professori Petworthi,' says Mrs Goko, 'Please sit down and take some coffee. We have much timi and these ladies have many questions.' Petworth sits down. The ladies look at him and ask no questions. The young man takes another photograph.

'First the coffee, you do not mind it strongi?' says Mrs Goko, 'Also a little rot'vuttu, to make it go downi?' 'Well, just a little,' says Petworth. 'Of coursi,' says the lady, 'Is that just nicei?' 'Fine,' says Petworth. 'These are my brightest assistants,' says Mrs Goko, 'As you see, three of them are ladies, and that one is a mani. In my country, no discrimination for sexi, yet still the ladies study the languages and filologies and the menis the heavy thingis, like to build bridges, although a lady can plan a bridgi just like a mani. Of course you interest in such sociological thingis. Please say now your namies to Professori Petworthi, so he knows you all.' 'Miss Bancic,' says one. 'Miss

Chervovna,' says the next. 'Miss Mamorian,' says the next. 'Picnic,' says the man, looking at him through his dark sunglasses. 'Now tell Professori Petworthi what you make your theses on and explain your enterprises. Please be as critical as you wanti, here we are always critical of our praxis and try to make our thinking always correcti.' 'I work on anarchistic nihilism of the proletarian novel of A. Sillitoe,' says Miss Bancic, 'I investigate his quasi-radical critique and his modus of realismus.' 'This should be interesting to Professori Petworthi,' says Mrs Goko. 'It is,' says Petworth, 'Tell me . . .' 'I work on the anarchistic nihilism of the drames of J. Orton,' says Miss Chemovna, 'I use a new concept of tragi-comedy and investigate his corruption-image.' 'That should interesti you very much, Professori Petworthi,' says Mrs Goko, 'It does,' says Petworth, 'Fascinating.' 'I compare the political poem of William Woolworth and Hrovdat,' says Miss Mamorian.

'Of whom?' asks Petworth. 'Yes,' says Mrs Goko, 'Please be as critical as you liki.' 'Hrovdat,' says Miss Mamorian. 'Our national poeti,' says Mrs Goko, 'Has translated Byroni and Shakespeari, was friend of Kossuthi.' 'You saw his statue when you came,' says Lubijova. 'Yes,' says Petworth, 'But who was the English poet?' 'Woolworth, author of *Prelude*,' says Miss Mamorian. 'I think you mean William Wordsworth,' says Petworth. 'Our visitor's criticism is correcti,' says Mrs Goko, 'Woolworthi is name of department storyi.' 'This is correct?' asks Miss Mamorian. 'Our visitor's criticism is righti,' says Mrs Goko firmly, 'And we must learn to put it into practicei.' 'And Mr Picnic, what are you working on?' asks Petworth, as Miss Mamorian gulps and begins, very quietly, to cry. 'I think you are bourgeois ideologue,' says Mr Picnic, 'Why do you come here to our country? How are you sent?' 'Professor Petworthi is guesti of the Ministrat'uu Kulturu Komutetuu,' says Mrs Goko, 'His visiti is approved by the Minister.' 'Who asks you?' says Picnic, 'Someone here on this fakultetuu?' 'I think it is time for your lectori,' says Mrs Goko, 'Because of Professor Marcovic's little sickness, I am agreed to introducei you.' 'I like answer please,' says Picnic, 'Is this invitation arranged by a person of this fakultetuu?' 'I don't think so, Mr Picnic,' says Petworth, 'Why do you ask?' 'Marcovic?' asks Picnic, 'You know Marcovic?' 'No,' says Petworth. 'You don't know who supports your visit?' asks Picnic, 'Varada? Plitplov?' 'I thinki we go now, to the lectori, where our studenti are waiting,' says Mrs Goko, 'The session is of two houri, you know the continental fashioni, with perhaps a fifteen minuti breaki for the lavatory or for smokings in the middle. You accept to take questions?' 'Oh, yes,' says Petworth. 'Then we hear your lectori and see if we want it,' says Mrs Goko, as Mr Picnic takes another photograph.

They walk in a crowd along the dark corridor, which has statues in gloomy niches, and many cigarette ends on the floor. 'The Presidenti of the University hoped formally to greeti you,' says Mrs Goko, 'Unfortunately he is not so welli also, in his chesti. He asked me to sendi to you his welcomes and his sentiments of scholarly amity and concordi.' 'Thank you,' says Petworth, 'I should like to send him mine.' 'Our studenti are of excellenti standard but perhaps you should speak just a little slowly,' says Mrs Goko, 'Also you do not mind if we maki tape-recording, only for educational purposes?' 'Not at all,' says Petworth. 'And do you have some special needi?' asks Mrs Goko, 'For a screeni or a big sticki?' 'No,' says Petworth. A few students stand huddled round an open doorway out of which comes a buzz of noise. 'Pleasi,' says Mrs Goko, ushering him in through the door. He is in a large raked auditorium in which, in stacks, students in considerable numbers sit. They rise to their feet as the party comes in; 'Thank you, sitti,' says Mrs Goko. The students resume their seats and a familiar form of coma, leaning hands on elbows or whispering to each other from behind notebooks. There is a podium with a very high desk on it, and behind the desk chairs for two. 'Now, pleasi, I introduce you, but one question. I note you were borni in the twentieth century but what is the datei?' '1941,' says Petworth. 'A year of destiny, I thinki,' says Mrs Goko. 'I've always thought so,' says Petworth. 'On the deski a glass of water,' says Mrs Goko, 'All is welli?' 'Yes,' says Petworth. Mrs Goko then rises and goes to the high podium, cranes over the top of it so that her head is just visible, and begins to speak, while Mr Picnic, in the doorway, takes a photograph of the audience.

'Cam'radakuu,' says Mrs Goko, 'It is a greati pleasurum to introduce our guesti Professori Petworthi. Doctora Petworthi is lecturi of sociologyii at the Universitet of Watermuthi.' 'No, no,' says Petworth, leaning forward in his chair. 'He is authori of monographic achievementis to the number of seven, inclusive of An Introducti to Sociologyii, Problumi in Sociologyii, Sociological Methodi, and so forthi.' 'I'm sorry for interrupting,' says Petworth, 'But a confusion has occurred. I'm not that Doctor Petworth.' 'You are not Prifessori Petworthi?' cries Mrs Goko, fuming at the podium. 'I am,' says Petworth, 'But I'm a different Professor Petworth.' 'You are looked up in *Whosi Whosi*,' says Mrs Goko. 'I'm not in *Who's Who*,' says Petworth, 'That's another Professor Petworth in another university. He's a sociologist. I'm a linguist.' 'Don't you give lectori on prublumi of English sociologyii?' asks Mrs Goko. 'No,' says Petworth, 'On the English Language as a Medium of International Communication.' 'But that was the approved lectori, approved by the rectori,' says Mrs Goko, 'It is not permitted to give it on something else. I must cancel, tell them all to go away.' 'Mrs Goko, in the approved programme he is giving lecture on the English language,' says Marisja Lubijova from the front row, 'That is on the programme of the Mun'stratuu.' 'But he must give the lectori approved by the rectori,' says Mrs Goko, 'I think he should give the lecture approved by the Mun'stratuu,' says Marisja Lubijova. The two hundred or so students sitting in the room stare, delighted, like all students everywhere, by confusion; Petworth stares back at them, red in the face, like all lecturers everywhere, when, as is so frequent, lectures do not go as they are meant to. 'I think we take a break for fifteen minuti,' says Mrs Goko, 'Please to come back here and don't go awayii.'

'I'm terribly sorry,' says Petworth when they all huddle, a moment later, in the corridor, 'It is easy to confuse the two of us. I sometimes get his letters by mistake. I bet he never gets mine.' 'It is not your fault,' says Marisja Lubijova, reaching in her shoulderbag and producing a file, 'See here, please, here is written the programme of Petwurt, all quite clear.' 'The Mun'stratuu has changed the programme approved by the rectori,' says Mrs Goko, 'We have applicated for this subjecti. Is this man a qualified scholari?' 'Isn't Mr Plitplov here?' asks Petworth, 'He's met me before.' Picnic, who has been taking photographs, comes nearer. 'Dr Plitplov is not so welli also, in the head,' says Mrs Goko, 'Well, I think I must telephone now the Mun'stratuu for confirmation and also the rectori so I am not to blami.' Mrs Goko bustles off, to her office. 'Petwurt, you don't embarrass,' says Lubijova, 'These people have made their own mistake and must take a responsibility.' 'How is this mistake occurring?' asks Picnic, approaching, from behind his sunglasses. 'Obviously this man is an agent,' murmurs Lubijova to Petworth, 'They are in all universities. Do not tell him so much.' 'Do you have ident'ayuu?' asks Picnic, 'And Plitplov, you are friend of Plitplov?' 'The Mun'stratuu of course has checked all ident'ayuu,' says Lubijova, 'You must look somewhere else for the cause of this error.' 'So, very welli,' says Mrs Goko, coming back, her face looking white, 'You are righti, there is an error. But now I do not know how to introduce him. Also some of these studentis are studentis of sociologyii. Their English is not so goodi. You must tell one sentence at a timi, and I do translati. Now we go back.'

'Cam'radakuu,' says Mrs Goko, when the audience has settled itself again, 'Here is another Professori Petworthi. He is very famous scholari who has authored many famous books on topicis, and he speakis now on "The Englishi Languagi as Mediumi of Internationali Communicationi." Welcome him please.' A strange noise follows, as Petworth rises and steps up to the podium; it is, as he sees when he peers out over the high top of it, the sound of the students, rapping with their knuckles on their desks, though whether in appreciation of the brevity of Mrs Goko's introduction or in polite appreciation of his own presence he does not know. He puts the well-used lecture in front of him, and takes off the paperclip; he stares out. The stack of faces, looking at his poor haircut and his small head peering at them over the podium, reaches ever backward: big faces and small ones, male ones and female ones, light ones and dark ones, civilian ones and military ones. It is a familiar ecology, a world to which he is well used. In the front row sits a recognizable selection of likely lecture-goers: a white, tense-looking Lubijova, a black spectacled Picnic, looking more at the audience than the speaker, the three girl assistants, with Miss Mamorian still visibly watering at the eyes, a professorial looking person, with an ironic manner and a V-shaped grey beard, a stout middle-aged Indian lady in a sari, a few more female assistants in cardigans, then a male one, wrapped in wiring and holding a tape recorder. Yes, it is known ground, a usual party almost complete, save, he thinks, for two possible guests who have sent their apologies: Mr Plitplov, and, alas, brilliant, batik-clad Katya Princip.

Petworth looks down to his ill-written text, his web of old words; he starts the lecture that has caused so much stir at Slaka airport, and is now causing so little here. The students stare blankly as he begins his explanation, arguing that in the modern world the English language has quite changed its function, become a new lingua franca, so that the most common speech acts in which it is now used no longer involve native speakers at all, but those who use it as a second language: a Japanese talking to a Norwegian, an Indian to a (insert, says the text, local example) Slakan. 'Pleasi, I translati,' says Mrs Goko, tapping his elbow, and stepping forward to speak. They mumble a little to each other as he explains that a new form of language is emerging in the world, divorced from its original cultural associations, dislocated and displaced, a Spranglais of potent proportions, manifest everywhere. Signs and advertisements everywhere employed it; newspapers and novels were constructed in its terms, from African polyglot fictions to *Finnegans Wake*. Politics and love affairs were made out of it; planes went up and down, and generally managed to avoid hitting each other, through its use. Behind the language was a world culture, itself divesting itself of its traditional rooted signs; a new world of the plurilingual and the distorted, of the sign floating free of the signified, was upon us. Petworth is talking, says Petworth, about language in a new state of volatility, the world after Babel. The students murmur amongst themselves, or grow tired and stare into the air; Mrs Goko takes his own words and makes them something else; the faces in front of him grow blank to his eyes. But then they grow real again, for at the back of the room a small door opens, and two late arrivals come quietly in, slipping into back row seats. The other people are strangers, but these are not; for one, besuited and crisp as a lettuce, is Mr Steadiman, and the other, wearing a white scarf neatly tied round her neck, and the batik dress, is Katya Princip.

II

The business of a lecturer is, of course, to lecture; this is why lecturers exist. Petworth has not come this far, crossed two time-zones, found other skies and other birds, simply in order to answer toasts, to visit tombs, to worry about domestic disorders, to catch himself in the thorny thickets of sexual confusion, split loyalties, divided attachments, to know desire or despair, to fall in love with lady writers; he has come to perform utterance. This is why planes have flown to bring him here, hotel rooms been booked, food set before him on plates; this is why he has left his house, home and country, brought his briefcase, made his way to this point. His head may ache with peach brandy, his wrist may hurt, his split lip blur his talk a little; his heart may be troubled, his spirit be energyless, poor, lacking the will to be, let alone the will to become. He

211

may be a speech without a subject, a verb without a noun, certainly not a character in the world historical sense; but he has a story to tell, and now he is telling it. And telling it, he becomes himself an order, a sentence that grows into a paragraph and then a page, a page and then a plot, a direction incorporating due beginning, middle, and end. His text before him, he becomes that text; and, though he may be before an audience that has come to hear another lecture, from another lecturer, it does not matter. Petworth, for this moment, exists, in his hour of words. A bell rings in the corridor, and he knows his words and his existence are up. But, sitting down, in the great auditorium, while Mrs Goko utters a few last sentences of translation, Petworth knows that he has been.

The knuckles rap on the desks; the audience stands politely as Mrs Goko leads the way out of the room. In the corridor, reaching for a cigarette, Petworth feels his old empty self come back. 'Really I think this goes quite welli,' says Mrs Goko, her spectacles hanging round her neck, 'It is not whati we expected, but it is interesting lectori. The speedi is finei, and you may telli by regarding their faces how well they graspi what you speaki.' 'Comrade Petwurt, I tell you we expect some remarkable talks,' says Lubijova, 'Well, I think you give us quite a remarkable one.' 'Perhaps now you wishi to go to the mani's room for a little relief,' says Mrs Goko, pointing to a door with F on it, 'Do go there, and then comei back pleasi to my roomi, do you remember? We have fifteen minutis, and is just a little brandi more in the bottlei.' 'Aarrghh,' says a voice, 'Good stuff, old chap. The last fellow was pretty boring, actually. Sent the audience off to sleep.' 'English for Soporific Purposes,' says Petworth, 'Do you know Mrs Goko?' 'I'm Ster Ster Steadiman,' says Steadiman, 'Cult cult cultural man at the British Embassy. Professor Marcovic was kind enough to invite me.' 'Marcovic?' says Mr Picnic, taking a photograph. 'I am sorry,' says Mrs Goko, 'Professor Marcovic has a little sicknessi today.' 'I've never man man managed to meet him,' says Steadiman, 'I hope one day.' 'There are many political complicaties,' says Mrs Goko, 'But if he survives these I expect he will be welli again.' 'It is really Wordworth?' asks Miss Mamorian, catching Petworth just as he enters the door marked F, 'Not Woolworth? I am only a little way into my project, and I don't read yet any books.' 'Yes, Wordsworth,' says Petworth, pushing open the door, entering a place of cold tiles and hissing pipes.

When he comes out again, the crowds that have just filled the corridor have gone; only one figure stands there, back to him, looking at a poster. 'Oh, you are funny behind this so high desk,' says a lady writer, turning, 'Do you know Fonzy Bear, of Muppets? You are like this. Mr Petwit, walk with me a minute on the stair.' Round the corner, on the stone staircase, where cold statues stand in niches, Katya Princip says: 'I came, you see. Of course this is foolish. But I think about you last night, and I know I like to see you again. Do you mind it?' 'No,' says Petworth. 'I wish we talk again,' says Princip, 'But I think is not possible. Soon you leave Slaka.' 'Yes, tomorrow,' says Petworth. 'Do you have lunch with all these people?' asks Princip, leaning against the wall and looking at him. 'That's what often happens,' says Petworth. 'I like you to come with me,' says Princip, 'I like to take you somewhere. Do you want it?' 'Yes,' says Petworth. 'You know it is foolish,' says Princip. 'Yes,' says Petworth. 'Then we let fate decide it, like in a good story,' says Princip, 'Of course if we know how we should give it some help. Let us just say, we try. If we are lucky, we know we are lucky couple.' 'Good,' says Petworth. 'Watch for me when your lecture stops,' says Princip, 'They do not know me but perhaps I come to you. Do what I tell you, I am good witch. Now, go to them, they wonder where you went. And wish, wish, wish we are lucky. In my books wishes often work.' In the long corridor to Mrs Goko's room Mr Picnic stands in his dark sunglasses; 'You take a long time,' he says, 'We wait you.' 'Brandy, drinki it quickly,' says Mrs Goko, giving him a glass, 'Already it is time to go backi and meeti once more the studentis.'

But back on the podium, as Petworth talks again, his spirit rising, about the things he knows so well, about EFL and ESL and ESP, of EAP and EOP and EST, he sees that the audience has strangely changed. The numbers are much the same, but new faces have been traded for old ones, fair for dark, women for men, military for civilian. Only the front row remains as familiar as ever, save for one new figure, a man who sits on the end of the row, holding up a copy of *P'rtyuu Populatuuu* to cover his face, though the sharp striped trousers that show below it suggest a possible identity; on the back row, still, sit Steadiman and, looking at him warmly, Katya Princip. 'I think we permiti some questions,' says Mrs Goko, after Petworth has sat down, and the knuckles have rapped, 'Also any criticisms. As you know, Professori Petworthi, always we are criticali, according to revolutionary principles.' There is the statutory long pause, and then a few questions, a few criticisms: the man with the V-shaped beard rises, to denounce, in English, English as the language of capitalist oppression; Miss Mamorian also rises, to suggest the thinking is not correct; Mr Picnic observes that the lecture fails to unravel the hegemony of forces underlying the process to which it refers. 'Professori Petworthi,' says Mrs Goko, 'You have given us a fascinating lectori of importance to all who study Englishi. Also we are pleased you speaki it very welli. You have heard some very good criticisms, and we thinki your visit will not be wasted. We thinki it may make your changi your theories, and so all have profited.' 'Theories exist to be changed,' says Petworth. 'So thank you, pleasi, for your good lectori, and may we acquaint you that here in our country we make a languagi revolution with the aimi of devising a true popular language consistent with history. We hope you study.' 'I shall,' says Petworth.

It seems to Petworth, as he leaves the hall, that a dispute is now breaking out among the audience; indeed Picnic now stands at the podium he has just left, addressing the students in the language Petworth does not know. But there are other matters to attend to. 'Perhaps I make mistaki to refer here to the language revolution,' says Mrs Goko, 'But you are linguisti, I think you interest.' 'Yes, very,' says Petworth. 'I like to tell you more at the lunch with our faculty arranged to followi.' 'Ah, I see,' says Petworth. 'So, my friend,' says the man from behind *P'rtyuu Populatuuu*, who is no other than Plitplov, 'This was quite a good lecture of bourgeois linguistics. Of course the criticisms of Madame Goko and others are most potent.' 'Very good,' says Miss Mamorian. 'I hope you excuse I miss some of your wise words,' says Plitplov, 'As I tell you last night at a certain party, I have many obligations.' 'Oh, yes, a party?' says Lubijova, 'You ate and then you went to bed, all by yourself? I don't think it any more, Comrade Petwurt.' 'Oh, here is Miss Lubijova,' says Plitplov, 'It is nice to see you in our university.' 'You have seen me in it before, I think,' says Lubijova, 'Perhaps you forget because you have a headache. I do not think a party will help it. It does not help Comrade Petwurt's face.' 'I'm Ster Ster Steadiman,' says Steadiman, coming up to Lubijova, 'I gather you're Dr Petworth's guide interpreter.' 'I am not to blame for Dr Petwurt at all,' says Lubijova, 'I try to make him good but he is naughty. How do you know him?' 'Dip dip dip,' says Steadiman. 'Oh, Mr Petwit, so good a lecture,' says a certain lady novelist, coming up, 'Do you know I understand nearly all of it?'

'You are all friends?' asks Picnic, coming up beside Petworth, 'How do you meet? Who knows who?' In the dark corridor stands much of the gallery of his Slakan acquaintances. Petworth stares at them, this one talking to that one, compounding his emotional confusions, unravelling or complicating his lies; he no longer knows the answer. 'Oh, you are Mr Plitplov?' cries Katya Princip, 'I have read your articles in the newspaper with an interest.' 'You are good to notice,' says Plitplov. 'You are Katya Princip?' cries Mrs Goko, 'Welku, welku.' 'Oh, look, here is Miss Lubijova,' says Katya Princip, 'You see I took good care of Mr Petwit and left him very nicely at his hotel.' 'Oh, yes?' says Lubijova, 'I think it is good thing he leaves Slaka tomorrow.' 'I hope you arrange a nice lunch for him, he does very well,' says Princip. 'Mrs Goko has arranged a lunch,' says Petworth. 'No,' says Mrs Goko, 'I telli I like to arrange a lunchi, but is not possibli. Marcovic is not welli, and he alone can spend the departmenti fundis.' 'Oh, cancelled?' says Katya Princip. 'Well, let's all find a rest rest restaurant,' says Steadiman. 'I cannot comi,' says Mrs Goko, 'Many duties in university.' 'I know a nice place,' says Plitplov. 'Which one?' asks Picnic. 'Come, we will follow Dr Plitplov,' says Lubijova, 'We must hope his head is all better.' 'We have learnied very much of you,' says Mrs Goko, shaking hands, 'Now I like to say thanki.' 'Is really Wordworth?' asks Miss Mamorian, as the assistants, in their cardigans, line up to shake hands, and Picnic takes one last photograph for what must now be quite an extensive collection.

But then the occasion is suddenly over, as these formal occasions so suddenly are. The remaining party descends the great stone staircase into the great gaunt front hall of the university: Steadiman and Lubijova going ahead, talking together, perhaps about his clandestine last night, Petworth following behind, flanked by Katya Princip and a panting Plitplov. 'So, your lecture has gone very well,' says Plitplov, 'Perhaps at lunch I can make a few suggestions for your improvement. You will see our academical standards are very rigorous, and we expect a special clarity of analysis.' Porters peer at them out of glass booths as they go out of the building; a few students with briefcases stand on the steps. 'I also found it interesting,' says Katya Princip, 'And I think you spoke a little slowly for me.' 'Always you are of fine quality,' says Plitplov, 'But of course in our context a few dialectical errors will become apparent. We are not so much pragmatist as the British. But definitely I did not make a mistake to come there. You know well you did not really disgrace yourself.' They step out through the colonnade onto the street, which looks out onto a square where the sun shines brightly. Across the square stands the statue of Hrovdat, that Wordworth of Slaka: the national poet who has been, like all such national poets, in all such countries, a romantic revolutionary, who has translated Byron and Shakespeare, written plays, fought the nation's oppressors from the east and the west, the Turks or the Germans, the Macedonians or the Swedes, known Kossuth, fought and declaimed on the barricades of 1848, fled away into exile, discovered conspiratorial friends, returned in disguise, gathered new forces, gone back into battle and in it fallen, his last and bravest poem loud on his lips; the pigeons strut on his head now, and the party, with many explanations, stares across the street at him.

'And now do we all eat together?' says Plitplov, 'I think you all follow me.' 'But I think there is a nice restaurant just this way,' says Lubijova, leaving the side of the umbrella-ed Mr Steadiman. 'Oh, but please, this is my university,' says Plitplov, 'I know there is better a Balkan one this way. I go to it often.' 'Oh, that one,' says Lubijova, 'But it is spicy, and often there is no food.' 'I know a nice one in the town,' says Steadiman, 'I believe they take American Express.' 'Well, all depends on what people like to eat,' says Lubijova, 'Comrade Petwurt, what do you like? The spicy or the plain?' 'The fishes or the meats?' asks Plitplov. 'The typisch or the modern?' asks Lubijova. 'All of them have no food,' murmurs Princip, 'Well, it is always so. In Slaka people will talk so long about where to have food they never eat any.' 'The place in town is awe awe awfully good,' says Steadiman, 'Not sure how to get there from here, though.' 'The one that way is better,' says Plitplov. 'The other that way is cheaper,' says Lubijova. And so, in front of the colonnade of the university, the group falls into one of those huddles of indecisiveness that such groups are prone to, when no one quite wants to defer to, but neither to offend, anyone else, and no one can quite go anywhere. Petworth stands, and a hand slips through his arm: 'While they talk, I just take you to see the statue of Hrovdat,' says Katya Princip, 'Don't you think you must see it?' 'He has seen it from the tram,' says Lubijova, turning. 'Then I think he sees it properly,' says Katya Princip, 'You will take ten minutes to make your mind. I like to explain to him our national tradition of poetry. Don't you think you must know more about our writers?'

'Well, yes, I do,' says Petworth. 'So we are back in a minute,' says Princip, leading Petworth across the busy road. The statue stands up, a man in metal on horseback, romantically falling while his flag still stays aloft. 'So, you see him, Hrovdat,' says Princip, 'This was a very good man and he did brave things and believed very much in liberty. And so we still like him and his poems are remembered, and we can speak them from our hearts. It is nice to be a writer like that, to have a little courage. Now, do you have a little courage, Petwit? Do you jump with me on this tram?' 'On the tram?' asks Petworth. 'I think fate smiles on us,' says Princip, 'Quick now, while they don't look this way.' 'I don't think it's a very good idea,' says Petworth, 'They're all waiting for us, they'll all . . .' But his considerate thoughts are evidently too late; Princip has him by the hand, is tugging him along, is standing on the steps of the old metal tram and drawing him up after her. Across the street he sees Lubijova staring as he is dragged up into the huddle of passengers; a metal shutter closes behind him, and the tram begins to rattle off. He is in a press of bodies, but through the rough glass of the window he can see, across the street, the uncertain huddle of prospective diners break open, line the roadside, stare after the rattling vehicle. Plitplov and Lubijova stand still; Steadiman, with characteristic courage, lifts his umbrella and, waving it, begins to run down the middle of the street, after the tram. 'They saw,' says Petworth. 'Oh, yes,' says Princip, laughing in front of him. 'We can't just disappear like this,' he says. 'Of course, my dear,' says Princip, putting her arm through his, 'I am your witch. I make you disappear just when I like it, into the air, down a hole. Just like Stupid in my story.'

III

'And here the place I want you to see,' says Katya Princip, in her batik dress and white scarf, as they sit, a little later, in the quiet corner of a restaurant that lies somewhere just beyond the end of the tram-route, with fields outside the windows, 'It is very special to me, do you see why I like it? Once it was hunting lodge, for some imperial princes. From here they took out their guns and went into that forest. Now still are cooked the wild things. Isn't it better?' Petworth looks round at the room they have much to themselves. Only two other couples are here; they sit at a white-clothed table, near to a log fire, in a room of dark wood, with ornate carved beams and painted walls, where the horned fragmentary skulls of many creatures, the sad severed heads of deer, the brute rooting faces of wild boar, stare down on them. 'It's delightful,' says Petworth, 'I just hope it wasn't a bad idea.' 'Oh, Petwit, please don't worry,' says Katya Princip, putting her hand on his, and looking at him with clear grey eyes, 'Of course it was not a sensible thing. But don't you think we all need sometimes to do a foolishness? Tomorrow you go away, perhaps I don't see you again, and I like to see you. That dinner is cancelled, I think fate likes us to meet. And we are here together, we can be happy if we like. Now, my dear, look around you, please. Look through the window. The sun shines there, the rain has gone, it is warm day, the fields and trees are very beautiful, don't you say so? And now look please at me. We sit here, there is nice fire, we drink, our knees touch underneath, we look into the face of one another, and perhaps I am a bit beautiful like those fields. Don't you think we could be happy? Most of the time is sadness, happiness is only a little time. But don't you think it is good to take it?' 'Yes, I do,' says Petworth. 'Yes, you do,' says Princip, squeezing his hand, 'Now I think we eat something.'

Princip waves to a waiter in a long white apron, who comes

to the side of their table, holding his pad. 'Now what do you like?' asks Princip, holding the menu out to Petworth and smiling at him, 'Look, I explain you. Here is massalu, this is a fish just like a dentex. Here is valpuru, made of the brain of a little cow, very nice to eat. Natupashu, this is what a bull has, and you too, I hope. What do you call, is it testicle?' 'Ah, yes,' says Petworth. 'Do you eat it?' asks Princip, 'It makes you love better, that is what we say here. But perhaps you don't need it, you look strong to me. I tell you what is best to eat here, the *wilde*, what do you say, the wild things. Here is lad'slatu, that is the boar, they live in the forest not far away. This is what I have, do you eat it too?' 'Marvellous,' says Petworth. 'Not a testicle?' asks Princip. 'No,' says Petworth. 'This is right,' says Princip, 'Something wild, because we are a little wild. And some wine, don't you say so. So we can drink to our foolishness?' 'Please,' says Petworth. 'Oh, that is good,' says Princip, when the waiter has gone, 'And now, Petwit, tell me something. When, please, do you make your next appointment?' 'Tonight at seven,' says Petworth, looking at his programme. 'And this girl who looks to you, she comes then to your hotel?' 'Yes,' says Petworth. 'Well, I will make some plans for you,' says Princip, 'Tell her you have been to see the city, to look at the castle. She will be suspicious, but you are a free man, I think. And what you must do, you must take her a flower. Then she will think you are not so bad, everyone likes a flower.' 'I will,' says Petworth. 'And so you have all the afternoon,' says Princip, 'It is the same with me. Well, we will enjoy it.' 'Yes,' says Petworth.

'Oh, look,' says Princip, laughing, and taking his face in her hands, 'Still a long face, down to here. My dear, I will explain you something. In my country, people do not like to do a thing that is noticed. They like it to stay quiet, and they like quiet in others. Don't surprise, don't be excellent, it makes troubles. Well, your friend here is not like that. I am just a little bit excellent, do you notice?' 'I do,' says Petworth. 'I have a good mind I like, and a good body I like, and I like to use them, to make display of them. I do many things people tell are foolish, because, you see, my dear Petwit, if you do not do them, you are nothing, and you make everything else nothing. Of course I can be sensible, you saw it yesterday, but sensible is nothing. Do you see why I came to your lecture?' 'Yes,' says Petworth. 'No, you do not see,' says Princip, 'Because I do not explain it so well. I come there because I like you, do you see it, and if you like somebody it is nice to do something about it. I think you are looking at my charms.' 'I am, indeed,' says Petworth. 'Do you like them?' asks Princip. 'Very much indeed,' says Petworth. 'Oh, do you, very much indeed,' says Princip, laughing, 'I do not mean those charms, the charms here on my wrist. Do you see them? Always I wear them. They are magic, you know. This hanging here is a fish, well, a man can ride on the back of a fish, and go to another world. Here a key, with a key all you must do is find the right door. A stone, well, give a stone and you get a story. And here is a heart, you know what you do with a heart. You think they are nice?' 'Yes,' says Petworth, fingering the bracelet round Princip's white wrist. 'Well, my dear, I give you one,' says Princip, 'Let me think which one. Not the heart, you have one already. Not a key, I need it. I think the stone, because I like you to have a story. Find a string, wait, I have one in my bag, and put it please round your neck. I want to find it there when I meet you again. Oh, look, here is our drink. Now we can drink to foolishness.'

'Foolishness,' says Petworth, after the waiter has served them, raising his glass. 'You see, the stone works already,' says Princip, 'Now do you have a story to tell me?' 'I don't think so,' says Petworth. 'Oh, you are dull,' says Princip, 'Well, I am the story-teller, I tell you one. What do I pick? Oh, I know, an old one, the man who goes to Glit.' 'Very appropriate,' says Petworth. 'Do you go there?' asks Princip, 'Well, this is a story from old times, about a traveller from afar who made a journey in our country. He wanted to make his journey somewhere interesting, and on his way he met a man who told him that

221

Glit was a place of good streets and beautiful women and the finest things to buy. He went to Glit, but just as he could see the city, he met on the road with a marvellous thing. A young woman with fine eyes stood under a tree looking at him, and he knew he was in love. The woman smiled and things happened, you know how it is, my dear. He spent some days with her in her little house, but after some days, well, the eyes did not seem quite so beautiful and he did not think so much about love. He had waited too long in this place, passed all these nights, and it was time to make his journey again. So one morning when she goes off to the market to buy food, he packs up his baggages and goes on to Glit. But as he travelled he thought all the time of the young woman, and he knew she had bewitched him and was trying to find a way to see him again. But he must make the purpose of his journey, and he is a man, so it is not love. He entered the gate of Glit, it is still there, and saw a woman walking down the street toward him, an old peasant carrying some sticks under her arm; her body is bent but her face is the face of the girl. He walks on through the streets, and all the women walking there, clean or dirty ones, old or youngs, just the same. He looks through the windows; there are women sewing, women cooking, women in bathtubs, all the same face. Oh, see, he brings our food, wasn't that quick? Doesn't it look nice?'

In a metal dish between them, a meal of meat and vegetables bubbles and seethes aromatically; the waiter fills their glasses with wine. 'It looks very good,' says Petworth. 'Put your plate here,' says Princip, 'I serve you.' 'You will finish the story?' asks Petworth. 'Oh, my dear,' says Princip, 'If you like it. In my country the women are quite feminist but with a nice man we still like to please. Well, my dear Mr Petwit, the man has business on his mind; he likes to buy a ring. He goes to the house of a fine merchant of Glit and makes some good trade; for not so much money he gets a beautiful ring. The merchant is kind, and asks him to stay there the night. He calls his wife and asks her to take the man to a beautiful room with bed. In the room the wife looks at him. It is the same face, the same body, surely the same person as the young woman by the road. The traveller tells that they have met before. "No, we don't meet," says the wife, "But you must leave at once. I like you, and I know my husband means to kill you in this bed tonight, and take back his ring." The traveller looks round. The doors have no handles, the windows don't open. "There is only one way to leave," says the woman, "I am a witch. If you give me one kiss, the doors will all spring open and you will be free." The traveller makes the kiss, mmmmnn, the doors open, he takes his luggages and runs from Glit. He looks on the road for the house he has been, but all he sees there is bundle of rags. After long travellings, he comes to his home and his wife. He gives her the ring, makes her the kiss, mmmmnn; and then he sees she has the face of the lady of Glit. This is the story, do you like it?' 'Did you make it up?' asks Petworth. 'It is a very very old story,' says Princip, 'How could I make it up? Of course it is very fantastical, not real at all, but you see I do not believe in reality.'

'You don't believe in it,' says Petworth. 'No, I have tried it and I do not believe it,' says Princip, 'Reality is what happens if you listen to other people's stories and not to your own. The stories become a country, the country becomes a prison, and the prison comes in your mind. And everywhere more of the same story: the people do not steal, they make miracles of production, they all love Karl Marx. Soon it is the only story, and that is how comes reality. Well, I will tell you something, my dear, if you give me one kiss, even if you don't. I have only one I with a me in it, you the same. The world is in your own head, and they put it there, with a me and a you in it, so we can make our own stories. And this is how I like to use my own head, which you see right in front of you, a nice one, I hope. Not to make some more reality for other people to live inside, but some space for my mind to grow. And now you tell me, Comrade Petwit, that my position is not correct, it does not advance history and truth. And I tell you, my nice friend, that history and truth are your stories and not mine. And then you tell me, well, you had better drive a tram. I can do it, too. Do you think I am a witch?' 'Perhaps,' says Petworth. 'Of course it is possible,' says Princip, 'In my country we talk of rational projects and economic plannings, but really we are still peasants and magicians. Do I witch you a little bit?' 'Yes,' says Petworth. 'Well, I try,' says Princip, 'Now, do you like some coffee?' 'Yes,' says Petworth. 'Then we ask for a taxi and we go and find some,' says Princip, 'I know a place where it is better.'

'Wasn't it nice?' asks big, blonde Katya Princip, sitting beside him in the small orange taxi, her arm through his, 'You see now why I like so much that place. I hope you like the next one.' 'I'm sure I shall,' says Petworth. The taxi is driving toward the city, at some speed; loud honkings from the other traffic surround them. 'Here our drivers do not look behind,' says Katya Princip, 'They look always forward, into the social-ist future. Look, here on the hill, the castle. This is where you are going this afternoon, so please remember just what it is like. Inside is big and dark, and there are many small rooms of stone. You have been in castles before, I think. In the rooms, the nice metal suitings for the very little soldiers, with plumes in the helms, and on the wall some pictures of all the old battles. Then you see some old guns and a wine press. Then downstairs some cold prisons with no windows, for the tour-ists, not for them to live in, just to look at. We do not treat our tourists so badly. There is fine exhibition of our Slakan past, with many maps and drawings of the old invasions. Upstairs the bedroom of Bishop Vlam. You know he was, what do you call him, a man who likes too much the ladies.' 'A rake?' asks Petworth. 'That is a rake?' asks Princip, 'Then what do you clean the leaves with?' 'Another rake,' says Petworth. 'So, two rakes,' says Princip, 'This one has a fine bedroom with a bed of four posts. Or perhaps now three posts, he was very rough with his ladies. He put them down a hole also, remember the hole. So, do you see it all?' 'I think so,' says Petworth. 'Good,' says Princip, 'Well, now you have been there, so we go somewhere quite different. I think I tell this driver to slower, don't you? He is running over much too many people.' Princip leans forward to talk to the driver; Petworth stares out at the cityscape of urban Slaka, where in grey and khaki the people walk, in the day's sun, and the streets flicker past. He stares, feeling separate, pleasurably hijacked; as he does so, a certain small thought occurs to him.

It is the curious thought that he is happy. He is, for a brief spell, in the company of a woman, blonde, batik-clad Katya Princip, whom he finds gay, and amusing, and beautiful, and whose gaiety makes him feel gay too. But there is more to it than that; for Dr Petworth, sitting there in the foreign taxi in the foreign city, clutching his lecture, is not a man much used to feeling that he exists. Over the years he has grown older, seen some greying of the hair, watched his teeth deteriorate and be on occasion extracted, lost his youthful humour, grown more anxious and solitary, felt some centre in him, some ground of being where value ought to be, grow fragile and dissipate. The world about him, as he has come to know more of it, has grown not more real, but less, and life not more living but a parody of itself. People have become repetitions of people already known, desires become an absurd biological urgency, vague therapeutic hungers for variation and complication. The wife who was once everything seems slight now, a drifting mysterious presence and absence; women who appear in his days and dreams as possible lovers have not tugged him with the necessary intensity of emotion. The objects of will have deteriorated, like his teeth; he has trouble in summoning up enough substance to be, to stir, to feel, to say. He has come to feel contentless, wordless, not there, grown more used to inner absence than to presence. But now, though he knows he should not be here, though he thinks with anxiety and guilt of the three lost diners, talking about him somewhere in any one

225

of a dozen possible restaurants, though he can think of no adequate explanation for himself when explanation is needed, he feels a curious small sense that exist is what he does.

'This taxi driver is very interesting,' says Katya Princip, the presumed source of these emotions, turning towards him, 'He tells me he is no more in love with his wife.' The taxi driver, a big hairy man, turns and nods. 'He has seen me and now he loves me, and he wants me to go and take some drinks with him. I explain no, I am busy with my lover, you do not mind I say that?' 'No,' says Petworth. 'But now he wants to kill himself,' says Princip, 'Sometimes people are like that here.' The taxi stops, in the middle of a quiet urban street with linden trees along it, and behind the trees rows of old high balconied apartment buildings; the driver turns and speaks volubly to Princip. 'Do you please get out, my dear,' says Princip, 'I come to you in a minute. I just have some more words with him.' Petworth gets out and stares up and down the street: no one walks in it, and the doors are all shut. 'So,' says Katya Princip, climbing out of the taxi, 'I think I persuade him not to do it. I take a drink with him tomorrow. Often such things happen to me, I don't know why, of course. Well, we just walk a little, and we are there.' 'Where?' asks Petworth. 'Where we are going,' says Princip, 'I think you are liking some coffee. We go to a place we can get some. It is called my apartment.' 'Ah,' says Petworth. 'I look at you and I think you are very tired,' says Princip, 'Perhaps you need a rest and a shower, before you do your next thing. I will make you some terrible coffee and give you an awful cake. It is just here, we go in this door. Press the button and the machine opens it. Now we go in quickly, I do not want everyone to see you. I am smuggling you, Petwit.'

They enter a dark lobby, with a lift in a cage at the end of it. 'Come inside it, quickly,' says Princip, 'Look, I show you how it works, in case you come here again to see me. I hope another time you will want to, do you think so? Look, in this box on the wall you must put in a small coin, ten butt'uun. If you do not do it, the machine does not march. If you do, well, pouff, there it goes.' In the clanking cage, they rise up together through the building. Princip is close against him; stone landings float past, lined with closed wooden doors. 'Now here is my floor, the top,' says Princip, 'Aren't we lucky, there is no one to see us. Now, where is my key, and then I make you disappear again.' They step out onto the stone landing, and Princip puts her key to a blank wooden door. 'When it is open, go quickly inside,' she says, 'We do not like the world to know all the things we do.' The door opens; inside is a small narrow hall, a hall so narrow and small it is hard to know whether it has been designed to increase human intimacy, or entirely prevent it. The walls press them together: 'You see, you are come,' cries Princip, laughing, her face just below his, 'I hope you don't think this is all I have. There is some more apartment inside.' In the tight space, it is difficult not to find one's arms around the person with whom one is pressed; Petworth's, certainly, are now round Princip's waist. 'Oh, Petwit,' says Princip, gently removing his hands, 'Don't you know I brought you here for a rest? Of course; you must be tired after such a lecture. Do you like also to be a rake? You are such a thin one, perhaps really a rake of the other kind.' 'I like you,' says Petworth. 'Oh, yes, I understand it,' says Princip, 'I also to you. But I am a little bit elusive, my dear. I like to talk a bit with you. And we have so much time, isn't it nice? All the afternoon, and for us to stay together. Unless you like better to go to the castle? Do you prefer it better?' 'No, I like to be here with you,' says Petworth. 'Well, you have good sense,' says Princip, 'Now come inside and I show you my flat.'

7 – OPER.

I

It is, this room that Petworth now steps into, a small, tight room, short of space for human endeavour. But human endeavour has been here, and humanized it: two antique chairs stand to either side of a fine wide modern sofa, which elegantly fits into the bookshelves on the wall, a wall on which hang three modern paintings of violent and erotic concept, and two small ikons. The rest of the wallspace is taken up with bookshelves, from which many hundreds of volumes tumble; and books, too, lie scattered on the tables and on the large wide desk standing by the window, on which sits also a telephone, a typewriter, a jumble of loose papers which flutter in the small draught that comes through the curtains above. 'Well, my dear, I hope you don't expect a special place,' says Princip, taking off her white scarf, 'Here in my country, the apartments are small, the heat is bad, the telephone usually does not march, the men do not mend a thing when it makes wrong. Of course, you do not have such problems in your country.' 'I suppose not,' says Petworth. 'Really, do you say so?' asks Princip, laughing, 'You think I have not been there? Don't you know I was in London once?' 'You were?' asks Petworth. 'My dear, of course. Perhaps I saw you even in the street, and did not know it. If it was so, would it not be sad? But I think you have those problems too. Especially at my hotel. Some things grow the same all over the world, I think. It is a time when life is not so easy. Well, it is not so good, but I hope you like. Do you like these paintings of my friends? And my nice antiquated chairs? Do you know they are from before the revolution? Some of those things still exist. And my desk where I work, do you like it? Here is the private place where I make all those books. Oh, they are made here in my nice place, but then of course I must go to the world and put them to the market. That is the hard thing, to go to the market. To please those people at the Union. To value their wise criticisms. Well, you don't come here to criticize me, I hope.'

'No,' says Petworth, 'I like your room.' 'Well, it has a good taste,' says Princip, 'Or so I try. And, for a time, it is ours all. No one else comes. We have it for today. So please sit down, my dear, take a nice chair, make some music with the player, take off your shoes. And do you know what I do now? I go to the kitchen just to make you some coffee and bring you some cake. That is what you came for, I think, well, you must be served.' Princip goes into the kitchen; Petworth walks about the small, cramped room, evidently living room, study, and bedroom, for a nightgown lies under the sofa pillow. 'What do you look at?' calls Princip from the kitchen, 'I hope you don't read what I write. It is very private, until it is finished. But of course, you do not know my language. In a minute maybe I will teach you some.' 'So many books,' says Petworth, looking in the bookshelves, where the unbound volumes with their Cyrillic titles lie. 'Yes, every day I read them and I become some more a person,' says Princip, 'Look please in the street. Does anyone watch?' 'Watch the flat?' asks Petworth. 'Of course,' says Princip, 'Don't you know this is a main work for many people? To sit there in cars and watch the others? And I am a writer, not reliable, often they like to watch me for a while. Also to photograph me now and again, and make list of who my friends are. Of course perhaps it does not mean anything. It comes in useful perhaps for some later day, when I am not any more a person to invite to an official lunch and meet a nice foreign visitor.' Petworth goes to the window and leans over the typewriter, where a page of unknown words spirals out; beyond the net curtains the street is quiet and empty, except for one parked car.

'There's just one car,' he says. 'Is it a black one?' asks Princip. 'Yes,' says Petworth. 'And do you see someone in it?' asks Princip. 'I can't tell,' says Petworth. 'Yes, of course,' says Princip, 'It is a state of mind, you know, to be watched. We like, don't we, to see our lives from the inside. But if you are watched you see them from the eyes of those others. You can't remember any more if you have really an inside, or if the inside is already the outside. You become like an actor, or those girls in a dress photograph, what do you call?' 'A model,' says Petworth. 'Well, perhaps now we are all so,' says Princip, 'Perhaps the inside was always just a little illusion, a false secret. But we like that secret, don't we? And then, one day, they stop you perhaps, and take you to a place. They do not arrest you, it is just for a day and night, to ask you some little questions. So you can help a little the state. They are often nice, with cigarettes and drink. But they open your file and it is fat and everything is there, the notes and the pictures. And they tell you what you are and what you do. They know more than you, they remember everything, the things you don't ever remember that you did, but you did them. They tell it, you say, "It is not me, I am not like that, I was never there." And they tell: "Yes, it is you, really you, the other is your illusion." They have made your story, a bad novel, and you are in it for ever. And here is what is strange. You begin to agree it, because it fits, because it has your images, your voice in a tape. You begin to confess it, yes, I am like that, how well you know me. And they are right, because in all of us is a doubt, that we do not know ourselves at all. We all feel a bit guilty to exist. And this they know very well. To be is the crime we commit, and anyone will confess it. Don't you think you would do the same?' 'Yes,' says Petworth.

'Well, I am nearly ready,' says Princip, 'Put on please some music, my dear. Do you see my records player? Do you know how to make work that thing? I expect you are a little bit a mechanical person.' 'Yes, I can do it,' says Petworth, finding the machine and switching it on. 'You cannot read my books, but of course you can hear my music, that is a language we can all know,' says Princip, 'Do you find my records? What do you pick?' Petworth sifts through the shelf of records in the bookcase; most of the covers are in the language he does not know. 'Do you like the classical or the modernismus?' asks Princip, 'There are both.' 'Classical,' says Petworth, 'Here's some Mozart.' 'Oh, do you like?' asks Princip, 'Well, he is civilized. Now do you sit down and take off your shoes.' The courtly music comes through the speakers; a civil guest, Petworth sits on the sofa-bed, and removes the shoes from his feet. 'And now here is your awful coffee, your terrible cake,' says Princip, coming in in her batik dress, carrying a silver tray, 'Also a little peach brandy that will make you better. I hope you do not mind to fatten a bit. I think it is good, really you are too thin. But I think in the West the thin is very popular.' Princip sits down with him on the sofa, and hands him a plate: 'I am sorry I am so long,' she says, 'But I do not make many foods. I like to eat in a restaurant, with my friends. But it is nice to have a friend who is here with me. I think you are one now. We make a little risk, but I think it is worth it. It is only what civilized people do, to make the frontiers go a little bit away. I think you would give me tea if I meet you in London.'

'So you went there?' asks Petworth. 'Yes, I have been, I know where you come from,' says Princip, 'It is not easy to get travels, you know that. But I am a writer, that gives sometimes certain privileges. Also there were other reasons.' 'What were they?' asks Petworth. 'Well, you see,' says Princip, smiling at him, 'One of my husbands was high once in the Party. He was even for a little while minister. Of course then it was very easy to get travels. You see, here in Slaka, always there must be someone who can help. A person with a power who can pull for you some strings. We learn to live in this way. And if you have a nice body also, this is help. You make some love the way you join the Party. If you do it the right way, you get a nice reward for it. A very good meal at a restaurant, a place at the opera, a ticket to make travels. An apartment with a nice viewing, a place on a list. You become clever to do all these things very carefully. That is the way you get somewhere. Perhaps you think it is bad. Perhaps you think your life is not like that.' 'I suppose I do,' says Petworth. 'Oh, do you?' says Princip, 'Well, perhaps you are simple. Don't you think that is your nice illusion? Don't you think everywhere all life is an exchange? What makes your people marry? What makes them choose their friends? Why do they say what they say, think what they think? And their desire, how do they make their desire? We have nice words, love, and friendship, and faith. But don't you think there is, what do you say, a calculus? Perhaps what we do in Slaka is not so strange. Your coffee, you don't like?' 'Yes, it's very good,' says Petworth, 'So that was one of your husbands. Have you had many?'

'Oh, not so many,' says Princip, laughing, 'I just had four. Some people like to collect the stamps or some china. Now you get idea what I have liked to collect.' 'And now?' asks Petworth. 'A husband, now?' asks Princip, 'Oh, no, I don't, now. Now I am lonely in quite a different way. And what about you, Petwit. How many wives do you have had?' 'Me?' asks Petworth, 'Oh, just one, actually.' 'Only a one?' cries Princip, 'Really that is not very much at all, almost none. I think perhaps you are not very ambitious. And this one, you had her a long time?' 'Yes,' says Petworth. 'And she likes you?' asks Princip. 'Well,' says Petworth, 'A little.' 'Oh, not enough!' cries Princip, 'Do you tell me she does not care for you so much?' 'That's my impression,' says Petworth. 'She likes some other?' asks Princip. 'I don't know,' says Petworth, 'She seems quite fond of her dentist.' 'And you think he fills some more cavities too?' asks Princip, 'Well, perhaps you are not so nice to her. If you are lonely, perhaps she is lonely too. Don't you think it?' 'I think probably she is,' says Petworth, seeing the view down the garden. 'And she is warm, she is good at the bed?' asks Princip. 'Not very,' says Petworth. 'Really, my dear,' says Princip, 'This does not sound at all right. My husbands are always very good in that. Very bad in other things, but in that always very good. And what do you do? Do you take many lovers?' 'Not really,' says Petworth. 'I do not understand you,' says Princip, 'Perhaps you mean you like to, but do not have the courage. Well, if you do not, that confirms me. You are not a character in the world historical sense.'

'You think I should?' asks Petworth. 'It is not for me to advise you,' says Princip, 'But I think you must have a will and a desire. Otherwise you are empty.' 'Well, in my country there is a saying,' says Petworth. 'Of course,' says Princip, 'If a country, always a saying. What is yours?' 'A man needs a good woman,' says Petworth, 'And when he's found her he needs a bad one too.' 'My dear, I do not know if I like this,' says Princip, 'Do you like to tell me I am a bad woman?' 'No, I didn't mean that at all,' says Petworth. 'Oh, continue, please,' says Princip, 'You tell me you hope I will be your bad woman. You like to make me a little insult. Perhaps in your country you make a compliment, but it is not, here.' 'You've misunderstood,' says Petworth. 'I don't think so,' says Princip, 'My English is not so good, but I am not foolish. You see, here in my country we like to be a little bit admired. Even though feminist attitudes are very important, we like to think we make a little respect.' 'I admire you greatly,' says Petworth. 'That is different,' says Princip, 'Now you have convinced me. Remember, I am not your bad witch, I am your good one.' 'I know,' says Petworth. 'You see what I have done,' says Princip, 'I have changed for you the weather. I have made you disappear. I have brought you to my room. And now you do not know what I will do with you. Do you like that cake? Perhaps it makes you feel sleepy.' 'Not really,' says Petworth. 'I think so,' says Princip, 'Don't you know you are careless? In a fairy story, you do not eat a cake. Or talk at all to the people with the red hairs. Or open a locked door, or go inside a room that is forbidden. If you do, things will change for you, and perhaps

233

it will not always be nice.' 'Well, I know,' says Petworth, 'But that's in a fairy story.' 'And you are not in one,' says Princip, 'No, you are not. And the cake is just a terrible cake and I do not even make it, just a shop. But I think you are tired, because you have been busy. Do you like to take now a shower?' 'I'd rather talk,' says Petworth. 'No, I think you must relax,' says Princip, 'Beside, I arrange it for you, while I make the coffee. There is a nice bathplace just behind the kitchen. You find there towel, hanging at the door. The soap is scented and very nice. It is all ready, please go now.'

'Well, very well,' says Petworth, getting up from the sofa. 'And take please your time, my dear,' says Princip, smiling at him, 'We are lucky, this is our afternoon, you do not need to hurry. I can put away these plates and tidy for you my room, I did not expect such a visitor. Do you find it? You go through the kitchen and there is a little white door.' Petworth goes, through the kitchen, through the white door, into a small, tiled bathroom with bare pipes and a great green mirror. In the mirror his body glints as he undresses, hanging his safari suit behind the door. A dull gloom goes with him, as he thinks of his confession, the admission of his wanting sexuality. He stands in the tub, turns the taps, feels the surge of water come over him, cold first, and then turning to hot; he thinks of his dark wife, who dyes her hair, and paints dark paintings in the lumber room, and stays silent, a dull dark anima at the end of a long tunnel. Like wasted words the water splashes over him; the heat grows, the mirror where his body shone fades and blurs. There is no shower curtain; the thick pipes roar; the flood washes over his face. He turns his head away, to realize that, in the steamed room, a person is standing there. 'Who is it?' he asks. 'You don't mind I come in?' says Katya Princip, 'You see after a cake, I like always to weigh, and my machine is here.' 'Please,' says Petworth. 'I hope the shower makes you fresh after your lecture?' says Princip, a vague shape in the steam. 'Yes, it does,' says Petworth, naked and white. 'Here is my machine,' says Princip, 'Now, do I get fatter? My weigh, fifty five kilos, that is not so bad. My high, one meter sixty five, that does not change. Other traits, grey eyes, blonde hair, all as usual. Special marks, not any. Rate of pulsation, normal, except when I look at you. You do not mind I look at you?' 'No,' says Petworth. 'The soap, do you like it?' asks Princip, close to his side in the steam, 'It is special, a present from France.' 'It's very nice,' says Petworth. 'And this water, it makes itself hot enough for you?' 'Yes, just right,' says Petworth. 'Often it does not work so well,' says Princip, 'I just try it with my hand. You are my guest here, it is not right that you burn your shoulders. Oh, it is good today, perhaps a little hot, you are sure it is not too much?' 'No, it's just right,' says Petworth, politely, standing there bedraggled in the steaming shower. 'Oh, look at you, my dear,' says Princip, 'Such a thin man, doesn't it hurt to be so thin?' 'Not at all,' says Petworth, 'I've always been like this.'

'Oh, you think I criticize the way you look, please, I do not,' says Princip, 'Really you look so nice there in the water, your wet body, very nice. But I hope you admit your lecture was open to an ideological criticism?' 'Too pragmatic?' asks Petworth. 'Exactly,' says Princip, 'Do you like me to soap you, and we can talk also about your deviations?' 'Well, yes,' says Petworth, 'It seems a good idea.' 'Perhaps it is easy if I come there in the tub with you,' says Princip, 'I do not want to get wet with this dress, do you like it, I paid for it much money?' 'I love it,' says Petworth. 'Yes, I am nice in it,' says Princip, fading into the steam, 'But I am nice without it too. We must not be bound by fetishism of the commodities. I hang it up and come back to you.' Without it, Princip emerges again from the steam, her naked back a blur in the mirror. 'Make please a room for me,' says Princip, 'It is not such a big tub. Yes, you are easily disproved. Stand still, please, I put this soap on you, oh, what a soft skin. Yes, you see, my dear, in our histories, we both have an old grey man.' 'Do we?' asks Petworth. 'Is good? You like?' asks Princip, 'Oh, yes, one is Marx, and the other Freud. Naturally my thinking has much of Marx. My husband the apparatchik, he talked to me much of Marx.' 'Does he have to be here?' asks Petworth. 'My husband is nowhere, Marx everywhere,' says Princip, 'Of course he is here. My dear, it is you should not be here. You know if I make you a guest in my apartment, if I give you some terrible coffee and a nice shower, I should report this contact to the authorities? That is our law, of course I do not do it. Don't you wash me now, I think you are very clean.' 'Yes,' says Petworth, 'Certainly.' 'You do not know Marx, but I think you know Freud,' says Princip, 'Isn't this water very nice?'

'Yes, I do,' says Petworth, his hands moving over the soft contours of no-longer batik-clad magical realist novelist Katya Princip. 'Marx explains the historical origins of consciousness,' she says, 'Freud quite ignores this, neglecting the ideological foundations of the mind. Yet it must be admitted he made some essential discoveries. He knew that it is nice to put a certain thing you have into a certain thing that is mine. For this he made a contribution to the progress of thought, don't you say?' 'Yes,' says Petworth. 'So you are deviationist, but not entirely to be condemned,' says Princip, 'Both thought-systems have their deficiencies. Do you think it is possible to make a dialectical synthesis? If we do it well, it might not produce a false consciousness. Do you like to try it? Oh, Petwit, look at you there, already I think you do. No, no, wait, my dear, my dear, I do not think we succeed like this, do you? For some problems in philosophy, Plato shows it is best to think lying down. Don't we go back there to my bed, isn't it better, oh, what do you do to me now, my dear, oh do you, oh do you really, oh isn't it nice, perhaps I am wrong, perhaps we stay, isn't it too wet, don't we fall down, no, we don't, I think we stay, yes, we stay, yes, yes.' 'Yes, yes,' says Petworth, an unattached signifier amid steam. 'Da, da,' says Princip, 'Da, da, da, da.' The water showers over them; for a moment there are no words. 'Oh, yes,' says Princip, a little later, 'This was a real contribution to thought. But now I bring you your nice towel and we dry. I think we go back to my little room and consider again our positions. Oh, Petwit, you are lovely.'

'I am sorry I do not have a nice little bedroom for you to lie in,' says Princip, back in the sitting room, 'Here for everyone only so many metres of space. I am lucky, I am approved writer, I have certain privileges. But only so much space, others are not so lucky even. My sofa is my bed, I make magic and it changes. Look, I just press here and now you have a bed to lie on. Lie, please, it is very comfortable. You must make strong again. Remember, you are only just started here. There are many more things for you to do in my country. Oh, our music has stopped. Were we so long at the shower? Well, I put some more on before I come to you, what do you like better, the woods or the strings? Here is some army songs, I don't think you like to hear that. Here is Vivaldi, here Janaček? Do you like charming or sad? Of course, you told me your taste, it is Vivaldi for you. Now I come to you, my dear. Are you warm? No, don't move, I just like to kneel here and look down at you. So thin, really there is not much of you. Your nice wet hairs, a thin white chest, so neat the thigh, is that what you call it, and what a good present for me in the middle. You know, you are just a little bit beautiful, Petwit. And me, do you like me? I am very good at the top, I think, but perhaps too fat for you at the stomach. Here we think a fatness there is just a little erotic. That is our cultural characteristic, but not so much in the West. All the ladies flat like a table, don't forget I have been there. Well, in any case, my dear, my weigh goes down. So perhaps I please you more when we meet again, do you think? Do you believe it, we meet again? Or do you go home away soon to your country and forget all about me? Yes, I think you do, it is natural.'

'No,' says Petworth, lying there on the sofa which has so magically become a bed, his head against books, looking up at Princip, big over him as she leans on one elbow to stare down into his face. 'Oh, listen, you are so sure,' says Princip, 'Well,

I am not. There is a world out there, my dear Petwit, do you forget it? Of course we have made a very nice exchange, each one gives the other something, all so simple. Oh, such nice touchings and chattings, but they do not last long, not like history. Sex is good, but is not information. Here, you see me, I look at you, and what do I know? I know you have a sad wife, I think you are sad too, perhaps you have many problems. I know you are not character in the world historical sense, I try to make you better, but I don't think I do. You are confused, you are good person, you have a desire, or you would not come with me, you are a little bit in my heart. And you look at me, and what do you know, I could be anyone, your good witch or your bad. You know I have had four husbands, and I have written a book you could not read. Now you know I have a body that you can read, it has been your book and you have read it in a certain way, for the pleasure. Well, I hope it was a good pleasure, but did you learn much, do you think you will pass the examination? Well, perhaps it does not matter. Often the best relations are between the peoples who do not know each other so well. Perhaps it is silly that people get to know each other very well, often it is nothing but disappointment. Who is ever as interesting as ourselves? Who can love us enough to drive away all the lonely and the terror? And to be known, that is often dangerous, especially in my country. No, I think I am a thing that happens to you once, in a foreign place, not a part of time, not a part of your true life.'

'I don't think so,' says Petworth, 'You're more than that.' 'Well, of course, it is possible to reach in a sudden into a soul, and find a friend,' says Princip, 'This is what I felt when I saw you at the awful lunch of Tankic. Such an apparatchik, I know that kind. Did you know at once I wanted you then, I felt an ache? Perhaps you made me a little foolish, you know I did not behave well. But something happened, I wanted you in my life, I wanted to give you a story, make you a character. And I think you wanted that too, you are not a character, not yet, but there is something in your eyes, always looking. Yes, we liked each other, I believe that. Of course we did, or we would not do these things. But what is liking when it is so easy? Oh, we made the bad world go away for a minute, that really is what love is for, but when it comes back, we have of course to live in it. Make all the loves you like and you still do not escape. Most lives are a prison, here in my country of course, you know, but I know also in yours. Do not forget, I have been there. If yours is not, you are very lucky. And all the lovings in the world, they do not make these things go away. The sad wife in your bed at home. The black cat that waits outside, did you see it? The water that dries here on your skin that is like me going away. Oh, yes, my dear, we have made our nice secret, all so natural. But of course it is not so natural. As my grey father Marx tells, it is also cultural and ideological, economical and sexual. It is part of all the systems, and each time you choose or you do, you enter one of them. I make you a certain kind of man, you make me a certain kind of woman. What a nice bed this would be if it was not in the world, but it is. Petwit, do you listen, do you go to sleep?'

'No,' says Petworth, 'I listen very carefully.' 'But you don't like what I say,' says Princip, 'No, this is why love is sad, this is why people after love lie on beds like we do, and do not feel happy. My dear, excuse me, please. In my country, after an event, we make always an analysis. That is our cultural characteristic. But you see, my dear, I want to give you a better sense of existence. Petwit, you know, to exist, that is not so very fantastic. Any fool can do this. All that is needed is for two people to make the nice little secret, just like you and me, and pouf, another in the world. I don't think this happens this time, Petwit, don't look so bad, of course I make a certain protection. But so we come into existence. And the problem is not to exist at all, it is to make importance of it. We are not just stones that sit in a field. I don't think so. Are you a stone, Petwit? I am not. Don't we have to find a desire, make a will? Don't we go always somewhere toward something? Of course to do it is hard as well as nice, it is even dangerous. No teacher is pure. No witch is safe. Oh, Petwit, my dear, I upset you. Now, I see it, you are the one who is sad. Well, perhaps I meaned it. Not to hurt you but to learn you. Stay quite still, please, one minute, I just do something to you. Do you like it? I kiss your feet. It is something we do here. Perhaps not in your country? Well, it was worth your travels. Oh, Petwit, you go soon, I don't like it. I wish I could keep you here for always. Perhaps you do not wish it also. Well, remember, a witch is not so easy to lose. I will not be far away when you go into the forest. And even if you do not come back, you will not really forget me.'

'I won't,' says Petworth, 'I really won't.' 'Listen, I think I tell you just one more story,' says Princip, 'Not a very interesting story, it is just about me, a true story, how I became writer. I was married then, with one of my husbands, not the best one. It was the one I told you, the minister, the apparatchik. He sat all the day in an office, with fat secretary, he drove inside the official cars with the curtains, he was high in the party, at all the meetings, he came home each night nice in a dark suit. I was student then, I read many books, I was clever. I studied with him his work, I advised his awful decisions, all those corrupt things. But always he told, please, be a good wife, an apparatchik must have a good wife. Well, he was not such good man, but I was pretty good wife. I made the dinner parties, I sat at the table, not this one here, of course then there was an apartment, very good, I said amusing things, I spoke in Russian and English, I talked the music and the art. Not the politics of course, oh no, not permitted. Well, on a certain night, he brought round our table some very important men, to talk about a national affair. I knew all about these things then, I listened, I understood, I wanted to say something. Well, I made mistake, I began to talk. These men, they were not so bad, they listened quite politely. But they turned round and round their glasses, they looked at each other in a certain way, I knew of course they want me to stop. Well, at first the things

I said were sensible, but then they became foolish, because, you see, they were not wanted. But I knew if I stopped they would all turn right away, and I did not want it, so I could not stop. My face was red, but I talked and talked, and then I got up from there and ran to the door and outside, and always still talking. I went out into the park, and I waited till the cars came for those men. Then I turned back to my husband, he stood in the room in his nice suit, and so angry. Do you know what he told me?'

'No,' says Petworth. 'He told, when you give a party again, you say nothing, never again do you speak in this way,' says Princip, 'Well, he came home the next day in his nice suit, and I expect he called for me, but I was not there. I was somewhere else, with someone else, and already I was writer. I could not live in a world where you think words you cannot speak. Of course, if people make of reality a prison, then others will wish to escape from it. I wrote down my words, the nonsense and the not nonsense, the words I could speak and the words I was trying to learn to speak, the words that were not yet words. I learned then a certain sense of existence. This is what I thought. But in case you think it is easy, no, it is not, because those words are like love, they do not go out of history. I feel toward the free, but I am not free. And no one is free, which is why the words are as sad as the love. My life is not better, but it is mine. I am sorry, my dear, really it is a very dull story. The others were much better. It is boring to be true.' 'What happened to your husband?' asks Petworth. 'This one, the apparatchik?' asks Princip, 'Oh, there was a political change in my country. What was right was now wrong. Who was in now was out. Well, we had been given some nice privileges. We builded a nice dacha, a little house, out in the forest, not so far from here. One day he went there in his nice suit, and he shot himself. He was allowed to be a hunter and to keep a gun. It was better for him than a trial and a prison. This also is remembered about me, by those who do not like me. For him, I am afraid I was not such good witch. For you, I hope I am much better. Now you see why I can tell so much about history. I have learned in the best places.'

'Should we have done this?' asks Petworth, looking at her, as they lie there in the small room, where a faint wind blows the net curtains, and rustles the papers on the desk, and the light begins to fade down in the sky beyond. 'Now you think you commit a crime against the state,' says Princip, 'Now you wish it had not happened. Well, it is not a real offence, even under Marx. Not if you do it with a good ideological attitude. Of course, if you find your position is not correct . . .' 'Well,' says Petworth, looking at their bodies infolded into each other, 'It looks quite good to me.' 'I think so,' says Princip, laughing, 'Perhaps you like to improve it some more? You see now I know how to teach you.' 'Yes,' says Petworth. 'Then I will help you,' says Princip, 'I told you you had many things still to do in my country. Hold me so, see me please as a comrade-of-arms of the struggle. Think with your mind you build a great and startling project. Feel with your heart you reach the great laws of human universality. Know with your strong you contribute to the historic advance of the proletariat.' Live grey eyes are staring into his face; a body beside him is a fundamental mass with a living motion; there are hands on his own body, drawing its shape and design, drawing it out of shape and design. 'Yes, something is happening to you, do you feel it,' says Katya, eyes, hair, flesh leaning over him. 'Oh, Katya,' says Petworth, looking at the face, alert, moving, the eyes open, reaching out to touch the mass and feel its architecture, the bone order beneath the fleshly pads, 'Katya.' 'Oh, Petwit, do you remember my name?' says Princip, 'You have not said it before. Do you call me a person? Well, perhaps I am Katya, someone like that, but please, it is not the person, it is cause that matters. Take me into yourself, do you do it better if I come on top of you, don't you say?'

There is a body elevated above him, shaped against the light. 'Petwit, now I am magicking you,' says Princip, 'I will take you somewhere, on a nice journey, I am your guide.'

242

'Oh,' says Petworth, 'Oh my god.' 'Petwit, please, no god,' says Princip, swinging the top of her body across his face, 'Don't you know our task is secular? Try please to relate your subjective to your objective, your spirit to history. In this way you will grow free of errors. Yes, I am your guide, we make it together, our special journey. Do you remember Stupid, do you think you know now how he climbed the tower, perhaps he did what you do, perhaps he found the witch was the princess also. Well, I am your sex princess, I am witching you, I am taking you where you cannot go, think of a word you do not know, I am that word, try to understand it, do you come nearer?' Above him is skin in its long planes, hollowed here, puffed there, the outward thrust of breasts, the inward tuck of the navel, the feel of an intricate yielding crease. 'Yes, you come nearer,' says Princip, 'is there a meaning, is there a place, you go into that place, I put you in that place, you come there and I come there with you, and we are together. You don't have a sad wife, you have me only, no other, all the bodies are my body, do you feel it happen, I do, you do, I know you do, yes, yes.' There is light and dark, inside and outside, arrest, explosion, light following dark, a room of books where curtains blow. 'Wasn't it my best story?' says Princip, 'Didn't I magic you nicely?' 'It was better,' says Petworth. 'Of course,' says Princip, 'Only one thing wrong.' 'What's that?' asks Petworth. 'Look at you,' says Princip, 'Nowhere to pin on you your medal. Petwit, do you think we found a place that is ours?' Petworth leans up; with a dull, dragging, mechanical note, the telephone on the desk under the blowing curtains begins to ring.

'Oh, no,' says Princip, looking at him, 'Who is this? Quick, go please and put on clothes. Wait, what is time?' 'Time?' asks Petworth. 'On your watch,' says Princip. 'It's a quarter to six,' says Petworth, hurrying, heart beating, into the bathroom. The steam is fading slowly off the green mirror, a naked Petworth refracts emptily at him, the pipes in the tub rattle and groan, Katya Princip's batik dress swings loose on the hook behind the door. Dressing quickly, tugging up clothes, he can hear, beyond the thin wall, the stop and start of a voice, in rapid irregular conversation in the language he still does not know. Telephones and time are of this world; something in the world, half-remembered, presses on him, a worry. In the other room, the telephone clicks down; then Princip, big, naked, her face sad, stands in the door. 'Oh, Petwit, be quick, you must go now,' she says, 'Someone comes here soon, I cannot stop it. Find please my dress.' 'Here,' says Petworth, handing it to her, watching her body scurry, become disorderly, as she pulls it onto her. 'Oh, why don't we have time?' she says, 'And now you will go away, and perhaps I will not see you again.' 'We have to,' says Petworth, 'I'm back in Slaka in ten days.' 'Ten days, it is long,' says Princip, 'And things will happen on your journey, perhaps you will not want then to see me. And you have not been good visitor today, they will watch you, it will not be easy. Oh, I know how it is done, they will make you suddenly busy, they will change your programme. Or they will perhaps invite me to make a little journey from the town. All of a sudden they need my new book, go, please, to the dacha for writers in the country, it is all arranged. For people not to meet, that is easy to fix, we are experts. Wait, your hair, borrow please this comb, you must not look like that when you go. Oh, look, you are in my mirror, I wish I keep you in there. I have a love for you, Petwit, I don't know why, and no time to say it.' 'I have it too,' says Petworth.

'Come quickly, help me, we must turn back the bed,' says Princip, drawing him back into the small room, 'Oh, Petwit, do you truly want to see me again? Even if it is so hard and so foolish?' 'Yes,' says Petworth, as the bed becomes a sofa again. 'Well, you make good decision,' says Princip, 'It is foolish and it is right. So how do we arrange, how? Well, look, I write down a telephone for you to ring. It is not this one here, another. When you ring there, do not speak, wait till I answer. If another one answers, still do not speak, put it back, wait a time and then try again. If I answer, talk like we make a small business. Do not try the number more than two times, always people listen, they might interest in you. Do you understand all this? It is very important.' 'Yes, I understand,' says Petworth, 'But if I don't reach you, is there another way? Can I come here?' 'No, never come here, you understand that?' says Princip, 'There is the coffee house, you remember it, you know I go there. Oh, I hope you come back, I hope you find me, but now I know you will. You see, I did not finish the story of Stupid. Oh, look at you, Petwit, so intense and sad. Are you always so?' 'No,' says Petworth. 'Only in your spare time,' says Princip, 'It will be all right.' 'Yes,' says Petworth. 'Oh, Petwit,' says Princip, holding him, 'Well, I have put you in my story, you know. And I give you the stone, do you wear it? And here, from my pot, one flower, not for you, for your guide. And a coin to pay the lift, you know how to use. I cannot come with you, but Wang'luku, that is easy to find. You walk here to the end, then go three streets to the right, you will see before you Hotel Slaka. And on your journey in the forest, think I am with you, not far away.' 'I will,' says Petworth. 'Go now, quickly,' says Princip, opening the door of the flat, 'Be always careful, my dear. Oh, the lift is here, go, I watch you.'

The gates of the lift come to, the coin goes in, the cage goes down. He hurries through the empty lobby and into the darkening street. To his left, the black car still stands; he goes to the right, coming to a busy street along which pink trams clatter. In one hand he carries the tattered folder holding his tattered lecture, in the other the bouncing single flower. The street is busy, and the crowd comes toward him in bewildering profusion, faces too many to meet, shawled women, men in fur hats, young people in jeans, soldiers in khaki. There is a strain in his senses, a mild disorder in his body, a faint pain in his side, like the pain, perhaps, of existence itself, a feeling made half of pleasure and half of guilt. There is a throb in his groin, and in his mind a sense of a destination with a duty in it, though he cannot remember quite what it is. His breath pants; white-walled buildings rise on either side, and down the side streets domes glisten and glint. On the high government blocks, not very far away, the clocks begin to strike, like the rasp of a telephone; the notes in the air sound six, and he remembers what he is half-remembering, what he is half-striving for, that just at this time he should be at the hotel, calling his distant dark wife. The roof of the hotel shows over the buildings in front of him; he begins, now, to run toward it, the flower bobbing in his hand. The big square shows up in front of him; the flashing sign says SCH'VEPPUU. The square opens up, but the massed crowds that move toward the pink trams stopped in the centre obstruct. He pushes through, running dangerously in front of traffic; a pink tram clangs furiously at him. Breathing hard, he reaches the glass doors of the hotel.

On the other side of the glass, as he pushes at it, one of the dark whores, in a long velvet dress, looks out, smiles at him, inspects the flower he carries. 'Change money,' murmurs a voice in the crowds just inside, as he hurries in, stumbling over the luggage of a new bus-party which has just arrived and stands all round the desk. 'Pervert!' shouts a voice from somewhere in the crowd, 'Pervert!' The lacquered-haired Cosmoplot girl stands in her blue uniform behind the desk marked R'GUSTRAYUU, looking at him and angrily tapping her watch. 'My call to England,' says Petworth, pushing up to the desk. 'Don't you see this time?' says the girl, pointing at the big clock on the wall between Marx and Lenin, 'You are late five minutes.' 'I was delayed,' says Petworth, 'There's a lot of traffic. Can't you put me through?' The girl turns, and looks at a man in a dark suit, standing in a doorway marked DURUG'AYUU; the man shakes his head. 'It is cancel,' says the girl, 'You must be here right time.' 'Can I call later?' asks Petworth, holding the wilting flower. 'Tomorrow,' says the girl. 'I leave Slaka tomorrow,' says Petworth. 'Then you see why is bad to be late,' says the girl, 'Do you like key?' 'Please,' says Petworth. 'Ident'ayuu,' says the girl. Taking the key, going to the lift, Petworth sees the man in the dark suit watching him. In the lift, his image shows in the mirrors, a man carrying a flower; in his mind there arises the guilty image of his dark wife, yet the face is imperfect and not quite right, for it has the grey eyes of Katya Princip. He goes along the corridor past the floormaid; he unlocks the door to his big and empty room.

II

'Oh Petwurt, Petwurt, that is nice,' says Marisja Lubijova, in a fine blue knitted dress, with a white lace stole over it, when he meets her in the lobby at seven, 'You have brought me one flower. Look, I put it in my dress. It is just right to visit an oper.' 'I thought it would suit the occasion,' says Petworth. 'Also I think it means you feel a little ashamed, I hope so,' says Lubijova, 'This thing you do at lunch-time.' 'Yes, I'm sorry about that,' says Petworth, 'A small confusion.' 'Really you are very naughty,' says Lubijova, 'Your friends arrange you a lunch where you are guest of honour, and then you do not come. Of course everyone is very embarrass. They do not know what to tell each other. And your official from London, where you go last night and do not tell me, he thinks a very bad thing has happened to you. He thinks he will go to the police, or call London, do you like to start a world war between our powers, Petwurt?' 'No, not really,' says Petworth. 'It is happy Dr Plitplov thinks it is a small *affaire du coeur*,' says Lubijova, 'But you must tell your Mr Steadiman what has happened to you.' 'Can I call him?' asks Petworth. 'I think he goes also to the oper,' says Lubijova, 'Yes, you are very naughty, but you have brought me a flower, and you look very sorry, and we go to make a nice evening. So I will not be so cross with you. But look at you, please. We go to oper, where everyone dresses in the best, and you don't even put on your nice suit. Don't you like to go back and change yourself? We have time for it.' 'My suit?' says Petworth, thinking of it, ripped open at the flies by Budgie Steadiman, 'I'm afraid it needs pressing.' 'Very well,' says Lubijova, stiffly, 'Come then in your bad clothes. Let us find a taxi. Or perhaps you feel better in a tram.'

As they sit in the orange taxi, driving off through the evening streets of Slaka, Lubijova turns toward him. 'So, Comrade Petwurt,' she says, 'You went away with your lady writer. Did you make a nice afternoon?' 'Oh, very pleasant,' says Petworth. 'Perhaps you go somewhere quite interesting,' says Lubijova. 'Oh, Miss Princip wanted to take me to see the castle,' says Petworth. 'Oh, really, that is nice,' says Lubijova, 'The castle of Vlam?' 'Yes,' says Petworth. 'And you like it, it is good?' asks Lubijova. 'Yes, very fine,' says Petworth. 'I am glad you impress,' says Lubijova, 'The castle is closed for some weeks, for a restauration. That is why I do not take you there already myself. But of course your friend is a very famous writer, who has important contacts. I expect she has used her privileges so that you can go inside.' 'I expect so,' says Petworth, feeling uneasy. 'And do you see in there the tomb of Vlam?' asks Lubijova. 'The tomb of Vlam,' says Petworth. 'In the baroque style,' says Lubijova, 'All over it the cupids.' 'Ah, yes,' says Petworth, 'It's very good.' 'Oh, really, you think so?' says Lubijova, 'I did not know there was one. I have just myself invented it. Don't you think I would make a nice lady writer too?' 'Well, yes,' says Petworth. 'I wonder what you really do,' says Lubijova. 'We just looked around,' says Petworth. 'Petwurt, Petwurt,' says Lubijova, 'You are such a trouble to me. You lie to me about last night, now you lie to me about today. I don't know about you, Petwurt. I don't know why you are here, but I know I must think of you in a new way. You are not a good visitor. And don't you know I might be in some troubles if you do bad things here?'

'I'm sorry,' says Petworth, 'But it's all quite harmless.' 'Is it?' asks Lubijova, looking at him, 'Perhaps you are quite clever or really quite simple. How do I know? But if you are simple you are not in a simple world. Don't you remember, when I bring you to your hotel from the airport, I told you something? That here in my country it is always good to be cautious? Don't you listen to what I say? Don't you think? And I am your poor guide who is responsible. Well, perhaps I will trust you a little bit. I don't know why, perhaps I like you. In any case, we go away tomorrow away from Slaka. Perhaps you will make a new start.' 'I'll try,' says Petworth. 'You try,' says Lubijova, 'Well, we shall see. But let us in any case enjoy our evening. It ought to be our nice time. You do not mind to sit for five hours for an oper in another language?' 'Aren't all operas in another language?' asks Petworth. 'Yes, well, tonight you have interpreter,' says Lubijova, slipping her arm in his, 'And it is very good oper, by one of the great musicians of my country. For a long time this work was lost but then under socialism it was discovered again. Many have seen it as the prefigure of many other great oper works, like the Figaro Wedding of Mozart or the Seville Haircutting Man of Rossini. Now it re-lives, and everyone is very excited, including many foreign peoples. Here come all our workers, and also the important visitors. Even the naughty ones, like you, Comrade Petwurt. I wonder what you are really doing, all that aftenoon, my bad friend, with your little lady writer?' 'Really, just a little tourism,' says Petworth. 'Oh, yes, do you?' cries Lubijova, taking the fleshy part of his arm between her fingers, and squeezing it, 'Well, perhaps I must not ask you to describe the places where you make this tour. Perhaps they are not so polite. Perhaps you embarrass if you tell them?' 'Not at all,' says Petworth, 'I just don't know where we went. I'm a stranger.' 'Not so strange, any more,' says Lubijova, 'On your neck, isn't it a bite?'

The taxi has stopped; the high, well-lit dome of the opera house is above them, and bright lights illuminate the great windows. Outside, on the gaunt pavement, a great crowd mills, as fine-looking couples descend in large numbers from orange taxis or big black Volgas and cross from the curb toward the great marbled entrance. 'I hope you make it your mind to escort me nicely, Comrade Petwurt,' says Lubijova, 'Here at the oper we like always to make a very good style. Please put my shawl nicely round my shoulders, I think you know how to be a gentleman. Now do you have some vloskan to pay this taxi? I think he likes very much to be paid.' 'Yes, of course,' says Petworth, reaching down into the pocket of his worn trousers. On the pavement, Lubijova, in her stole, the flower in the bosom of her dress, tucks her arm through his as they walk to the entrance. Big posters show singers in false beards, with their mouths wide open; *Vedontakal Vrop*, say the inscribed words. A few, but just a very few, of the universal armed men stand by the glass doors as they sweep with the press into the lobby, part of a great tidal drift of human motion. Inside, from the glinting chandeliers, a thousand lights shine; Petworth feels tired, very tired, and his body, from the exertions of the day, has a certain pained fragility to it, while his mind runs troubled about what Lubijova has found out about him. But the city of betrayals and disappearances, watchers and listeners, seems curiously behind him as they pass, in the crowd, through the lobby and up a great curved stone staircase, where the wall-lights glint and glisten, and so, too, do the necklaces and tiaras and fur-wraps of the handsome ladies who stand in line at the mirrored cloakrooms, waiting to de-cloak.

'Well, do you impress?' asks Lubijova, as they stand in the great plush foyer. 'Splendid,' says Petworth, standing in his old clothes, as the ladies in front of him expose black dresses and décolletage, and the men stand neat as penguins in their dinner jackets and evening dress. 'Yes, you surprise,' says Lubijova, laughing, 'Of course we are a music-loving nation, and since socialism the loving has much increased. The tickets are sent to the factories for the best workers and they come with a great pleasure, as you see. Of course they do not explain you these things in the newspapers of your West. You think we are just some factories and food shortage; we know what you say about us. Well, now you know it is different. Now you see we make really a very nice life.' 'These are workers?' asks Petworth. 'Yes, you see our people like to make good display,' says Lubijova, 'Only you, Petwurt, not in the best, look at you.' 'I didn't know it would be such a gala occasion,' says Petworth, seeing himself, in his sagging safari jacket, reflected back from the mirrored walls. 'Well, we know you are foreigner, a bit strange really,' says Lubijova, 'So perhaps we all make a little excuse for you.' A high-ranking soldier passes them by, chest heavy with ribbons; on his arm is a tall fine woman, her cleavage so complete it displays the navel and almost visits the crotch. 'They're hardly all workers,' says Petworth. 'Perhaps some are party officials,' says Lubijova, 'You like them to have a relax after all their hard work, I hope?' 'You realize this whole derned thing could be in some foreign language?' says a middle-aged lady, wearing a diamanté-ed trouser suit, in the accents of Texas, to Petworth's side. 'Yeah, well, just listen to the music,' says her escort, a middle-aged man in bright tartan trousers. 'Also people from everywhere in the world,' says Lubijova, 'They travel many miles to hear our arts.'

The engulfing human motion continues, as the people press through the plush-walled foyer, which curves in a circle around the central auditorium. Perfume wafts from bosoms; faces appear and disappear; the heat of humanity grows. 'I think perhaps you wait for me here,' says Lubijova, 'I go to collect our tickets, also to find a programme that is English. Always they make one for our special guests from abroad. Now, you don't go away? You only wait here? If some pretty lady comes, you don't leave with her?' 'No, I'll wait here,' says Petworth. 'All right, I trust you,' says Lubijova, leaving, 'Perhaps I am mad.' In her white stole, she moves off with the crowd; Petworth stands, reflected in mirrors, lighting a cigarette. The press continues; bright couples slide through velvet curtains into boxes, offering him brief glimpses of the great lighted auditorium within. Led by an official guide, the Vietnamese ladies from the hotel swarm by; they have set aside their dark blue work suits, and are clad now in fine silk cheong-sams.

The bodily strangeness that has been overwhelming Petworth for most of the day becomes a physical unease; like water down a drain, the self he thought within him seems to be draining out. The lights glitter; the mirrors glint. 'Isn't it Dr Petworth? Isn't it my good old friend?' says a voice; in a dinner jacket worn with a fine white sweater, Plitplov has somehow emerged from the crowd and stands in front of him, his bird-like eyes looking hard at him, 'You are well? You are safe? No bad thing has happened to you?' 'Oh, you're here,' says Petworth. 'Of course, everyone comes here,' says Plitplov, 'Well, all day I am making a worry for you.' 'There was no need,' says Petworth. 'Of course,' says Plitplov, 'In my country, when someone is lost, all the friends grow upset and wonder if a bad thing has happened. Of course, there is usually a simple explanation. I expect you have one.'

'It's quite simple,' says Petworth, 'I was just taken for a little look around the city.' 'A little advice, my friend,' says Plitplov, looking around, 'Please do not smoke. It is not permitted in a public place. And it is not so good to draw an attention to yourself. A little look around the city, well, that is very nice. And your guide the excellent Miss Princip?' 'Yes,' says Petworth. 'A very fine writer,' says Plitplov, 'I have reviewed myself her books, did she mention so?' 'Actually, no,' says Petworth. 'Well, it does not matter,' says Plitplov, 'So, you like to disappear. Well, I do not mind it. It is true I made many special efforts to come there to your lecture and take a lunch with you. But of course I understand. Your field is literature and this is a writer. Also I do not have those nice charms. And of course it was noticed very much in Cambridge you liked always the ladies. A man is not so interesting to you. But of course here is not Cambridge, I have told you this already. You like to be absent, well, my friend, it is not so hard to be absent in my country. But don't you know you make a risk for everyone? For you, for your writer, for your friends, for me. You know I had a hand to invite you? Do you like to make a difficulty for me? Perhaps that was the intention of your visit?' 'Not at all,' says Petworth. 'And your guide, your Miss Lubijova, does she know what you do?' asks Plitplov. 'I think she has a good idea,' says Petworth. 'And of course what she knows, all will know,' says Plitplov, 'And what do you do with Miss Princip? Do you make an *affaire du coeur*?' 'We simply went for a little—' says Petworth. 'Structuralism,' says Plitplov, 'I believe it has caused many intellectual searchings of heart in your country.'

'Oh, are you here, Dr Plitplov?' says Lubijova, coming up in her stole, 'You don't tell me this at our lunch.' 'Of course, I am opera lover,' says Plitplov, 'I perhaps also write a something in the newspaper.' 'But at our lunch you said you were going somewhere to dinner tonight,' says Lubijova. 'Well, it was such a sad lunch,' says Plitplov, 'Of course I was worried for my old friend.' 'Well, you did not need,' says Lubijova, hoisting her stole, 'He makes a very interesting afternoon. He goes with a lady writer to the castle of Vlam.' 'That is nice,' says Plitplov, 'But I think the castle is closed now, there is nothing there.' 'But there are ladies who know special ways into castles,' says Lubijova, 'You know what is said: the way into a room is not always through the door.' 'I see, my friend,' says Plitplov, 'You make a little mystery for us.' 'Perhaps it is not so hard to solve,' says Lubijova. A bell rings: 'Don't you think it is time to take a seat?' asks Plitplov. 'Well,' says Lubijova, 'I am afraid there is just a certain small confusion.' 'Really?' says Petworth. 'Not a difficulty,' says Lubijova, 'Do not worry. They have been very efficient here, and sold our seats two times. An American tourist sits in your place.' 'We won't be able to see it?' asks Petworth. 'Of course, you are an important visitor,' says Lubijova, 'They will make certain arrangements.' 'Please,' says Plitplov, 'Sit down please on this banquette. I have certain influences here. I will speak to some people I know very well.' 'Already I have spoken,' says Lubijova. 'I think perhaps I know them a little better,' says Plitplov, 'I have a certain skill to make some arrangements. It will not take long.'

'Of course it is arranged already,' says Lubijova, sitting down, 'This American is not so important as you. They will take him out and give him ticket for another night. Now, while we wait, I explain you the programme. There is also a small confusion with a printer and they do not have now a text in English. But it is simple, I interpret you, do you like?' 'Of course,' says Petworth. 'Well, I am your good guide,' says Lubijova, reaching into her small red evening bag and taking out her big red spectacles, 'So, here on the front, the title, *Vedontakal Vrop*, do you understand it?' 'No,' says Petworth. 'Well, how does it mean?' says Lubijova, 'Do you know, the secret that is not a secret, the secret found out, how do you says? Like your afternoon. You think you have done something hidden, but everyone knows it.' 'The secret unmasked?' suggests Petworth. 'Exact,' says Lubijova, 'The secret unmasked. Now here inside is explained it is oper bouffe of two hundred years. You know bouffe? It means is very funny. Here is explained it is played in a typical style, but with some modernizations. The technic is influenced by China oper of Sichuan province, but also by Bolshoi. The play has always been lost but now is found, except part of acta three. But with brilliant improvisations this small difficulty is triumphantly overcome. The story is from the folk, but Leblat, who makes the liber, has changes all things round to make them more unusual, so it is not the same any more. And now here is the story, do you like I tell it to you, in case we do not find some seats?' 'Yes,' says Petworth, 'Please.'

'Well, it is difficult,' says Lubijova, turning over the written pages, while in the auditorium the buzz and chatter of the audience rises, 'But I try. In acta first, a student paramour falls into love with a beautiful girl who has bad father, who forbids a marriage. He is a magician who is sometimes turning people into a bear, and of course this makes laughable confusions. Also the boy has cruel father who does not understand him. That father tells he must not marriage but make travel to the big city and make his examen to become a government official.

254

The girl is sad and disguises herself as boy to go after him. But the boy is sad and decides to stay, so he disguises as girl. Also his mother is loving an uncle who disguises himself like a king from a foreign country so he can make visits. But also there is naughty maid and a silly servant who is sometimes in love with this maid but often not. These two also are disguising all the time, but of course in oper nothing is as it seems. By two scene, the confusions are very bad and then come more people, like a tough aunt, a man from Turk, a soft-wit brother who is more clever than he looks, and a priest who is perhaps policeman. I hope you understand it now, a bit? It is not so easy for me.' 'Yes, I think so,' says Petworth. 'Why don't those people leave now?' says Lubijova, looking up, 'Perhaps they like to make protest. Sometimes this happens. But our ushers are always very efficient.' And indeed the curtains leading to the auditorium now part, and, between two black-suited ushers comes a couple, he wearing bright tartan trousers, she a diamanté-ed trouser suit. 'Jesus, when will you guys ever learn to run a country?' says the man to one of the ushers, in a Texas accent. 'Do you know this is the third goddam night this has happened?' says the woman to the other. 'You see how easily our little problem is solved,' says Lubijova, rising, 'Now we go in. Please take my arm, we do it nicely.'

The auditorium, high, round, and ornate, is a monument to the baroque taste. Three tiers of boxes run round it; in the boxes sit, in a buzz of chatter, shining people with white glowing shirt fronts and bright dresses. The great proscenium arch is finely plastered and decorated with cupids; only the cusp in the centre shows history's workings, for, where damaged plaster shows the arms of an imperial power must once have stood, there is emblazoned a red hammer and sickle. 'Our seats are in stall,' says Lubijova, as they are led to the second row from the front, 'That is nice, we will see everything. And not even late: only now does the orchester come. Perhaps they wait for us. Of course this orchester is very fine, our players are in the class of the world. Perhaps sometimes they have just

255

one little problem.' 'Oh, yes,' says Petworth, sitting down, 'What's that?' 'They like to work hard, like all our people,' says Lubijova, 'So when it is rehearse often they are too busy, and must send their substitutes. Then at performance, well, of course always they play very well, but often they do not understand what the others do. But it will not be so tonight. They are playing together one night already. And now here is coming the conductor. It is Leo Fenycx, geboren Prague and if quite young also very famous. Perhaps you know of him already?' 'I'm afraid not,' says Petworth, as the audience begins to clap, and Leo Fenycx, in his white tie and tails, bows his head. 'No?' cries Lubijova, clapping, 'Many fine evaluations have been written of his work. You don't read them?' 'No, I haven't,' says Petworth, as the conductor turns toward the orchestra and the bright lights of the house begin to dim.

'Oh, Petwurt,' says Lubijova suddenly, squeezing his arm, 'Who is that?' 'What?' asks Petworth. 'Someone waves you, at the loge up there, in the second tier, where sit the party officials,' says Lubijova. But the boxes are deep dark circles in a near blackness; and now, with a great plucking of strings, a romping, bantering overture begins. 'Who was this?' whispers Lubijova. 'I didn't see,' whispers Petworth, 'A man or a woman?' The bassoons come in loudly. 'Of course,' murmurs Lubijova, 'Another lady. In a red dress.' 'I have no idea,' murmurs Petworth. The noisy brass enter. 'Of course you have idea,' whispers Lubijova. 'I don't suppose she was waving to me at all,' whispers Petworth. There is an arabesque of wood-winds. 'Yes, to you,' murmurs Lubijova, 'Petwurt, you are like romantic little boy. Everywhere you go, there are ladies.' 'No, not really,' murmurs Petworth. The fiddles come in to state a second theme. 'Perhaps you are an American,' says Lubijova, 'Do you like to think of sexing all the time, like those people?' 'No,' whispers Petworth. The new and darker theme begins to swell, while the light woodwinds play the first theme against it. 'I think so,' murmurs Lubijova, 'Is this why you come to Slaka? To make your romantic life? I thought you are here to make some lectures.' 'I am,' murmurs Petworth. The brass come in, to restate the first theme more strongly. 'Only two days ago you are coming to Slaka,' says Lubijova, 'You are telling me you know no one. Now is two days, and everywhere there are ladies. In the morning, the afternoon, the night, always some ladies. Who is this one?' 'I really don't know,' whispers Petworth, conscious that along the row heads are swivelling to look at them. 'Please,' says a voice in English from the row behind, 'We try to listen this music.' 'I'm sorry,' whispers Petworth, turning. 'Oh, is it you, my good old friend,' says the voice from behind, 'Do you make a quarrel? Something has gone wrong?' The overture swells and rises, the two themes become one. 'Not you, Comrade Plitplov,' murmurs Lubijova. 'Oh, we sit close,' says Plitplov, 'What a good coincidence.'

But now, in a cloud of dust, the great curtain in front of them ascends. A three-dimensional painted landscape of very bosky aspect is disclosed, with barrel-shaped tree-trunks rising up to branches that shake paper leaves. Centre stage is a papier-mâché cave; from the cave comes a young man dressed as an old man and wearing a long grey beard. He sings lustily at the audience: 'Tells he is a very old man with a long grey beard,' whispers Lubijova to Petworth. In the orchestra pit a flute-bird twitters; from stage left comes, tripping lightly, a young girl dressed as a boy. 'Tells she is a young girl dressed as a boy,' whispers Plitplov from the row behind, after a moment. 'Of course the old man does not know she is really girl,' murmurs Lubijova, 'Because now she is telling him she is soldier.' 'Also she does not know he is really her uncle,' whispers Plitplov, 'Because he tells her he is really the king of another country.' But now, backstage, a singing boy, wrapped in a very large cloak, has appeared, slinking through the cardboard trees, and singing. 'Oh, what a silly boy!' cries Lubijova, laughing, 'He tells he is a young man in love with a girl who is lost.' 'That is this girl,' whispers Plitplov. 'But he cannot marry her because all the fathers forbid, so he hides in

257

the forest dressed like robber,' says Lubijova, 'He tells he likes to take from the rich to give to the poor.' 'To spend on his bets,' says Plitplov. 'To give to the poor,' says Lubijova, firmly, 'Now he sees the old man and thinks he will steal his purse, so everyone will know he is robber.' 'Look, he steals it,' whispers Plitplov. 'But the girl wants to show now she has the honour of a man,' says Lubijova, 'She tells that boy she fights him to a duel. Doesn't she know he is her best lover?' 'No,' says Plitplov. 'Look, they both pull out their arms,' says Lubijova, 'Oh, what a pity. He shoots her and she falls. She sings she dies of a plum in the breast.' 'A plum?' asks Petworth. 'The plum he has shooted from his arm,' says Lubijova.

'Bullet,' whispers Plitplov, 'Plum is a make of fruit.' 'I am right, plum,' says Lubijova, 'Now he sings he is sorry. He thinks he will bend to loosen her blouses. Perhaps he will find there a very nice surprise, don't you think so?' 'No,' says Plitplov, 'Because now is coming a man who tells a wizard has turned him into a bear.' 'It is funny,' says Lubijova, laughing. 'The old man laughs at him and says he was always a bear!' 'But he tells he was not bear before, but only dog,' whispers Plitplov, 'Because he was always servant and a servant is only a dog.' 'Now they help the one with the plum,' whispers Lubijova. 'No,' says Plitplov, 'Because now comes a man who says he is a Turk who comes from Turkey, but really he is the brother of the girl.' 'Also comes a girl who sings she is the maid of the mother of the girl,' says Lubijova. 'He says he must hide from this maid or she will know him,' says Plitplov. 'She tells her naughty plan to marry the mother of the girl to the father of the boy, because they are always loving each other.' 'But first must die the father of the girl and the mother of the boy,' says Plitplov, 'That is why she carries here a pot of poison from an apothek.' 'From a magician,' says Lubijova. 'You tell it wrong,' says Plitplov. 'I tell it right,' says Lubijova. Meanwhile the stage fills with an extravagant crowd of people, some in costumes of relative realism, others resembling animals. 'Here some people who go to make a festival in the forest,' says Plitplov. 'They stop to sing a chorus about making some nice cakes,' says Lubijova. 'About the coming of the spring,' says Plitplov. 'Now they see the girl who is dying of the plum,' says Lubijova. 'Of the bullet,' says Plitplov. 'And now steps forward one to take her off to the cave of the magician.' 'The shop of the apothek,' says Plitplov. The chorus ascends, the girl is lifted, the singers move, the curtain falls.

In the dark auditorium, heads all round them have turned to stare. Two bassoonists rise to peer critically over the top of the orchestra pit at them. 'I think we're disturbing everybody,' murmurs Petworth. 'Comrade Plitplov, I think they will stop this oper if you are not more quiet,' says Lubijova. 'It is you,' hisses Plitplov. 'Well, we don't talk,' says Lubijova, 'I explain you all in the interlude, Comrade Petwurt.' 'In the interval,' whispers Plitplov from the rear. 'I am interpreter, I am right,' whispers Lubijova, firmly, 'See, again arises the curtain. Now we will be quiet and perhaps you will make the sense for yourself. Look, the cave of the magician.' 'The shop of the apothek,' hisses Plitplov, before he subsides in the row behind. Left to his own resources, Petworth stares up at the great stage, where the voices sound and the complex musical codes continue to unwind. One thing is clear: whatever the *mise-en-scène*, during that brief dropping of the curtain, much has changed in the imaginary world of artifice that is being composed and constructed just above his head. Perhaps much stage-time has passed, or everyone has died, or turned into something quite different, for the mind and senses are evidently being taken toward a new landscape of deceit and desire. Continuities may exist; the boy who was previously dressed as a robber could well be the same boy who is now dressed as a girl, though this could be an error; the coquette-ish maid in the dirndl who formerly carried her pot of poison might well be the girl now dressed as a cavalry officer, with moustaches, though this could be an optical illusion. Sexual arrangements are clearly other than they were. The boy-girl with the plum in her breast has either made a rapid recovery, or died, along with everyone else, but her erotic attention is now devoted to the magician or apothek, whom Petworth had previously understood to be her father. Meanwhile the boy dressed as a girl is being wooed by the young wife, or mistress, or perhaps assistant, of the magician, or perhaps apothek, though whether because she has unmasked his disguise, or because her tastes are oblique, or because she is a man who thinks he is a woman, is hard to surmise.

Shards and fragments, chaos and Babel; Petworth sits in his plush seat in the great auditorium, where from the circle of boxes the audience in their costumes of bland civility stare down onto the stage, and looks at the spectacle. Above him the faces move, painted and prettified, the cosmetics and the false beards gleam, the cadenced words, in the language he still does not know, spill out in their mysterious series, high sound that flows out erotically over him, as if his body is being washed in a shower of noise. The operatic confusion seems entirely in tune with that tumultuous exhaustion, that waning of utterance, that fading of self into contingent event that comes over a man in the midst of a difficult journey. Yet the mind, even when worn, still seeks order; lost in the garden of forking paths, where the narratives divide and multiply, he struggles to find a law of series, a system of signification, discover a story. But the author of what is being enacted in front of him seems to have little regard for the normal laws of probability, the familiar rules of genre and expectation. It is no longer clear to him who desires whom, nor which of any two partners is of which sex, nor, if he or she is, whether he or she will remain so. Identities have no proper barriers; people seem facets of each other. A singer appears who does not sing. The magician, or perhaps apothek, has big shoulders and many gold teeth; his wife, mistress, or assistant, has a fine neck and a mole above her right breast. Only impersonation seems true, the charade itself, the falsehood that is being created, the codes that proliferate and turn into counter-code. His mind drifts, dislodges, seems to find a room somewhere else in the big dark city he knows he is in, a room where water pours over him, and his body is being warmly touched.

His body is being warmly touched: 'Do you like it, do you like?' a voice asks, while someone shakes at his arm and tugs his hand. He opens his eyes; he is in the great baroque auditorium, with the lights ablaze. The orchestra has left the pit, the curtain is down, the stacks of boxes high above him are emptying of the party officials, the generals, the décolletée ladies. 'I hope you like it, they make it very well, I think,' says Lubijova, her hand on his arm, 'Of course, that poor boy, for him it is very difficult. He asks himself, is that man a woman, or the woman a man? And if there is this confusion, how many more? No wonder he is puzzled, and cannot believe his eyes or his senses.' 'Quite,' says Petworth. 'But in the ending all comes clear, if not in the way those people intend,' says Lubijova, 'Well, for an oper, such confusions are essential. Always an oper is a little bit erotical. Now, do you like to go in the foyer and make a promenade?' 'Do I?' asks Petworth, looking around. 'Yes, you do,' says Lubijova, firmly, pulling her stole around her, and rising, 'That is what we always like to do at the interlude.' 'Perhaps you like to visit also the men's room,' says Plitplov, solicitously, from the row behind, 'The next act is very long, and I will come with you.' 'Don't you like to take a drink that is a bit like champagne?' asks Lubijova, leading the way toward the aisle, 'Or if you like it, a pancake that is often very good? And perhaps also you will see your nice lady in red who likes to look out for you.' 'I don't think she was looking for me,' says Petworth, struggling along behind. 'Of course for you,' says Lubijova, 'Do you think we do not know what is your favourite interest?'

In the wide aisle, the people flow toward the exit; in her stole, Lubijova hurries in front. Following, Petworth stumbles, over, he finds, Plitplov, who has somehow managed to drop his programme and has bent down to retrieve it. 'My good friend,' hisses Plitplov, rising suddenly, and clutching urgently at Petworth's sleeve, 'don't you see now how foolish you have been?' 'Foolish?' asks Petworth, looking at him. 'Please talk quietly, pretend you discuss the opera,' says Plitplov, walking beside him, 'Of course, you have compromised everyone who is your friend. Now that one, your guide, knows everything. She sees right to your heart. Of course she knows what relations you have made this afternoon. And with what a nice lady.' 'That was a private matter,' says Petworth. 'Oh, my friend,' says Plitplov, 'Do you think you are in the Cambridge of Russell? What is a private matter? You cause trouble for that lady, I think also for me. Do you see I cannot trust you any more? And so you think this work contains a problematic of identity? Of course, you are right, with your sharp critical acumen. Ah, Miss Lubijova, I hope we don't make you wait. We dispute a little this opera.' 'But you miss the promenade,' says Lubijova, leading them out into the foyer, 'And I think that is really why people come to an oper. To see and to be seen. It is one of our events, don't you like to join it?' 'My dear lady,' says Plitplov, bowing, 'Clearly you are our guide.' Petworth looks around; the foyer has been strangely transformed. Evidently many intervening doors have been thrown open, to create a long curving corridor that leads, through plush passages, from one mirrored room to another, in a great circle round the entire building.

And round the opened-out concourse the people walk, in stately procession, some in one direction, some in the other: the party officials, the military figures, the décolletée ladies. The clothes are fine, the dresses bright, the shirt fronts glow; they walk slowly, as if to some civil dance, the music from the opera still in their heads. Some carry glasses of sparkling wine, others fine food on plates; the high-ranking officer walks by, on his arm the cleavaged lady, her hair in a bun, her body seemingly split bare and open down past the ribcage, and each of them carries a large ice-cream, topped with artificial foam. 'They say if you walk here at the oper you will soon see everyone in the world you know,' says Lubijova, as they join the moving slow circle, with Petworth to one side of her, Plitplov to the other. 'Of course not everybody likes that,' says Plitplov. 'I think now you are learning our country very well,' says Lubijova, 'You see our academical life, at close quarter. Our literary life, at very close quarter. And now our cultural life, which all support, the workers and their wives.' 'Oh, these are the workers and their wives?' asks Plitplov, chuckling. 'Oh, who do you like to say they are?' asks Lubijova. 'Of course,' says Plitplov, smiling, 'The apparatchiks and their mistresses. 'Well, there are workers of the head and the hand,' says Lubijova. 'And some other parts of the body also,' says Plitplov, 'You know what we say, some advance on their knees, some on their backs. Well, I think it is not hard to recognize those who make a horizontal progress.' 'Ah, I understand you,' says Lubijova, 'You like to say that the wives of our leaders are horizontals.' 'So you admit they are our leaders, not the workers,' says Plitplov. 'So you accuse our party officials of sexual crimes?' says Lubijova.

'Well, my good old friend,' says Plitplov, suddenly putting out his hand to Petworth, 'I hope you enjoy your last night in Slaka. I am afraid this occasion is not so pleasant for me. I think I go now, so let us say farewell.' 'Oh, no, you don't leave?' cries Lubijova, smiling. 'I expect my wife has a headache, and she does not see me all day,' says Plitplov, 'Also you know I rose very early to complete my businesses, so I might hear a little piece of your lecture and make a lunch with you. It has not been a day of great pleasures, but I try to do my duty. Still, I know now you have this guide who is watching you. I hope you will be careful in your journey through the forest.' 'I'm sorry to have disappointed you,' says Petworth, 'But I hope we'll meet when I come back to Slaka.' 'Oh, I don't think it,' says Plitplov, 'I like to make many affairs all over the country.' 'Comrade Petwurt also,' says Lubijova. 'So I say goodbye, my friend,' says Plitplov, 'Take please a very good care. You are not always so sensible. And when you turn back to England, give please my love to your Lottie. You know I am fond of her. Tell her I am well, except for some headaches. Also that I succeed quite well, despite some petty criticisms and enemies. Perhaps she gave you a message for me when you telephoned to her?' 'Well, no,' says Petworth. 'Oh, yes your telephone call tonight,' says Lubijova, 'It was successful? I hope you did not forget that important thing I have arranged for you?' 'No, I didn't forget it,' says Petworth, 'I just wasn't able to make it.' 'You don't make it?' asks Lubijova, stopping suddenly. 'No, I reached the hotel desk just too late,' says Petworth, 'I was only a few seconds after six, but they wouldn't let me call.'

In the great mirrored corridor, under the gleaming chandeliers, Lubijova stands and stares at Petworth. The promenading circle behind them, halted in its passage, backs up; somewhere a glass is dropped. 'Oh, really, yes, what a pity,' cries Lubijova, angrily, 'How my nose bleeds for you. Yes, it is very difficult to leave a lecture at noon and be at a hotel desk by six.' 'So you don't speak to your Lottie?' asks Plitplov. 'You go off all afternoon with your lady writer, and then you are late to call your wife?' says Lubijova, 'And what does she think now? Don't you wonder it?' Their movement arrested, the promenaders behind are forming a curious circle around the quarrel: the party officials in their evening dress, the generals and the air-force marshals, the Vietnamese ambassador, perhaps, in his denim workclothes, with his retinue, the Russian ambassadress, perhaps, in her tiara, with hers. 'I'll call her tomorrow,' says Petworth, 'I don't think she'll worry.' 'You do not call her tomorrow,' says Lubijova, 'Tomorrow you go to Glit, very early. And from there a call to the West takes perhaps one week. Also don't think I try to arrange it. I have tried for you, Petwurt, and I see what you do.' Troubled, disoriented, Petworth stares round the curious grotesque circle of official faces, and it even seems that there are some he recognizes. But if this confusion, how many more; he cannot believe his eyes or his senses. The chandeliers are bright, and even the ceiling is mirrored; up there is Petworth, standing on his head. Looking up, Petworth suddenly sees himself enfolded by the redness of a dress; then lips are descending on his face, a kiss is planted on his cheek. 'Angus darling, how wonderful,' says Budgie Steadiman, fine in a long velvet dress and cloak, with a tiara, 'Aren't you enjoying the opera? And don't you wish I was in it?'

'Oh, Budgie,' says Petworth. 'Petwurt, Petwurt,' says Lubijova, 'Not another one. I think you are impossible.' 'Who's your nice little friend?' asks Budgie, 'You must meet mine.' A small, round, bald man in a worn dinner jacket, holding a cigar, steps forward: 'Hey, Professorim Petwort and guide,' he says, 'Still very tough lady, hah, I think so.' 'Good evening, Mr Tankic,' says Petworth. 'Felix is engaged tonight,' says Budgie, 'And, yearning for opera, I succumbed to the attentions of another.' Tankic grins mischievously, and raises his cigar in salutation: 'You keep secret?' he says, 'A little assignation.' 'And dear Mr Plitplov,' says Budgie, 'My second favourite dinner guest.' 'Oh, do we meet somewhere before?' asks Plitplov, slinking obscurely toward the safety of the crowd. 'Only at my drunken table last night,' says Budgie, 'Strange how one always meets the people one knows at an opera.' 'Who is this?' whispers Lubijova, 'Who is your friend?' 'It's awfully rude to whisper,' says Budgie Steadiman, 'Come into our box. We're drinking champagne.' I do not think we are expected,' says Lubijova. 'In official box, all are expected,' says Tankic, lifting a velvet curtain, to reveal the dark red gloom of the space inside, and the bright lights of the auditorium gleaming beyond. 'And then we're going on to a strip club,' says Budgie, 'You really must come, Angus. I should love to take you there and strip you. Oh, do meet the rest of my party.' In the darkness of the box, on red plush chairs, two people are sitting, a couple, holding hands. 'Oh, well, it is the feder man,' says Professor Rom Rum, rising from the darkness and smiling, smart in a tailed evening suit, 'You enjoy the piece?' 'And you must meet . . .' says Budgie. 'I have,' says Petworth, staring at the other chair, in which sits, not in batik but in a low-cut black gauzed dress, the blonde magical realist novelist Katya Princip.

8 – TOUR.

I

In the bright clean early sun of the next morning, Petworth sits amid ferns in the great quiet lobby at the Hotel Slaka, awaiting the arrival of his guide. The arrangements for his departure from Slaka have gone competently well. A limping porter has brought down from the gaunt, troubled spaces of his great bedroom the luggage – the blue suitcase, the battered briefcase of lectures, the depleted plastic bag that still declares 'Say Hello to the Good Buys from Heathrow' – which Petworth has quickly and carelessly packed in the half dawn before going down to early breakfast; he has eaten that breakfast, the same breakfast as yesterday, and the day before, though he has made an order for something quite different. He has collected his passport from the blue Cosmoplot girl who bustles under the portraits of Marx and Wanko at the great desk in the customless lobby, and it rests hardbacked in his pocket; he has signed the great bill that will go to the Mun'stratuu, the cost of his three painful nights. The angled sun falls across the dust and into the red plastic chairs of the lobby, where only a few figures move, and where they are just taking down the shutters on the small stall that is marked LUTTU. It falls, too, on the ancient façades around the quiet square outside, where only one or two pink trams move, and even the newspaper seller has not yet begun his work of the day. Petworth sits in his chair and looks out through the great plateglass windows, looking out for a sight of the big black car that, according to the

267

programme he also carries in his pocket, will take him off with Lubijova on his journey through the forest, his journey to new lectures, new intellectual duties, to the familiar story of his travels. It is good to be moving again; to leave, on a clean new day, Slaka behind, its confusions, its pains, its sadnesses, its treacheries, to go back to the life he should never have left.

In the corner of the square, a big black Russian Volga, with a great grinning grille, comes out of shade into sunlight. It moves slowly, and stops under the hotel portico. In the front is a big-necked driver in a grey shirt; in the back sits Lubijova, in the coat in which she had met him at the airport. Lubijova gets out, and waves through the glass; Petworth gets up, and gathers together his baggage. 'Oh, you are ready, really I didn't expect it,' she says, coming over to him, swinging her shoulderbag, 'And do you sign already the bill at the desk?' 'Yes, I've done it,' says Petworth. 'And your baggages all here,' says Lubijova, 'Today you are very efficient.' 'I am,' says Petworth. 'Well, I think perhaps that means you want to be very good on our trip,' says Lubijova, 'I hope it. Of course already I worry about it. You know, Petwurt, you are not like my other tourists. But now we are going to be together really for quite a long time. So I think we try a bit to enjoy it, don't you say so?' 'Yes,' says Petworth, 'Of course.' 'And I understand perhaps you are very sad of last night,' says Lubijova, 'You have had a disappointment, I know it. I think I realize very well why you are so sick in that nightclub.' 'I was sick in the nightclub, was I?' asks Petworth. 'Oh, don't you remember it?' asks Lubijova, 'Do you make your mind a nothing? Well, perhaps you are right. Perhaps what is good is a new start for everything. Really we could have a nice time, I believe it. And do you see what a nice sun we have made for you, for your journey?' 'Yes, it's a lovely day,' says Petworth. 'So, no more things you must do?' asks Lubijova, 'You don't forget some things, your shirt at the laundry? You carry your passport? You pay them all your small bills? You pack your suit away?

You don't want to make a nice kiss to the girl at the desk?' 'No, thank you,' says Petworth, 'Yes, I'm ready.'

'So we go,' says Lubijova, 'Give me your documents case, and then we can move these baggages by ourselves. Look, it is a very fine car. Now you will ride like an apparatchik. I am sorry there are no curtains today for the windows, but even for a famous lecturer there is not always everything. Give this driver your baggages, he will put them away.' Outside, in the sun, the big-necked driver meets them and takes the luggage round to the car's great bulbous rear. 'Now, where do you like to sit?' asks Lubijova, 'In the front with a view, or in the back with your guide?' 'Oh, in the back,' says Petworth. 'Good,' says Lubijova, 'Then I believe you forgive me just a little for being angered of you last night. You understand me now, I think. I like to look after you and I am always for your good. I think you have learned a little lesson.' The big grey driver gets in; it is possible to recognize, from the familiar wart on the back of his neck, that this is the same man who, two days ago, took them up the hill to the Restaurant Propp. He turns, and Lubijova nods to him; he sounds an unnecessary flourish on a very fancy klaxon, starts the engine, and moves out into the square. 'So, now for more than a week you are leaving Slaka,' says Lubijova, 'Please say your goodbye to it. Do you think you will miss it? Perhaps now these things have happened you do not. In any case you go back there again before you turn back to England. Remember, you come back for our day of National Rejoicering, before you fly away. You will think it is just for you.' The car circles the square that Petworth has gazed down on so often from his great balconied bedroom, where the raucous nymphs play on the ceiling; now it turns up the narrow street, above which Marx, Lenin and Wanko hang, familiar now, on their wires. Petworth turns back to the square for a last view, to see that a big grey truck is stopping in it, in the empty early morning, just below the sign that says SCH'VEPPUU. The great, swaying hydraulic arm begins to ascend, with on the platform at the end of it three rocking workmen; then the square goes from sight.

'Plazscu P'rtyuu, you know that,' says Lubijova, pointing to the left, where the great vacant public open space is just visible, empty except for the guards standing like stone round Grigoric's tomb, 'Yes, it is pretty, the journey to Glit. The way is through the forest, you will like it. We take perhaps three hours, so I think you relax. You will see many things, the real visage of the country. In the big city, that is not the true life of a people. Perhaps all cities are everywhere the same. But always the country is different and more real, don't you say?' 'Yes,' says Petworth, looking out from the car at the usual central boulevard that leads through the city, where the neon signs still flash. 'Of course I will look after you to the best, and explain you what you see,' says Lubijova, 'You know I am very good guide. I remind you, I will be with you always, I come everywhere. Also don't forget, on these travels you do not take photographs, unless in the correct places. Especially forbidden to the camera, our industrial projects and our railways engines. They are very pretty, but you must not make an image of them. For other things, please ask me first.' 'I don't have a camera,' says Petworth. 'Then we do not worry, not a problem. So, we ride like a king and queen, and we stay at the nice hotels,' says Lubijova, as the car speeds on out of the city, passing the university to the left, with its statue of Hrovdat, and the great monumental crosses of a roadside cemetery to the right, 'Don't you like to wave through the window at all the people? But really there are no people, we are so early. And now we nearly leave the city. Over there the power station and the cathedral. Oh, what a pity, I think you didn't see it.' 'No,' says Petworth. 'Yes, always you are too busy,' says Lubijova, 'You like to follow a different religion, I have noticed. Well, it is not a matter, it is not so worth a visit.' 'No, I suppose not,' says Petworth.

The black car drives on, at high speed; the bright sun shines. It lights up the cloud of white dust that rises in the air above the cement factory, the plume of orange pollution spurting high from the huge ejaculating chimneys of the power station. It lights up the great white cliffs of the high-stacked workers' apartments, which, blank and repetitious, could well be anywhere in the world, except for the distinctly Slakan note of void public space, absence of cars, want of human figures. It lights up the hazy dust storm blowing between the buildings; it lights up the rubble and rubbish that is piled in the gutters, looking like the shifted snows of winter. It lights up, in the main road in front of them, a gang of soldiers who, so visible everywhere, are active here too, working in their vests on the roadbed, digging out holes and filling them with rocks. Their jackets and guns are spread over the white-trunked trees that line the route; a big military truck stands by, with an officer on top of the bonnet. 'Always you see we are working,' says Lubijova, 'Here we make better our roads, always good. And always our industry, developing all round you. Here are many great and startling projects.' Petworth looks round, and sees a large lumber yard, in which vast hoses are spraying outjets of water onto high stacks of wood, turning them black. Then, suddenly, peripheral Slaka, a city without suburbs, ceases; there is straight road and brown plain in front of them, and beside the straight road a small wooden hut, with many Cyrillic signs on it, and in it a number of the blue armed men. The driver turns and speaks. 'Tells he must just go to this police post, and report where into the country he takes you,' says Lubijova. The car stops, and the man goes into the post; Lubijova turns to Petworth, smiles, and puts her finger to her nose. 'Perhaps with him you try to be just a little cautious, if you can,' she says, 'You know these people, they are such officials, and they make report. See, he comes back, it is all right. And now we take you into the dark forest.'

The black car moves again, up the white straight road that cuts ahead over the dark brown plain; sun splashes into it. In her corner, Lubijova sits, her shoulderbag on her knee; Petworth sinks into the limousine's deep cushions, his head on the crocheted headrest, and gives in to the innocence of sight, the flat pleasure of the unfamiliar world before words and the mind have familiarized and named it. 'Now, do you remember where you make this journey?' asks Lubijova, 'I hope you do, it is all written in your paper. Today is Glit. That is a nice place, very old, and we spend there three nights of a very old hotel of a typical kind. There is a fine castle and we will go there; also here you speak two lectures at the university, you know what they are. Then is Saturday and we leave, to Nogod. This is also a good place, of course it is, because we have there a whole weekend and we would not want to make a weekend in a bad place. There will be some amusements, I expect, and you find there a lake with fishes. We go there with a train, because this driver must turn back before then to be with his wife. On Monday you make also two lectures, and then to Provd by another train. Provd is different, you will impress. It is a part of our country that had some backward people and was very silly, but now they make many remarkable new projects. You will see them. Here also two lectures. Then on the night in Wednesday, we take a plane, because it is quick, and come back here again to Slaka, so you can see the National Rejoicerings. Rejoicerings?' 'Rejoicings,' says Petworth, 'Celebrations.' 'Well, permit please just one little mistake,' says Lubijova, 'You know usually I am always translating you very well. I hope you are glad of it, now I am with you always.' 'I am indeed,' says Petworth.

The sun shines in, the great car speeds across the wide flat plain, which spreads out toward a distant horizon; here, faintly seen, are the mountains toward which they are heading. If landscapes have the variety of paintings, some coloured and warm, some plain and pastelled, thinks Petworth, staring out, then this is a landscape of very limited palate: matt, abstract, simplified, almost black and white. Few things move in it; there are no hedges or divisions. Wide tracts of green-brown space spread everywhere; in sheens of light, water sits in moraines and marshes. 'The Vronopian plain, very typical,' says Lubijova at his side, 'Also I think a little bit dull. Quite different are the forests and the mountains, where all our visitors like to come. You will enjoy them very much.' Heat and stillness prevail; on the green-brown land, a few white specks wander, the small ducks that move everywhere; occasionally great static flocks of white and brown sheep appear, guarded by single, rigid, upright human figures, shepherds who in their black suits and white shirts somehow resemble Methodist lay readers. The heat grows; Petworth begins to nod. 'Here more duckses,' says Lubijova, tugging at his arm, 'And do you remember the word for it? Do you get proficient now in our language?' 'Crak'akuu,' says Petworth. 'Oh, you are very good,' says Lubijova, 'What a pity that in the towns we go to those words are no good.' 'No good?' asks Petworth. 'Oh, we have so many languages here,' says Lubijova, 'Don't you know it? We are such a mixed people, all different. Of course our government likes very much to help and give us one language so we can talk all to one another. I am sorry, this plain is perhaps too long, but it will be very interesting in one hour. Perhaps you like to make now a little sleep, and I will wake you when you are in nice place? I think you are very tired of last night.' 'I am, rather,' says Petworth.

'Of course,' says Lubijova, 'You had only a very small time at your bed. Perhaps you know now it was not such a good idea to go there to that club, when is finished the oper. But of course you must go, of course you must listen to your lady friend.' 'Who?' asks Petworth. 'Petwurt, you know who,' says Lubijova, 'Your new lady friend, the wild English one who goes with Tankic. Who is she? Where do you meet her?' 'Oh, that's Mrs Steadiman,' says Petworth. 'Oh, she is his wife?' cries Lubijova, 'Really he likes to marry her? Then I think both of you do not choose your ladies very well, she is not such good friend. Once it is famous that all the British are reservated, but not any more, I think.' 'She is quite energetic,' says Petworth. 'Energetic, yes, I think so,' says Lubijova, 'Well, she nearly makes you some very bad trouble. But perhaps you think it is nice to visit a prison.' 'Not at all,' says Petworth. 'Well, I think you nearly did it, last night,' says Lubijova, 'You know, Petwurt, to me, you are such a strange man. Always you are making yourself problems that are ridiculous and no one knows how to help you. How can I understand you?' 'It seems very understandable to me,' says Petworth. 'But don't you think of anything serious?' asks Lubijova, 'But, no, I suppose you think it is nicer to go to a topless.' 'A topless what?' asks Petworth. 'Of course, that topless club where the strip lady makes the dance of the seven scarves. And you are taking one of those scarves to give to your energetic English lady, and the policemen make you turn it back to her.' 'I did that?' asks Petworth. 'You don't remenber it?' asks Lubijova. 'No,' says Petworth, 'Was it before or after I was sick?' 'Oh, before,' says Lubijova, 'It is lucky you were sick only after those policemen take you outside. When you had poured your drink all over the suit of poor Professor Rum.' 'I poured drink over Professor Rum?' asks Petworth. 'Of course you were angry,' says Lubijova, 'You did not like him to leave with your good friend the lady writer. You are lucky he understands it, and likes to be gracious and forget about it. Also that Mr Tankic knows so well those policemen, and comes with you when they take you in the police van to your hotel. Or perhaps you would not now be here with me.'

In front of them the driver, with his square neck, sits solidly. Evidently he possesses some kind of élite or official status; for, when he sounds his curious klaxon, cars draw to the side to let him pass, horse-drawn carts tug suddenly to a halt, even peasants leap into the ditches, under their own volition. Occasionally the unobligingness of one of the drivers of the few cars he passes offends him; he sticks a baton through the window, draws to a halt, and walks back to speak to the errant owner. 'You see he likes to treat you as very special guest,' says Lubijova, 'Don't you think you should be responsible?' 'Yes,' says Petworth, desperately delving in memory to try to recover the events of the previous late evening. He remembers some things: the departure in a crowd from the great warm womb of the opera house; the group of well-dressed uncertain people standing in the warm street, disputing where to go next; the cramped taxi ride, with a backside imprinted on his knee; the dim dull cellar of a state nightclub, a cellar and nothing more, where the people sit on iron chairs at plastic tables, drinking a warm light beer, the only drink on offer; a limp floorshow, with a gloomy Fifties singer in a pink ballgown, a choir of ten militiamen singing upliftingly in close harmony in their uniforms, and yes, one small blonde strip artiste, slowly and artistically removing gauzy veils from her thin body to the drum-rolls of a besuited, bespectacled three-piece band, and wearing, in addition to her diaphanous harem costume, a large earthenware pot on the top of her head. He remembers more: the disappointment when the seventh veil around the thin thighs is about to fall, and the lights cut, leaving only, in some bleak and deceitful exchange, one single spotlight which illuminates no longer the girl, who has disappeared into total blackness, but the earthenware pot, which wobbles, teeters, is steadied by a momentary hand, held upright, and the act ends. But the faces of his company are hard to recover, though he suspects that round the table were a laughing Budgie, a grinning Tankic, a silent Rum, a with-drawn Princip, an icy Lubijova, with only Plitplov having neglected to come.

The driver turns and says something: 'Tells here in this village there is a different name for a goat,' says Lubijova, 'And look now, here start our dark forests, very green. Also some mountains you cannot see so well, because there comes now a fog, but do not worry, I will describe you. Now do you see what a nice tour we make? And now is not so far to Glit. Don't you like it?' 'Yes,' says Petworth, looking out at a small huddled settlement of unpainted wooden houses, and the rising forested hills, and a hazy solid mass beyond, 'So what else happened, last night?' 'Really you don't remember it?' asks Lubijova, 'Well, perhaps you must ask your energetic friend.

I do not think she is the best for you. Really, in my country, it is not so polite, if a stripteasing is just a little bit boring, to stand up in a club and make a better one yourself.' 'She did that?' asks Petworth. 'And you helped her,' says Lubijova, 'Why do you think are coming all those policemen? I don't think it is a wonder your lady-writer disappoints, and is sad, and likes to leave.' 'I see,' says Petworth, 'She left then, did she?' 'She tried it,' says Lubijova, 'And then you tried it to stop her. Naturally Professor Rum speaks to you, he is her protector. And then you are very noisy and asking for a fight of him. I did not think it of you, Comrade Petwurt. Of course I know you are jealous and you like to think she likes you. But I do not think it was so intelligent to do this, do you?' 'Well, no,' says Petworth. 'Don't miss please our forest, it is very good,' says Lubijova, 'Our tourists enjoy it very much. And here still live, do you know, the wolfs and the wild pigs. Strange things happen here, don't you wish you could get out to look? But, of course, you cannot. We must go on.' 'Quite,' says Petworth, 'And what happened then?' 'Oh, you poured your drink, and the policemen taked you outside,' says Lubijova, 'And that is how you go to your hotel, not a very good way for a visiting lecturer.' 'No,' says Petworth, 'And Katya? She went with Professor Rum?' 'Oh, Petwurt,' says Lubijova, 'Don't you understand it, I have always been right. I have told you it is not so wise to like so much this lady. Well, now you know that one is not what she seems. She is strange, well, of course, she is a writer. Now, over there, the Storkian mountains, do you see? Many people like to come there in the summer to make the trails of horseback, and in the winter to make ski. I wish you could see them better, but one day you will come back.'

The road, lined with thicket and trees, now climbs a rocky defile, reaches a peak, stares down into a deep gorge. In the black car, high in the dark forest, Petworth stares into one too. 'She is not what she seems?' he asks. 'I try to make you understand,' says Lubijova, 'And I think she does also, with her story of the witch.' 'I see,' says Petworth. 'And last night you are very silly,' says Lubijova, 'And she will not like to see you again. Oh, Petwurt, I am sorry for you, I know how you like to think. She is free, she is courageous, she is a good woman who waits just for you. But really you know nothing, about our life here, what it is like, how we must live. Perhaps she does like you, it could be so. But to survive here, that is not simple, when we must always be reliable. And I think even your friend likes to survive, that is why she needs her protector, why she goes with Professor Rum. Of course he is a little bit dull, a little bit old, perhaps nothing much there in the bed. But he is important man in the academy, and also very high in the party, and with our Politburo. People need such friends, who can look after them very well. Perhaps you think you can do it, but I don't think so.' 'No,' says Petworth. 'We have a saying in my country,' says Lubijova. 'Some advance on their knees, others on their backs,' says Petworth. 'Oh, do you know it?' says Lubijova, 'Perhaps you say it in your country too. But you must understand her position.' 'Very well,' says Petworth. 'She is artist, a little bit rebel,' says Lubijova, 'She likes to take a chance, perhaps not too much, or she would not be success. But you must ask why they permit her to write those books. Always there is a reason. Do you know what we call that here?' 'No,' says Petworth. 'Well, courage with the permission of the police,' says Lubijova, 'And to have it you must be always clever. And now you know why those two are always needing each other.' 'Yes,' says Petworth, staring down into the deep gorge that drops away from them beside the road.

'So I hope now you understand something,' says Lubijova, 'Why always we see them together. Of course it is a very good exchange. He likes her charms, and recommends everywhere her work; think how nice for him to be seen with a person who is beautiful and respected, and has a great talent and a little courage. And for her, well, she is safe, you should please. It is not so strange, such things happen in all countries.' 'Yes,' says Petworth. 'And so they go together, always, in the oper, in the theatre; even at an official lunch for an important foreign visitor, like Comrade Petwurt.' 'Yes,' says Petworth. 'And there you make a meeting,' says Lubijova, 'And who knows, perhaps she is a little bored, perhaps he has made a bad love, perhaps it is important to show that she is not one of those bureaucrats at all. So she makes a friend of you, and everyone notices. But of course it must have its purpose.' 'What purpose?' asks Petworth. 'Oh, look down there, how far,' cries Lubijova, suddenly clutching Petworth's arm, 'Of course that is expert driver, but I still frighten. This is bad road, and there are many accidents.' Petworth looks down from the road that narrows, dips, bends, turns this way and that in great hairpin bends that slowly bring them toward the green base of the great gorge below them. 'It's all right,' he says, patting the hand on his arm. 'Oh, Petwurt, I regret,' says Lubijova, looking at him, 'I hope you don't disappoint with what I tell you, I think you do. Perhaps you have made some feelings about it that are a bit indiscreet. Well, please, I think you try to forget them. Perhaps already things begin to change. Perhaps Professor Rum is not so powerful, perhaps is time to make some new friends, there are changes now in our country. Always it is well to know someone new as well as someone who is old. But I don't think that new one can really be you, Petwurt. Do you think you can really help a person like that?' 'Well, no, of course I can't,' says Petworth. 'Oh, what a shame, poor Petwurt,' says Lubijova, looking at him, her thin white hands clutching her shoulderbag, 'You come, you find your sexual princess, and then, what a pity, she is more complicate than you thought. Well, you know, people are strange in all countries, you must expect that. And in another place such signs are not easy to read. That is why you have with you a guide, I think, to read the signs. Oh, look, this famous waterfall, do you see it? Do you know what we call it? The waterfall of the virgin. I don't know why, there are none in my country. But it is very pretty.'

A great blind bend comes up in front of them; as they approach it, the big-necked driver suddenly turns his head, and begins to talk. 'Always they do this,' says Lubijova, 'I interpret you. Tells we are almost to Glit. Tells you will see it when we are come across the next hill.' Round the bend, down the twisting slope, and into the bottom of the gorge the huge black Volga goes; then it ascends again, climbing up till it reaches a new summit. From the summit there is a view; another large gorge, with thickly wooded slopes, and in the romantic landscape high houses, huddled together, red and gold roofs, a castle up on an eminence, with sharp, pencil-like towers. 'Oh, do you see it, Glit?' asks Lubijova, 'Now we are really in another place. You know, everything is different, the people, the language, even the foods. Do you know this place was once very famous, more than Slaka? Here came all the trade, many secret spices, some from Tashkent, carpets from the Turk, silk from the east. Always we like to tell many stories about Glit. It is very nice, always I like this town. Of course there is a fine socialist reorganization, but it is still not so very different from the old time. Naturally, many tourists like to come here for our fine mountains and valleys, and also the beautiful altarpieces of the churches. But you do not interest in those. Also there are many opportunities of leisures both in the country and in the town.' 'I'm sure,' says Petworth. 'We say, those who see Glit always come back,' says Lubijova, 'Look now please, the gateway of the town, very old. Over there a tower with a gold roof that is very interesting. A lady in a typical dress of the region. Notice the balconies in the style of the Turk. They tell of Glit that outside every house hangs one pot of flowers, and those flowers are the souls of those inside. Look into the rooms, you see some women ply at old trades. Now the market place, how those peasants love to sell the fruit and the flowers. Don't you like?' 'It's very attractive,' says Petworth.

'Of course not all is old here,' says Lubijova, 'There is a new town with a universitet and a technic, you will see it tomorrow. But today I think you like to enjoy just this nice town. Here a river, isn't it clean and deep, as always in the mountains. Our people like to fish here, what a pity you do not do it. And here, look now, it is our hotel, I hope you like. It is very ancient and very typical.' There is a carillon from the klaxon, and the big black Volga halts outside the small low building, which has a restaurant garden, filled with umbrellas, overlooking the deep rushing river. Taking their luggage inside, they go into a low shady room; at the desk there is no girl in Cosmoplot uniform, but an old woman in a headscarf. 'She likes please your passport and my permission of travel,' says Lubijova, 'Of course I stay here too. Now, go with that boy, he takes you to your room, I will attend all these papers.' Petworth is led along a corridor to a room, a small clean room, with a very narrow bed, a quiet innocent room with no misery attached, where nothing has yet happened. He puts down his luggage; water is splashing outside the window, the gurgle of the local river, quieter than Slakan traffic, a small hint of something closer to peace, though Petworth does not quite feel entirely peaceful. Putting away his battered briefcase, unpacking his blue suitcase, he remembers that there is an historical world, and that history means trouble. There is a knock at the door of his room: 'It is Mari, your guide,' says a voice, 'That room is good for you? It makes you comfortable?' 'It's very nice,' says Petworth, opening the door. 'Not so big, like in Slaka,' says Marisja, looking around, 'But for the country it is nice. Mine is just like it, but you have a river. Well, my dear Petwurt, you have an afternoon, all free. What do you like to do? You can make a tour by your own, or if you like it I can guide you somewhere. I would like to show you a castle, if you want it.' 'Please,' says Petworth. 'It is high,' says Lubijova, 'But I think you are still quite young. Please to finish your unpack and then you will find me in the lobby.'

When they go out of the hotel, Lubijova takes him by the arm. 'The car has gone, you see, that Volga,' she says, 'We are not his only work. And so we are together by ourselves. You know, always I like this town.' And indeed Glit seems a likeable town, with old balconied houses, narrow streets busy with people, high stone towers, squares crammed with old trucks and horse-drawn carts. Girls walk by in bright peasant costume; men sit by the walls on sacks. They begin to mount stone steps that lead them above the town: 'Now we go up quite a long way,' says Lubijova, 'Show me you can do that without a gasp.' But Petworth is gasping by the time they reach the cracked old wooden doors of the castle, flanked by two worn stone lions: 'Well, perhaps you are not so fit,' says Lubijova, pulling at a bell, 'But then of course you are a scholar. Does he come? Yes, he comes.' An old man in felt slippers opens the door, to admit them into a cobbled court-yard. 'You know he tells we are the only ones?' says Lubijova, 'Well, it is late for the tours. Now I explain you this castle. Once there were many rulers from elsewhere who liked to oppress us. They liked to live in this castle that looks at the city and watch what the people did. If they made some money, these men took some. If they had nice wives or daughters, also they took them. Look, here is a well, very deep. But you must not drink the water of it, do you know why? It is because here were dropped the people of the town who were not so good, who did not like to pass away their wives or their daughters or their gelt, their coins. Throw down a stone, see how deep. Yes, they were very bad, those people. It was not so nice to live when they were here. But the people had their secret, it was inside them, they knew those big proud rulers in their fine clothes were not real. They had just invented themselves and they could blow away in the air. And they blew away, and they are dead. And now the people have this castle, which they can enjoy, and because those bad people left one good thing, we can forgive them just a little. But not too much, just a little.'

There are great towers going up into the air; up on the towers, pigeons coo, dropping their detritus onto history. 'Over here, Petwurt,' says Lubijova, 'This is, what do you say, the lattice?' 'The latrine,' says Petworth. 'Well, in case you do not think it, here you see that some things in the world are improved,' says Lubijova, 'You would not like to make

281

business in that. I think now we go inside, and then I take you up a tower. Here a capella, notice please the altarpiece. A very good carver has made it. Do you recognize his subject? This is Saint Michael, see how he battles with the worm.' 'The worm?' says Petworth. 'What do you like to call it?' asks Marisja. 'A dragon,' says Petworth. 'Well, we teach something to each other,' says Marisja, 'It is a dragon. Next time I shall be better guide. And here in the glass tomb, what do you call it? Is it a skillet?' 'No,' says Petworth, looking into an exposed tomb, cased with bubbled glass, in which there lies a skull, a ribcage, a bone system, all still clad in the tatters of some ancient finery, the scraps of a dusty feathered hat, embroidered coat and waistcoat, frogged trousers, high boots, 'A skillet's something you cook with. This is a skeleton.' 'What a pity he has no one now to mend his cloths,' says Marisja, 'But, you know, I think he lies there to teach you something. I hope you learn, or for all these years he has been wasting his time.' 'I think I get the point,' says Petworth. 'Over here, the nose mummy of a saint in a case,' says Marisja, 'And then we go up a tower that is very nice.' From the tower, there is an oceanic, pastoral horizon to look at, with waving treetops. 'Well,' says Marisja, when they reach the top, 'My dear Mr Petwurt, I think today you have seen really a castle. Not like the other time, when you made your tour in a different place. Oh, don't worry, I am not going to ask you more about your day with the lady writer. I think here we like to forget her. And it is easy, with such a nice view.'

Later, as the sun has begun to fade, they go back down toward the old town of Glit. 'Do you like to eat something?' asks Marisja, 'I know near here a place you will like. You can try in it the special eatings of Glit.' In a back street, they find a small old restaurant, with low ceilings; a good many people occupy its tables. The occupiers are, it seems, tourists, for some are talking in German, some in what Petworth thinks is Bulgarian; they are tourists not of Petworth's kind, but those for whom travel has something to do with pleasure and desire, and they are happy, happiness being what tourists are supposed to have. The menu comes, and a familiar litany begins. 'Now, what do you like?' Marisja asks, 'Here is the veal of a sheep, or do you like to eat a brain? Here a soup with feet in it, and here a typical thing of the place, a cream with a cumber made of the chords of the yurt.' Petworth stares at the written list, but the words are new again, and his head is tired, from a sleepless night, an uphill walk, a rural air, a beating sun. The pleasure of the strange is not what it was: 'An ordinary soup and a plain omelette,' he says. 'Oh, Petwurt, I disappoint,' says Marisja, 'I thought you came to enjoy all our customs? You told me that, do you remember it, right when I met you at the airport, and you wanted my embrace? But perhaps you do not delight yourself so much now? Perhaps you don't like my country?' 'Of course I do,' says Petworth. 'Do you know how you look?' asks Lubijova, 'Like a girl who sulks because her love had gone wrong. You like to be British, so polite, but really you are very obvious. Well, I shall take a brain. I like to enjoy myself. You know this is a very special experience for me?' 'Is it?' asks Petworth, 'Why?'

'If you knew just a little my country, you would understand, but, poor Petwurt, really you don't know very much about the world outside your head, I think. Here it is not so easy to travel around, and stay in a provincial hotel, and eat like this in a typical restaurant. You must be a very good person with an excellent file at the police, and you must get a certain permission. Well, dear Mr Petwurt, I have an excellent file, and you are my permission. If you like to disappoint now, well, please do it, but don't want me to share it. I like to make a very good time. I know you travel a lot, it is all ordinary; this, for you, but it is special for me. Don't forget, I am not some lady writer. I don't have a great courage, just a very dull life at Slaka. I do not have admiring lovers and a famous academician who watches out always for me. I do not write and imagine wonderful things, I just make some interpretations, and read some menus for you, and keep you away from bad troubles. And I hope you don't think that is so easy, do you? So I shall have a brain and, if you want a good advice from your guide who tries always to help you, you will forget this lady. She is well looked after.' 'Looked after?' asks Petworth, 'Has something happened to her?' 'I don't think so,' says Marisja Lubijova, 'But perhaps she makes some travels too. She has some little troubles you have helped her with. Our writers' union has a fine summer house on Lake Katuruu. Perhaps she likes to go there. It is very peaceful and there she can meet some more writers and discuss there her obligations in a clear and constructive way. She will be very well there and you do not need even to think about it.' 'She's been sent there?' asks Petworth. 'I don't know,' says Marisja, 'Perhaps she remains still in Slaka. They do not tell me these things. Oh, here is the waitress to take an order. Do you like to make it, in the language of Glit? No, all right, I interpret you, I will do it.'

The waitress who takes the order wears under her white apron a hidden black purse, so that she looks pregnant with money. A single candle lights the table, shining on the ringless long white hands, the pale face and blue eyelids, of Marisja Lubijova. 'I am naughty, I order you a brain,' she says, 'Now, do you please forget altogether this lady. I don't think you saw a real person, any more than a real castle. A lady like that is very strange. I know a little bit her story, you remember I gave you her book, do you still have it? You know she has had many husbands, did she tell you so? One was a famous man, a minister, everyone here knew of him, he was popular. Well, one day, this man, he shot himself.' 'I see,' says Petworth, 'How did it happen?' 'I don't know, I don't know everything,' says Marisja, 'But they are happy together, always in public, and then one day no more. She is not with him, then she makes a book, and it is accepted. On the day it is in the bookstore, that man sits at his desk in his very nice dacha, for he is a successful man, and he has somewhere a gun, and he puts it up here and he shoots his head. Who knows why? A marriage is a very secret thing. We do not know who is betrayed, or how. Perhaps even it was not at home, perhaps at work, in the Party. But now she is a famous writer and all want her book, and he is not a minister or anything else. It is not your world, Petwurt.' 'No,' says Petworth. 'Always you are so intense and sad,' says Lubijova, 'Well, that is your privilege. Or perhaps it is the privilege of your people. You expect certain things, like an American, well, we are not the same. We know we have a duty to make some useful lives, and we can be content. You are not content, I think. You do not know why you are in the world, do you?' 'I suppose not,' says Petworth.

'Oh, my dear Petwurt, you are so strange,' says Marisja Lubijova, laughing at him in the candlelight, 'Always you are smoking and drinking and taking black coffee and looking at the girls. Oh, yes, I have seen you, you look so, at all the ones who are nice. And here of course there are many to look at. Our girls are highly pretty and they are feminine without being victims of an oppression. I think this is why Englishmen always like them and want to marry them, now and again.' 'I expect so,' says Petworth. 'Oh, my dear, I think you are a man of many vice,' says Marisja, 'And do you get a great pleasure of your pleasure?' 'Not particularly,' says Petworth. 'No, always you are looking for something, I feel it,' says Marisja, 'But I don't know at all what it is.' 'Neither do I,' says Petworth. 'Do you know what I think?' asks Lubijova, 'I think you have come here to make yourself some guilt. That is why you have come. Well, you have chosen the right place. Here they will be pleased always to hear your confession. I think some people know that already, don't you?' 'Who?' asks Petworth. 'Your good old friend,' says Lubijova, 'Your Plitplov.' 'I'd forgotten him,' says Petworth. 'He will not let you,' says Lubijova, 'After all, he knows so well your wife. What does he know? What does he find out about you?' 'I don't know,' says Petworth. 'You don't like to tell,' says Marisja, 'You know I am your friend.' 'I really don't know,' says Petworth. 'Well, marriage is a secret

thing, we do not know who is betrayed, or how,' says Lubijova, 'Perhaps it is so secret that those who are there do not
know it. But I hope you do not trust him, this Plitplov.'

They sit at their table, in another country; the aproned
waitress comes to them with a bottle of wine. 'And you, are
you married?' asks Petworth, as the waitress applies a knife to
the top of the bottle. 'Oh, me?' asks Lubijova, looking up, 'Do
you think so? Why do you think it?' 'Your name, Lubijova,'
says Petworth. 'Oh, no, it does not mean that,' says Marisja,
'It means I am a woman. Which I think you noticed, I believe
you notice women. Well, I am one of those. It is my maiden's
name.' 'So you're not married,' says Petworth. 'Well, it is
possible,' says Lubijova, 'Often when we marry we keep our
maiden's name. If you like to change it, you must stand in a
line for many hours. So perhaps I am married.' 'But are you?'
asks Petworth. 'You are very interested, of a sudden,' says
Marisja, 'Well, I am and I am not.' 'That makes it much
clearer,' says Petworth. 'You see, once I was, not any more,'
says Marisja Lubijova, 'When I am student, I marry a boy who
liked to be a doctor.' 'Are you divorced?' asks Petworth. 'No,
do you know what that boy did?' asks Marisja, 'He was very
political, his father was high in the Party. So as a doctor he
went away to Vietnam, to help those people against imperial-
ism. And I stay here and make my examen with your Plitplov.'
'And what happened?' asks Petworth. 'Of course he died,' says
Marisja Lubijova, 'Not with a bullet, he caught a small something that was not so small, and he was not such a good doctor
to make better himself. And this is what happened to him, and
also to me.' 'I'm sorry,' says Petworth. 'No, it was not such a
close relation, we were two students who studied together,'
says Marisja, 'But close enough that I have small son. You
must come a bit close for that.' 'A son,' says Petworth, 'Don't
you miss him when you travel like this?'

'Not so much,' says Marisja Lubijova, 'You see, this is my
work, and we like to put first our work here. I am interpreter,
I like my job, I think I do it quite nicely. Of course one pays a

little price. But it is good to make travels. I go quite often, I am one of those you see in the dolmetsch boxes, in the congresses, with the headsets. Four channels, you click so, Russian, German, English, French. No one notices you, you make the world happen.' 'And what happens to your son?' 'So many questions,' says Lubijova, laughing, 'Here we have very good families. The world is hard but we are close. He lives at a certain apartment where is my mother. She likes to look to him, she is happy. He goes to a kindergarten, he is happy. They teach him to march up and down like a soldier in the square. I come home and I bring good things. When I am not with you, do you know what I am doing? I am finding a line, buying some tins, perhaps some toilet paper. Or there are some nice jams from a hotel. Our lives at home are not so bad, but you do not see them. And this is why my son plays now with his toys in Slaka, and I am happy in a restaurant of Glit here with you. This wine, you like it?' 'I do,' says Petworth. 'Yes, it is not so bad, it is of this region,' says Lubijova, looking at him with her pale face and dark hair across the table, 'Well, now we have made an exchange. On the first night I have found out about you. You like to travel, you like the darks. And now you have found out about me. So I think we make again a little toast. Do you think you remember how to do it?' 'Yes,' says Petworth, lifting his glass. 'Oh, Petwurt, no, it is not like that,' says Lubijova, laughing, 'You have forgotten. I hope you have not forgotten all those lessons you learn in my country.' 'No,' says Petworth.

'Now,' says Lubijova, looking hard at him, 'Put up the glass, then the eyes. Remember you must be always very sincere. I like you, you are fine, I want you in my bed, my dear. Think it very hard, can you do it? I hope so. Of course you can, see, you look at me in just the right way. I am glad, your time here has after all not been waste, I was beginning to think so. But perhaps now you begin to learn something. So, my friend: what toast? To your tour in the countryside. No, that is not so good a toast, far too ordinary. Do you remember the other? Zu frolukuu daragayuu?' 'What's that?' asks Petworth. 'Yes, you forget everything,' says Marisja, laughing, 'Of course, to the beautiful ladies. This time sincerely. To the ones you met already, also the ones perhaps you meet now. And for your sake, I hope these will be the better ones.' The chatter chatters in multilingua from the surrounding tables; the waitress comes with a nameless soup made of dairy products. They eat the meal, while the candle gutters; they walk back through the darkness in the narrow streets of Glit to their hotel. 'If you'd like one more drink,' says Petworth, just outside the entrance, 'I still have my duty-free whisky.' 'Oh, you want to make some more toast?' cries Marisja, 'Well, in my country it is our custom to drink and talk very late, discussing the fine concepts until we are stupid. But, my dear, I think tonight, not. You must be very tired, and I am also. And tomorrow your lecture must be good. Also, don't forget it, we have many more times together. Yes, I think really you will need your bottle, in some more days, but not now.' They go inside the ill-lit lobby and part. Soon, in the clean narrow bed, by the gurgling river, Petworth sleeps. In a dream, there is despair: he is looking for a word for a thing, but he does not know what the thing is, because the word will not come. There is a desire to incorporate, to make what is outside inside; and it seems that a body is there, a body that presses itself against him, puts something to his mouth. But when he wakes in the darkness, he is alone, with the water running outside, in the tight narrow bed.

II

Over the days that follow, Petworth finds himself once more in a quite familiar world, following a quite familiar course. He is a visiting lecturer again, with a busy life: events come and go away, and so do the people in them, none of them characters in the world historical sense. A small battered car with a faceless student driver in it comes to the hotel in the morning, to take him and his guide through the streets of Glit and out to the campus of the university, a new university, out of town on a scoured and treeless hill. The pourers of concrete have poured and poured; the buildings sit straight and squat in the rounded mountain landscape. Like most new universities, it is, inside, a place of exposed pipes and frankly steaming ducts, and with numbers instead of names on all the doors. He walks along corridors where posters flap and the tiles have begun to crack; a small professor, a shy man called Professor Vlic, appears from behind a bookstack and greets him. 'And your poetic laureate? It is still the excellent John Masefield?' asks Professor Vlic, leading him into a very tiny study, with three miniature easy chairs and a coffee table, 'I always please to see a visitor from Britain. And your British disease, you still have it? Or does it go away and everyone likes again to work? Your Iron Lady, how does she? Does she perform, does she make her miracle?' It is lecture talk, and Petworth talks it; Professor Vlic dispenses coffee from a coffee-maker; a canary in a cage hangs tweeting from the bookcase. 'We hope you stay with us all day, we like to use you,' says Professor Vlic, 'In the morning I allow you an hour and some questions. I make a short speech to introduce, just some nice things of you. Our students perhaps not like yours, a little quiet, it is not their language. Of course they look forward much to your conference. You have your paper, do we go there?'

A little later, Petworth finds himself in a great auditorium, which rakes backward into gloom and darkness; smudged student faces sit there, gloomy too. At the back, at the end of a row, sits a man who is holding up a newspaper, *P'rtyuu Populatuuu*; for a moment Petworth thinks of Plitplov, but Glit, surely, is too far away for even that mobile man. A line of short stout lady professors sits in the front row, thinking Marxist thoughts and knitting. At the podium, a long introduction unfolds from Professor Vlic, in the language he still does not know, though a name roughly resembling his own sounds now and again, as, it seems, Petworthim does this, Petwortha once did that. The desks creak, and there is a wind blowing through the room. Taking a lecture from his briefcase, a piece on the difference between 'I don't have' and 'I haven't got' which has won some international acclaim, Petworth goes to the podium and begins to speak. The faces here seem darker, browner than they were in Slaka; the man with the newspaper does not put it down. The faces strive to look as if they are listening; at the end of the lecture there is only one question. 'I believe Marx was very pleased with the British Darwin because he destroys the telegogu and establishes at last a critical Utopia,' says one of the ladies in the front row, putting down her knitting; 'I believe so,' says Petworth. At the end of the session, when Petworth is led out, the students all stand up, except for the man with the newspaper. 'I hope you take some lunch with us and we make a dialogi,' says Professor Vlic, 'Most of our professors are women, as you see, and they have very good ideas and also some babies, so their day is difficult. Perhaps you talk to them now and this afternoon.'

Petworth is taken through the tiled corridors to the cafeteria, where he eats a cold bad lunch of a familiar kind off a tray at a plastic-topped table: 'And do you believe, as Boehme did, that there is one deep level of speech that sounds below all languages?' asks one of the short, stout lady professors. 'I enjoy very much your bog,' says another of the lady professors. 'My bog?' says Petworth. 'Your excellent bog,' says the lady, 'Of course I have read it.' In the afternoon, there is a faculty seminar, where the short stout lady professors continue with their knitting and their thoughts. 'Tell me please, Prifusorru Patwat,' says one of the ladies, 'You know perhaps that somewhere at around the dawn of our experimental century arosed a crucial question, not first time, but dominating all since; that question I refer is so. What is the relation between the objective and historical world, which our scientists and men of physics view as reality, and the inward world of the seer, do you say perceiver, the psychic ego, from which place only may such a world be known? As you know, the reconcil-iations of these thoughts have been many, from Hegel to Marx to Freud and your own Wittgenstein, who was not yours truly. Now, do you tell me, how do you reconcile this ultimating question?' 'Also,' asks another lady, 'Do you think it is possible to reconcile the reception-aesthetic of an Iser with a Lukacsian Hegelianism?' Perhaps we should leave Petworth for a moment and find the toilet as he deals with these questions, and other such matters that, in seminar rooms throughout the world, faculties discuss with visiting speakers: the poverty of the library; the folly of the university administration; the lunacy of a ministry that institutes an educational reform but fails to have it ready when term starts, so that the students are not told and the books do not come and classes must be cancelled and the students protest and the police come and the poor faculty are compelled to remain at home working on their own research. 'You have given us excellent afternoon and I like if you please to dine you this evening,' says Professor Vlic, as he leads Petworth out of the seminar room and toward the battered car, in which, after going back once for his briefcase, and again to collect the offprint of an article by one of the lady professors, Petworth returns to his small old hotel by the river.

So Petworth works, by the day, by the evening. That night at eight, Professor Vlic comes to the hotel with a gloomy elderly lady. 'My wife,' he says, 'She does not speak at all English. She will sit very quietly. She has a magazine.' 'Won't it be boring for her?' asks Petworth, at the table under the umbrella by the river. 'Not at all,' says Professor Vlic, 'She eats. And perhaps your guide will say some things to her. I hope you have tried all our nice foods, very good in Glit. There is a typical thing, a cream of cucumber made with the chords of a yog, or do you like perhaps to eat a brain? I hope you try our things. And how is your monetarism? You think it is working? I think now money is not making sense any more. All our economies are wrong, capitalist and socialist. Of course our disasters are more rational, we plan them better. And yet everywhere people seem to have some riches. New clothes, a television receptor, perhaps a little car. Even our people here have many possessions. But I wonder, do these things represent what truly we desire, or does money make us take them? I have an apartment to sit in, a car to go in, am I happier man? I do not laugh any more, my worries are bigger. You have been in United States?'. 'Yes,' says Petworth. 'Is it as Tennessee Williams portrays, a decadent nation?' asks Professor Vlic, 'Always people lying in hot tubs? And everyone divorcing to be singles? Did you take an analyst while you are there, to get your head straight? It looks quite a straight head to me. Did you go to a sex shop? And what do you buy there, I don't even know what they sell. Do they have topless seminars now in the universities, the topless physics, the topless mathematic? How is your ego and your id? Look, I now recommend the cake eskimo. It is a specialism of this place. If you like, I will ask them for it.' 'Thank you,' says Petworth. 'Oh, so sorry,' says Professor Vlic, after a long conversation with a sad waiter, 'It is eaten all. A fruit instead, perhaps? He has one orange.'

It has been a usual day, and the one that follows promises to be much the same. The battered car comes, and Petworth gets in it to travel to the university; in the same gloomy auditorium he stands to lecture on the Uvular R. The audience is smaller today, perhaps because the Uvular R is of less pressing interest, perhaps because of the gloomier weather, or because of the presence of a rival attraction – for somewhere outside there seems to be a noise of students shouting, and even the occasional celebratory bang. But the man with the newspaper has not failed to come, and today he looks even more like Plitplov than ever; for in some moment of curiosity he lets the newspaper slip, to reveal a neat white sports shirt of the kind that Plitplov wears, though others wear them too, and in any case it could be an optical illusion. Later, as they walk to the university cafeteria, a window or two seems to have caved in in the corridor, perhaps as a result of the morning's celebrations, and in the air there lingers a strange smell of acrid smoke. After lunch there is another faculty seminar, and Professor Vlic, evidently a liberal soul, says he wants it to be even more of a dialogi; he insists on explaining what a dialogi is. 'In dialogi,' he says, as they sit in the small seminar room, from which it seems possible to hear the sound of firecrackers going off, 'each partner must be considered consenting person and no one should be subservient and no one on top. Of course in dialogi different partners will have different priority and the objects of attention will not be quite the same. But if dialogi shall work well, and be a true coming together, the different elements will be fit to the satisfaction of both partners. A tendency toward individuation exists in dialogi, but should be criticized. Our aim is not partial dialogi, but whole dialogi. Now I call you to begin.'

The dialogi goes on most of the afternoon; afterwards, Professor Vlic leads him out to the battered car in the car park. Round about, the broken glass seems quite wide-spread, there are a few steaming canisters about, and several khaki vans with wire mesh over their windows and shadowy people sitting inside stand round the university. 'Has something happened?' asks Petworth. 'Oh, it is just a small thing,' says Professor Vlic, 'I think there has been just a little demonstration about our languages. You know, we have here so many, of the north and the south, of the Indo and the Turkish. All of them confuse, but all of them like to be the main language of the country, which is why now is a tiny problem.' 'I thought there was a language reform,' says Petworth. 'One reform, and some people ask always for more,' says Professor Vlic, 'Well, it is a little problem, and we solve it quite quickly. Your lecture is very good, and tonight we like to thank you. Please to be our guest at a special faculty dinner at a restaurant in the town. Your guide, also, please. Now the man takes you back. The policemen will let you through, it is arranged. If you can be ready at eight we collect you and take you to a very nice place.' There is time to change in his innocent quiet room overlooking the river; there is time to take a little pleasure in his pleasant visit to Glit. Then he sits with Marisja Lubijova in the hotel lobby until a very small car containing four of the short stout lady professors, who now wear bright flowered dresses and carry large handbags, stops and takes them off, through the cramped, quiet old streets of Glit, to an ancient timbered restaurant somewhere. Inside the restaurant, the Restaurant Nada, many are gathered together, the faculty faces of the day, and there is laughter; hands pat Petworth's arms, smiles flash in his face, and he is steadily pushed toward a seat in the centre of the table.

'Here is a white wine, here a red, here a juicy if you like it,' says Professor Vlic, who sits in the place opposite him. And down the table, to either side, stretch the long rows of lady professors, smiling and laughing, gossiping and talking. The restaurant has a low ceiling, and pots of flowers hang from it; a goat is looking curiously in through the window at the long, bottle-laden table where, in two happy rows, the learned people sit, chatting as, at faculty dinners, faculty diners do. 'I have read your great poet of debunkery, Philip Larking,' says a stout lady to Petworth's right, 'I like to visit him and talk to him for three days and make a thesis.' 'Do you know also a campus writer Brodge?' asks a lady to his left, 'Who writes *Changing Westward*? I think he is very funny but sometimes his ideological position is not clear.' 'You like it, Glit?' asks a lady across the table, 'Really it is very pleasant, except in the earthquakes. Then our buildings fall down and it is not so amusing.' 'Oh, my English, I wish it was gooder,' says another lady across the table, 'Your language, so difficult. Always those sentences that appear correct, but you must not say. I swim-med. This is the lady I want to eat.' 'And some things you may say in Britain but not at all in the United States,' says the lady to his right, 'Elevator, not lift. Hood, not bonnet.' 'When you visit the United States,' says the lady beyond her, leaning toward him, 'You should not say to a lady, please may I stroke your pussy. It is quite correct, but it has a meaning that is not intended. But I do not know what it is.' 'Oh, you don't know it?' asks the lady beyond, 'Then I will tell you.' Laughter spreads down the table; a sizzling pot of strange food appears on the table in front of him; more, and more, of an unusual wine is poured.

There are voices, strange voices, singing in Petworth's head, the words of an English that is not quite English, English as a medium of international communication. He is well attended, and the ladies all lean toward him; he talks himself, of Sod's Law and Hobson's Choice, of laughing like a drainpipe and not having a sausage, the happy small talk of the passing linguist. 'I have been in Wales, that was very dark,' says a lady across the table. 'You are in Glit,' says the lady next to him, 'Here always a strong oral tradition, we like to tell the stories.' 'Oh, yes, we are famous of it,' says the lady beyond. 'I believe you have some very bad inflations,' says the lady on the other side, 'We have some here also, but they are not the same.' 'Do you like to hear one of our stories?' 'The one about the tailor?' 'No, the one about the shah.' 'In Wales there are many tea-shops, always closed.' 'Each partner in a dialogi should be considered a person and consenting always to the part.' 'Do you think Larking likes to see me for three days?' 'Once in a certain kingdom, not ours, there lived a shah.' 'A tzar?' 'It is a wine made from a grappa that a frost has bitten.' 'Here ours is a Marxist inflation, caused not at all by the entrepreneurial processes of capitalism but by the workings of economic laws.' 'The shah had a beautiful fair wife, a great hareem, a big Turk slave and a fine black horse.' 'I have been to a place called Rhyl where always is showing the film *Going With the Wind*.' 'Oh, don't they love you?' whispers, in his ear, his guide Marisja Lubijova, as she makes her way out of the room, toward the lavatory or wherever, 'Oh, aren't you success? And how much you like to enjoy it.' Petworth looks up, and sees her walking away, swinging her shoulderbag.

The food comes, the ladies smile. 'The shah loved alike his wife and his horse, and one day when he had ridden the first he went for a ride in the desert on the second.' 'Of course we have abolished entirely the bourse and therefore our market is entirely scientific.' 'On that way he meets a wizard who sits under a tree, and the wizard tells to him: "If you can answer please my question, you can have all your desires, don't you like that? And if you cannot, I can have your beautiful wife. What do you say? Is it bargain?"' 'I hope you went to our castle, we have much history here.' ' "Now my question," says the wizard, "What is the strongest, the loveliest, the fattest, the most beautiful thing in the whole world?"' 'If you walk past there just a little way, you will come to a place that is very interesting.' 'And the wizard then tells: "Now you have fourteen nights, until the moon, to make your travels and find it out. Then at the moon you tell me, or I take your wife."' 'Do you like now to take some spirits, for the end of our nice meal?' 'So for fourteen day that shah makes travel, and then he comes back to the wizard, and tells, very sad: "No, still I do not know what is the strongest, the loveliest, the fattest, the most beautiful thing in the whole world."' 'A visky or a bols? A Tichus or a Blackuu and Vuttuu?' 'Because of these fundamental differences, therefore the two systems are not at all the same, but are subject to different historical forces.' 'I think he likes to try the custom of the country, give him rot'vuttu.' 'And so that wizard goes away with the beautiful wife, and the shah is very sad and lonely. Oh, do we pay? Please, not you. You are our very nice guest.'

A great pile of vloskan, that paper fiction, grows in the middle of the table, supplied from the purses of the laughing ladies. 'But, please, you don't tell us what is the strongest, the loveliest, the fattest, the most beautiful thing in the whole world?' 'I do not know, but if you find him, bring it to me,' says the lady professor, laughing. 'We thank you, a good visit,' says Professor Vlic, rising, shaking hands. 'Time to go, Comrade Petwurt,' says Marisja Lubijova, leaning across Petworth's shoulder in a wifely intercession, 'You have had nice evening, but tomorrow you take that train to Nogod. Kiss goodbye all the nice ladies, make them farewell.' 'Of course, you must kiss us all,' says the lady professor who has told the imperfect story of the shah, 'But then we take you back.' 'No, I think he needs some fresh airs,' says Lubijova, firmly, as Petworth makes his embraces, writes down addresses, lists the titles of some useful books. He is led outside; the small smoky restaurant has grown remarkably hot, and even the outdoor air of Glit is almost glutinous. In the streets, as he walks back with his guide, the moon shines, and the scent of flowers from the balconies fills the evening. In the market place, the fountain burbles – though here there is a new smell, the aroma of acrid smoke, and more broken glass lies scattered about the pavements. There is a tired hysteria in Petworth, a sense of being over-used, spent in some massive verbal orgy; he pauses by the fountain. 'Yes, look at you,' says Lubijova, standing and looking at him, 'Oh, yes, you please now. You feel better. Always you like to amuse, always you like to be with the ladies. Are you an American, Comrade Petwurt? Don't you think of anything but sexing? Do you dream to be a star? Do you think the world exists to make you feel very okay?' 'I'm tired,' says Petworth. 'Oh, you should be happy,' says Mari, 'I think they were all in love with you, and would like to sleep with you.' 'Really?' says Petworth, 'Why?' 'Of course,' says Marisjia, 'Because your speeches are a good success, and that is always erotic. And also in your eyes it shows always you like women, and they like to be liked. Even under Marx.'

Later, in the small innocent bedroom where nothing has happened, and no pain has yet come, Petworth sits on the clean narrow bed; his duty-free bottle of whisky is open before him on the bedside table, and he has a toothglass in his hands. Words are spilling through his mind, in strange excess, a medley of sounding voices that penetrate and confuse. But it is as Katya Princip, that deceptive novelist, has said to him, in another place, now distant: the more words, the more country. But what country is it? The English that is no longer English, the English of second language users, reels through his head, a head that hardly feels like his. The acrid smoke-smell from the market place is still burning strangely in his nostrils. His throat is still tanged with the strong sweet taste of rot'vuttu, which is never to be missed. His body feels an empty place, longing for some fullness; there is a misery of feeling about a relationship that has betrayed, gone. A little along the bed, also holding a glass, sits Mari Lubijova; her hair has come down, and her round grey eyes, in her white tense face, are staring at him. 'I don't know, I don't know what to think of you,' says Mari, 'You are a soft person, you come from a soft place, you are not like these men here at all. And you are the worst I have ever guided.' 'I'm sorry,' says Petworth. 'No, really, I should not say these things,' says Mari, 'Even I should not be here. But you must understand, perhaps I am always just a little bit jealous.' 'Jealous?' says Petworth, 'Why, of what?' 'Really, Petwurt, you can't think?' asks Mari, staring down into her glass, 'Then you are not very bright. But of course, I know what I am. I am just your guide, your interpreter. I am invisible person. A voice, a sort of machine, I do not have words of my own. Just your words to take there, the words of others to bring to here. Well, of course, it is my job. And I hope I try to do it very well.'

'Yes, of course,' says Petworth. 'And I hope you understand I try to look after you a little, or you would be always in misfortune,' says Mari, 'Perhaps you blame me for what goes wrong.' 'No,' says Petworth. 'I think you do, a little,' says Mari, 'And perhaps you are right. It is hard to know how betrayal works. Please, I take some more of your whisky? I think you do not like to carry it all the way home again.' 'Please,' says Petworth. 'You know, when you are interpreter, you are not supposed to like the words you hear,' says Mari, 'All your speakers are the same. But, what is funny, in public places, all the speakers say almost the same things. You can have all those phrases ready in your head; you know you will need them. We wish you amity, friendship, concord of the peoples. We make here a fine progress. We wish you all come together in new ways. And because you know what will be said, you learn to change things a little bit, sometimes to make them easier, sometimes to make them better. You like to help your speaker a little, you want him to succeed.' 'Yes, I see,' says Petworth. 'Perhaps you do that for yourself,' says Mari, 'Because if you are interpreter, it is easy to grow a little afraid. You speak all the time, but always the words of others. Then you wonder: is there inside me a person, someone who is not the words of those others? You think: can I have still a desire, a wish, a feeling? But of course if you think like this, it is bad for your job, you must forget it. You are not here for that, you are here to make those exchanges, to let the others talk, so the world can go on. But, excuse me, please, sometimes I do have a little feeling. And now, I am sorry, it is jealous.' 'Yes, I understand,' says Petworth, looking at her tense white face as she sits beside him on the bed.

'So,' says Mari, raising up her glass, 'At least I hope I have taught you some things. I believe you know how to make a toast; show me you can do it. I don't like you to forget the lessons you have learned here in my country. Raise please the glass.' 'I remember,' says Petworth, raising his glass. 'Now, wait, what do we drink to?' says Mari, 'Yes, I think dialogi, you have heard of it, I believe? Dialogi is a linkage of context and relation, made in the assumption that both partners like to enjoy the same things. The aim is not partial dialogi but whole dialogi. If dialogi shall work well, there must be a true coming together. All elements must fit to the mutual satisfaction of both parties. So, please drink to dialogi. Do it right. Look with the eyes, be always sincere, remember what to think: I like you, you are fine, I want you so much in my bed.' There is a face, Mari Lubijova's, curiously close to Petworth's, and coming closer; for some reason he momentarily recalls a grey-haired lady who smokes a cigarette in a dark London office of the British Council. The face is very near, and then it turns. 'No,' says Mari, dropping her head and putting down her glass, 'Is not such a good toast. I am afraid you will do something to me and I do not like it.' 'I will?' asks Petworth.

'Please understand,' says Lubijova, 'Really I do not find you at all attractive in that way. You are not a bit my kind.' 'No,' says Petworth. 'I hope you do not try to force me,' says Mari. 'Of course not,' says Petworth. 'You are bourgeois reactionary without a correct sense of reality,' says Mari, 'You are not serious, and no important thing matters to you. You live a decadent life.' 'That sums me up pretty well,' says Petworth. 'And no sooner do you go from one trouble than you find another,' says Mari, 'You have had one lesson with the ladies, don't you learn?' 'Yes,' says Petworth. 'Of course I like to offer you a nice tenderness, but not at all in that way,' says Mari. 'No, of course,' says Petworth, 'I wasn't going to . . .'

'Of course all this is not true, none of it,' says Mari, 'To me you are attractive, perhaps just a little bit beautiful, Petwurt, and strange. Perhaps not in your own country, but here. And you know those who watch us and listen to us, they would like us to make some love.' 'Who do you mean?' asks Petworth. 'Oh, please, you know them, they are always there,' says Mari, 'But I do not think it is their business. I think we disappoint them, yes?' 'Yes,' says Petworth. 'But I cannot go now,' says Mari, 'I think we turn out the light and be together very quiet for a bit. And if we say nothing, no one can tell anything of us.' 'Who would tell?' asks Petworth. 'Of course,' says Mari, 'Someone is always telling of you and me. So we are quiet together, and we make no words.' Outside the window there is the noise of the rushing river, and there is a scent of trees in the air. But it is totally quiet and entirely dark in the little bedroom, and there is absolutely nothing to hear or see. A clock ticks, but one cannot tell how much time is passing; certainly it is some time later when Mari, in the dark, says: 'Comrade Petwurt, now I go. You must sleep very nicely, don't forget you must make an early wake, to go on that train to Nogod. Thank you for the drink, thank you to be with me, thank you to be quiet. And perhaps even we did make some love, if not in the usual way.' 'Yes,' says Petworth. 'But there is nothing to know, nothing to tell,' says Mari, 'And I hope you understand now that I am really your very good guide. And always I like to look after you very, very well.' 'I do,' says Petworth. 'And now I will sleep next door, where they have put me,' says Mari, 'And I hope you do not mind if I think of you a little?' 'I'd like you to,' says Petworth. In the dark room, the door opens, and Mari stands for a moment in the light from the corridor; in his clothes, Petworth turns on his side, and sleeps.

III

'So now you go to another city, isn't it nice?' says Marisja Lubijova, as Petworth lifts his luggage aboard the train that has belatedly come to a halt at the single platform of the railway station at Glit. It has been a long wait, and many cups of acorn coffee have been taken by the few waiting passengers, under the eyes of the two or three armed men who walk the platform; but it has come at last, a train of old, red-painted coaches, drawn by an ancient black steam engine with a large red star on its nose. Telegraphic noises come from an office; a few black-uniformed railwaymen make signals; Petworth and Lubijova struggle down the central aisle and find a seat opposite two young soldiers, who sit under a window with a red sign on it saying NOKU ROKU. 'Yes, you will like it, Nogod,' says Marisja, opening a volume of Hemingway and spreading it on her knee, 'It is also old but not at all like Glit. There is a lake and some hills there, also a kloster and a kirkus. We will stay in a nice modern hotel, and have a good weekend of leisures, you have worked very hard. I hope you enjoy now a rest. Don't you like our train?' 'Yes,' says Petworth, as the rails rattle under them, 'But I suppose the signs mean I can't smoke?' 'Oh, dear, poor comrade Petwurt,' says Marisja, 'Do you want to? We don't so much like those things in our country. I think you find our regulation a little hard. Well, it is for your good, we do not like you to be ill.' 'I'll just go and stand at the end of the car,' says Petworth. 'I don't think is permitted there either,' says Marisja, looking down into her book, 'But if you like to look.' The soldiers stare at him as he rises; he walks to the end of the coach and stands by the door. Lighting a cigarette, he leans through the open window, and looks out.

The train is moving very slowly; beside the track, there are peasants walking along with produce who seem to advance almost as fast. It rattles over the stone and wooden bridges and through the short tunnels of the mountainous landscape; there is a sharp smell of woodsmoke, an ancient dust in the air. Forest closes round the track, and small streams bubble. Presently a man in a black uniform, with much dandruff on it, comes by; he points to Petworth's cigarette, and says: 'Nega-tivo.' 'Ah, da,' says Petworth, turning, and beginning to walk down the shaking train, looking for a place where the signs do not say NOKU ROKU. The train seems very empty; the corridors are wide between the seats, which are also wide and plush. Wooden doors divide the carriages into sections; at halfopen windows, curtains blow; the seats change colour from blue to brown as he walks on. He opens a door, and beyond is a dining car, its tables covered with dirty white cloths. The car is empty except for one grey-jacketed attendant and two men, who sit together at a table under one of the familiar signs that say NOKU ROKU. One of the men has a big black beard and gold bangles on both his wrists, and he smokes an aromatic Balkan cigarette; the other, his back to Petworth, wears natty sportive trousers and smokes a large curved pipe. The men turn to look at him, and the one with the pipe gets up suddenly. 'Well, is it really?' he cries, 'Is it truly my good old friend Dr Petworth? Are you also on this train?' Petworth stares: 'Well, Dr Plitplov,' he says, 'Fancy meeting you.' 'Such a strange thing,' says Plitplov, laughing, 'You are come to take a meal, no, is too early. You like to take a drink. Please, sit down here with us, we would like it.'

'I was looking for somewhere to smoke, actually,' says

Petworth, 'There doesn't seem to be anywhere on this train.' 'No, is not permitted, in such a public place,' says Plitplov, puffing at his pipe, 'But of course in my country many things are possible, if you know a someone. And this gentleman my friend here, I am sorry, he does not speak English, he knows well the crew of this train. He likes to make a lot of travels. Well, sit down, please, make a smoke, it is all right. Also we drink some very fine brandy. Please won't you take some? It is not too early in the day for you?' The attendant, prescient, has already appeared, with a clean new glass; Plitplov fills it from a very large bottle that sits on the table in front of him. 'Well, I think we drink to a very fine coincidence,' says Plitplov, raising his glass, 'Here I am going to make some businesses in Nogod, I think you go there too; and on the train who I meet except my very good friend! And your lectures in Glit, tell me? I hope they went very nicely?' 'I think they were all right,' says Petworth, drinking, 'You didn't happen to be there, did you? I thought I saw you.' 'In Glit?' cries Plitplov, laughing, 'At your lectures? I don't think so. Oh, my friend, I know in our academical life, lectures are most important, and of course I would like to be there. But really life is more than some lectures. How I wish I could hear you at Nogod, always you are quite fascinating, as I remember of Cambridge. But no, I must make a congress there. You know perhaps Nogod is a famous place to make a very good congress. But your nice guide, you have not lost your nice lady guide?' 'No,' says Petworth, 'She's further down the train.' 'How well that lady looks after you,' says Plitplov, 'Please, some more in your glass.' 'Only a little,' says Petworth, 'Too much.' 'I don't think,' says Plitplov, 'In my country your too much is only a little. Drink it please, it is a special brandy that is kept on this train only for certain people. It is good I am one of them.'

From time to time the train stops; the stations have no names and the train halts at nowhere. People with big suitcases get off, get on; the landscape as they move begins to flatten gradually. 'And your tour, you like it?' asks Plitplov, 'You are pleased to come?' 'Yes,' says Petworth. 'Then you are grateful to me?' asks Plitplov, 'You know I had a hand in the pie. Really I am sorry we do not make a bigger time together, but we all have our businesses, and we do not agree on all things, like Hemingway. Oh, you are wrong there, you cannot be right all the time. How was your strip?' 'My strip?' asks Petworth. 'Your strip after the opera,' says Plitplov, 'You know I did not come because I had headache.' 'Not terribly enjoyable,' says Petworth. 'Well, of course, these things, for tourists only,' says Plitplov, 'There are better things I can show you. But there is always your nice lady guide, she doesn't like it. In Nogod, where do you stay? What is your hotel?' 'I don't know,' says Petworth. 'Well, really there is only one, the Universe,' says Plitplov, 'I stay there also. Let us take together a little dinner. This gentleman my friend knows very well Nogod. He can meet you some ladies, find you some dancings, if those are your pleasures. I know you like to make nice time.' 'I shall be busy giving lectures,' says Petworth. 'Perhaps you will,' says Plitplov, 'Perhaps you will not.' 'I don't understand,' says Petworth. 'Oh, it is nothing,' says Plitplov, 'But here in my country we are having some little troubles, not very much. But it is the language reform, so a lecture on language could be even a provocation. But don't think of it, I am wrong to mention. Of course you will give your lectures, I wish I could hear them.'

The landscape flattens further; beyond the windows show the shores of a large lake. 'Perhaps you should find now your guide,' says Plitplov, 'In Nogod there are three stations, none of them with names. Take care, my friend, and I will find you. Is not such a big place. I may be a little elusive, but yes, we will make together a little dinner. Is it agreed?' 'If we can arrange it,' says Petworth. 'Of course,' says Plitplov, 'You know I like to make plans for you, plans of many kinds.' Petworth walks shakily down the shaking train, down the wide corridors, through the wooden doors. Marisja Lubijova sits reading in her spectacles: 'You are gone a long time,' she says, setting aside her book, 'Oh, comrade Petwurt, what are you doing? I let you go for a moment, and now you are smelling of drink.' 'I met someone, guess who?' says Petworth. 'I don't want to play game with you,' says Marisja, staring at him, 'Who is on the train?' 'Dr Plitplov,' says Petworth. 'Really, your good old friend?' says Mari Lubijova, 'And he goes to Nogod?' 'Yes,' says Petworth. 'Why does he follow you?' asks Marisja. 'I don't think he does follow me,' says Petworth, 'Our paths just keep crossing.' 'Petwurt, I think you are a very simple man, really you do not know anything about life, how to live it. Of course your paths cross. That is because he likes to follow you. But what is his reason? What does he want from you?' 'Nothing, as far as I know,' says Petworth, breathing brandy fumes. 'Oh, yes, he does all this for nothing,' says Marisja Lubijova, 'What does he know about you? How does he know you so well? And your marriage?' 'He just came to that course in Cambridge,' says Petworth. 'That is all?' asks Marisja, 'I don't think so. You know, I cannot even imagine him as student. That man, he likes to think he was borned knowing everything. Well, Petwurt, take up please your baggages. Look, we are nearly here.'

And beyond the windows there is an urban landscape, a blowing wind, washing hanging between tenements, a long black wall, an advertisement, very tattered, for *P'rtyuu Populatuuu*, a heap of coal, a smell of oil fumes, a platform with people on it. They descend from the train; there is a high glass ceiling, a line of parcel trucks, a concourse, a number of people waiting expectantly, a few armed men, a forecourt, a few orange taxis. Marisja Lubijova walks firmly to the head of the line and claims one; meanwhile Petworth notices, coming toward them with waves and shouts, Plitplov and the man with the big black beard. 'Quick please, inside,' says Marisja Lubijova, 'He does not come again in a taxi with us.' They drive through the town, which has a humid atmosphere and a somewhat Mediterranean feel. Unseen shouters shout in the streets, children run about, car horns hoot with abandon, behind half-screened open windows unshaven men at desks answer telephones. The Hotel Universe is a high modern hotel by the lake, with a pool and a pier; there are display cases of souvenirs in the lobby and a blue Cosmoplot girl behind the desk. 'You stay at the Universe,' says Marisja, conducting the formalities, 'I must stay at the small annexe behind.' Petworth's hotel room is the universal room, with bigger table lamps in it than has the rest of life, a small television set that will not switch on, and a card on the dressing table that says: 'Please tickle one: ☐ I like very much my stay; ☐ it is all right; ☐ I disappoint.' The cafeteria where, a little later, they meet to take a little lunch is called a Butter'um, and is like a hamburger joint, without hamburgers. 'Why does he come?' asks Marisja, over the salad, 'Now I think our nice weekend will really not be so well.' Through a glass wall they can see into the lobby: in the lobby stands Plitplov, talking to the blackbearded man, and a man in a big felt hat, and someone who looks curiously like Professor Rom Rum. 'We try not to mind,' says Marisja, 'We try to enjoy ourselves. The Mun'stratuu has been very efficient, and many things have been arranged.'

And many have. Over the weekend, Petworth is taken to various spots round the lake, to sit in cafés drinking light beer; he is taken by coach to a monastery high up a hill, where a little old moustached man issues him with very large felt slippers, which he wears to be shown, by a monk in a great vestment, an ancient hand-illustrated Bible in an alphabet that is now very little used. 'Those places,' says Marisja afterward, wrinkling her nose, 'How they love to sell their propagandas to the foolish people who think it is all so.' He is taken to a circus, the Kyrku Hyvardim, where he looks at the sad-faced lions, the romping monkeys, and feels curiously at home. He is taken to a state-run fish-farm, and given a lecture on rural reform; he is taken to a cinema to watch films, filmed in the style of heavy photographic realism, evidently shot by big cameras that are not easy to move around, about heroes of labour, campaigns for teaching things to deaf children, factories with steaming chimneys, and nuclear power stations. Occasionally Marisja Lubijova translates – 'Katrina advances revolutionary ballet by her prize posture,' she explains – but most of it is floating images, as the heavy urgent commentaries go on in the language he still has not managed to learn. Plitplov is not to be seen, until on Sunday night, after his guide has gone to her annexe behind the Universe, Petworth sees a sign saying CONGRUSS'UM. Two of the blue armed men guard an open door; through it Petworth can see a big hall with a platform with many flags on it. Men sit on the platform and in front of them are signs with their names on. Photographers stand at the side of the hall and step forward now and then, their cameras flashing. To the side of the stage, four translators sit in a box marked DOL'METSCHUU, their mouths moving rapidly. It seems to Petworth that one of the translators is Plitplov. One of the blue armed men closes the door, and gestures Petworth away; he goes to the lift and back to his room, where the big table lamps and the small television set seem to look at him, listen to him.

The weekend is over; in the morning it seems that the cycle will begin again. His lectures in a folder, he goes down to breakfast in the Butter'um; during the meal, of bad black coffee and bread rolls, Marisja is called away to the telephone. 'There is a small confusion,' she says when she comes back, 'Your tour will not be quite the same. I am afraid you miss your last city. You do not go after it all to Provd. What a pity, you would like it. But there are some little troubles there that make it not a good idea. Also your lectures here, perhaps you do not give them. Instead we take you to a nice state farm with tractors, you will have a very nice day. Also tomorrow we try to find you a ticket for a plane back to Slaka, so you have more time to go to the Wicwok shop and find some nice souvenirs.' 'Is it to do with the language reform?' asks Petworth. 'Something like that,' says Mari, 'It is not very important and it will all soon be solved. But what a pity for your tour. Now you will not be able to give your best lectures.' It seems to Petworth that when they go out into the lobby there are rather more of the blue armed militiamen than usual, and that, at the nice state farm with the tractors, as they trudge along furrows, Marisja Lubijova is whiter and more tense than he is used to. When they get back to the hotel, the sign saying CONGRUSS'UM has gone; after he goes to his room, the telephone rings. 'You are alone?' says a voice, 'No person is with you?' 'No,' says Petworth, 'Is that Plitplov?' 'Someone of that sort,' says the voice, 'You wonder about a dinner, you think you are neglected.' 'I haven't worried,' says Petworth. 'I think we make a raincheck, you understand this expression, it is American,' says the voice, 'I like to take now the way back to Slaka. I have an anxious wife, very delicate, and she has not seen me for three days. Do you make your lectures?' 'No,' says Petworth. 'Well, a little word of advice from an old friend,' says the voice, 'I think you tell your nice lady guide you like to go back to Slaka too. It is not so hard to arrange. You are important official visitor.' 'I fly back tomorrow,' says Petworth. 'Is good,' says the voice, 'I hope the planes go. Sleep very well, my friend.'

It is crowded at the airport at Nogod, when the taxi delivers them there the following morning. At the two check-in desks long lines contend. 'It is impossible,' says Marisja Lubijova, 'Wait here, please, I go to try to make you some arrangements. You don't go away? I don't lose you again?' 'No,' says Petworth, standing, as he has stood before, his back next to a pillar, his luggage tumbled at his feet. Around him, the crowd bustles in its unending business; faces, foreign, unfamiliar faces, but more familiar than they were once, surface for a moment and then disappear into the press. At the end of the concourse, a big clock ticks: a stall says LUTTU, another COSMOPLOT. Back in an old metaphysics of Petworthian absence, Petworth waits. The airport smells of carbolic soap; signs say NOKU ROKU, but everywhere the sweet scent of Balkan tobacco prevails. Buses stop outside the concourse, and the crowd thickens and thickens; there is no noise of planes taking off.

Then, after a very long time, he sees Lubijova pushing back through the crowd toward him. 'There is a small confusion,' she says, 'Perhaps it is not so small. All want to go to Slaka and the planes do not come so it is not possible. But a plane comes tonight and I think we go on it. You see, they treat you like a very important visitor. You don't mind to wait? They will send away most of these people. They think their tickets are good but they are not.' In a small crowded bar looking out toward the tarmac, Petworth sits out the afternoon, drinking rot'vuttu. 'You can tell always the usual travellers by Comflug,' says Marisja, sitting opposite, 'They bring their binoculars, to look at the under of those planes when they land. Then if it does not look right, they make change of the flight. But it is no use today.'

Airports are indeed much the same the world over: Heathrow last week, Nogod now. A few unwarmed planes wait on the tarmac, a few people are allowed to go to the exit gates, a flight or two, during the afternoon, takes off. Night begins to fall, the landing strip lights up, then the big beam of a landing light is switched on in the sky. 'We go to the gate now, this is our plane,' says Marisja Lubijova, 'You must carry on all your bags, we do not check them. Perhaps it is better I explain you. It is not because you are important visitor we go on this flight. I know the stewardess who takes it, I teach her some English. And she is mistress of the captain, so we get a place. Here it is always best to know somebody. Don't you think I am good guide?' They push out to the plane in a great crowd; at the steps, a long-legged green stewardess in a hard hat greets Marisja Lubijova, and embraces her. 'Here is my friend,' says Lubijova. 'Yes, it is your friend,' says the stewardess, 'Please walk the steps, and at top go right, not left.' At the top of the steps, the passengers with them turn into the forward cabin, where the stewardess seats them in neat rows, as if packing a box of people. But to the right is a green curtain, and the long-legged stewardess lifts it: 'Please, in here,' she says. Petworth walks through; behind the curtain is a curious world. For the

309

rear cabin seems filled to the brim with green stewardesses, lolling in most of the available seats. In their Comflug uniforms, they come in many kinds: some are young and some quite elderly; some are blonde, and some are arabesque; there are thin-faced ones with flashing eyes and big-boned ones with wide flat features. There is an off-duty look to them; their horse-rider's helmets are up on the rack, their shoes are scattered about the cabin floor. The bulkhead signs say LUPU LUPU and NOKU ROKU, but their belts are unfastened and an aromatic haze of cigarette smoke blows above their heads.

Petworth sits in a row with two young green stewardesses; Marisja Lubijova is found a seat on the other side of the aisle. The stewardess next to Petworth says something to him, in the language he has still not succeeded in grasping; 'I'm sorry, I don't understand,' he says. 'English?' says the girl, 'He is English.' 'English? Is he English?' say the three girls in the row behind, rising to look at him. 'Do you like a Russ cigarette?' asks the girl next to him, 'Do you like to take some vodka?' 'Yes, thank you,' says Petworth. 'I learn English,' says the girl, 'I like to make flight to the West.' 'I also learn it,' says the girl in the seat beyond. Outside, the engines fire, and begin to roar; there is an announcement over the intercom. 'Do you like that cigarette? Do you like that vodka?' asks the girl next to him, 'We buy them in Russ.' The plane is taxiing; the lights of Nogod disappear in the windows. 'Is that where this flight has come from?' asks Petworth. 'Tashkent,' says the girl, 'We are all off duty in Tashkent. It is nice there, at the autumn. You go, you goed?' There comes the great rush into airspeed; Petworth puffs on his cigarette. 'We say: you have been,' he says, never less than a pedagogue, 'No, I haven't been.' 'Oh, you should have been, when you have chance,' says the girl, 'I know you like.' 'Vulu suftu'un burdu pumfluttu,' says a female voice over the intercom., 'Plaz'scu otvatu ummerg'nucuna proddo flugsu'froluku.' One of the girls, holding a paper cup of vodka, stands and does a little mocking dance, pointing at the exits; the others applaud and raise their cups to her. 'Have

310

a nice day, I hope you enjoy your flight,' says the girl next to Petworth, 'Here, more vodka, you like?' 'Yes, I do,' says Petworth. 'This is a nice man,' says the stewardess. 'What a nice man,' says a girl in the row behind.

'Yes, he is very nice man, I like,' says the long-legged stewardess, standing up in the aisle, smiling at him, 'He is your man?' 'Oh, please,' says Marisja Lubijova, 'I am his guide, that is all. He makes a tour.' 'Oh, yes, I believe you, his guide,' says the stewardess, 'Listen, I like to ask him something. Do you interpret?' 'Oh, Petwurt, listen, this is nice, you have invitation,' says Lubijova, after a moment, 'She tells how she is the mistress of the captain who flies our plane. Well, it is this man's birthday and she likes to be with him. They make a party in the cockplace, what do you call it?' 'The cockpit?' asks Petworth. 'There,' says Marisja, 'And she likes to take you there because you are visitor here and such a nice man.' 'To the cockpit?' asks Petworth. 'Yes, they are making there some celebratings,' says Marisja. 'But this is a Russian plane, and I'm a Western visitor,' says Petworth, 'I'm sure it's not permitted.' 'But here is party,' says the long-legged stewardess, 'Everyone likes party.' 'Is it a good idea?' asks Petworth. 'Well, that man cannot leave his cockpit, you would not like that,' says Marisja, 'I think we must go to him. It is a very nice invitation. Come, we are going.' 'You said I couldn't even photograph railway engines,' says Petworth, but the stewardess beside him is pushing him up, and Marisja Lubijova holding wide the green door-curtain. Led by two stewardesses, Marisja and Petworth pass down the long aisle of the plane. The passengers, the men in hats, the women in headscarves, sit pressed together in tight rows, just as Petworth had been on his journey from London, a journey that now seems long ago; they look up, displaying a little curiosity, but not too much, as they all walk up the plane to the door of the pilot's cabin.

The cockpit seems curiously small and very technical; beyond its windows, up ahead, a great black darkness lies. But inside all is comfortable and cheery; the pilot sits in his seat, his co-pilot beside him, each holding plastic cups of peach brandy; the flight engineer, behind, takes, to save space, the second stewardess onto his knee. It is cramped, but the pilot rises very civilly, to shake Petworth by the hand, and then he shakes the other hands too, as explanations are made. 'Tells this is a new plane from Russia,' Lubijova says, 'Tells he likes to show you how to fly it.' In front of the plane, in the moonlight, the great massed bulk of mountains rises; the pilot pulls levers and ratchets for Petworth, who nods very politely. 'He asks if you like to sit down and fly it,' says Lubijova. 'Very easy,' says the long-legged stewardess. 'I don't think I'd better,' says Petworth, looking at a mountain top very close to the wing. 'You like rot'vuttu?' asks the stewardess. 'Oh, yes,' says Petworth. It is hard to pass drink around the overcrowded cockpit, but somehow it is managed, and when the long-legged stewardess sits on the knee of the pilot, and Marisja Lubijova on that of the co-pilot, there is more or less room for everyone. A flash of lightning illuminates the mountains; the captain raises his cup and says to Petworth, in English: 'Welcome, amity and concord.' 'Indeed,' says Petworth. 'Also amity and Boeing, amity and Tupolev,' says the co-pilot. It is a very good party, with much laughter: 'Now we all sing a little song for a birthday,' explains Marisja Lubijova, 'I don't think you have it in your country.' But all good times come to an end; a grid of lights appears on the horizon. 'Slaka, my friend,' says the pilot, tapping Petworth's arm and pointing. Petworth recognizes the jagged cup of mountains, spots, even, the orange pollution on the horizon. Handles are being pushed; something heavy bangs in the wing. 'He asks do you like to land it?' asks Marisja Lubijova, amid much laughter. 'Next time,' says Petworth, laughing too, looking forward into the night.

The world in front looks like a great black hole. In the hole it seems impossible to perceive a destination, except that there are lights, lights growing in size, lights becoming so big that they seem to be on collision course with the plane. There seems no sense in continuing in this direction, but the direction continues; something slaps up at them out of the darkness, with a white line on it, and the plane bounces and rocks. Brakes come on, machinery groans; there is a well-lit runway ahead. And, standing there in the cockpit, he bounces too, his brandy spilling into technical parts that other brandies cannot reach. There has been fear in him, he knows, and the fear will not go away. For now the big Ilyushin turns, taxis in slowly through the airport lanes. And even at night it is possible to see that quite a number of armed men are standing about at various points on the tarmac: clustered around the other planes that stand in line on the apron; gathered waiting on the stand to which the small van with a sign on it saying HIN MI that has appeared out of the darkness leads the great aircraft. A flight handler waves his lighted bats to bring the plane into parking position; blue buses begin to move from the ill-lit terminal; the armed men cluster round. The engines cut; steps are wheeled up to their side. 'Tells he hopes you enjoyed it,' says Marisja Lubijova, rising from the lap of the co-pilot, 'Tells he was very pleased to see you.' Through the windows, it is possible to see the passengers getting off, and going to the blue buses that will take them to the door marked INVAT. The pilot shuts down the plane; led by the long-legged stewardess, Marisja and Petworth, the flight engineer and his companion, walk through the now empty cabin of the Russian jet.

At the bottom of the steps, four of the armed men who wait around planes wait around the plane as Petworth descends with his companions, his hair awry. He should not be here; it is not right. He expects, perhaps even feels he deserves, disaster, a quick arrest. But the officer of the party salutes him, the flight engineer nods, and they go not toward the drab terminal building and the door marked UNVAT but to a quite different entrance, where there is a pleasant room, and the green stewardesses are there again, and there is another drink, and a number of warm embraces from the scented girls, with their wheeled flight-bags, and their neat neck-scarves, and then they are all on the forecourt where the blue-armed men walk, and Marisja puts him into an orange taxi, which is soon on the long straight road to Slaka. 'Oh, it is Pervert,' says the lacquered-haired Cosmoplot girl at the Hotel Slaka, 'Passipotti.' 'Now, dolling,' says Marisja Lubijova. 'I know, I know, he needs it,' says the girl, 'Tomorrow, it is late. I give you same room.' And late it is, as Petworth goes up in the lift, along the corridor past the floormaid, and into the massive bedroom where the cupids frolic on the ceiling and the tram gantries flash through the curtains. He looks down through the window, where, somewhere, Marisja Lubijova goes, disappearing into the mysterious life she has in Slaka; he turns toward the big duvetted bed.

9 – NATKULT.

I

With time to spare in Slaka, a lecturer with no more lectures to give, a tourist with nothing better to do than to tour, Petworth spends the next two days wandering the city – that idyll of north and south, west and Turkish, with its fine residences of stone and its rectorates of Baroque accretion. The events of the political world trouble him, he senses worry in the air; but everything in Slaka seems quiet. Waking in the morning in the all too familiar big bedroom, going down to breakfast, he stops each day in the lobby at the stall marked LUTTU to buy the red-masted party newspaper, *P'rtyuu Populatuuu*, hoping to find out a fact or two. *Intens'uu activuu, mass'ufu manufestu* say the headlines he reads over his pig-bacon and yurt. But though he is a linguist, though he has been in this country ten days now, and has promised to try the language in order to read Katya Princip's book, still in his luggage, the words below the headlines still do not manage to yield a sense. When Marisja Lubijova, in her grey coat, arrives in the lobby after breakfast, looking as formal as she did on the first day of his visit, he tries to find out from her what is happening. 'Oh, comrade Petwurt, I hope you don't worry,' she says reassuringly, sitting down in one of the red plastic chairs in the lobby, 'There is just a very small confusion, in a few universities, so we do not ask you to give your lectures there. But that is nice, now you have time to look around Slaka, and go to the Wicwok shops. They open again the castle, and you have not been to the National Gallery. Of course perhaps you could change your ticket and go home before, but that is not so easy, they are such bureaucrats here. And then you miss our day of National Culture, and you do not want that! Look, I have brought you a nice guide-book in English, we will find you some nice thing to do.'

So Petworth finds some nice things to do. He goes to the advanced glass-blowing factory, and to the National Gallery, where the frenzies of Post-lmpressionism and Fauvism and the work of the national Expressionist painter Lev Pric subside into the tidy narrative economies of socialist realism. He goes to the castle – 'this time *really* the castle,' says Marisja Lubijova, toiling by his side – of Bishop 'Wencher' Vlam (1675–1753, according to the guidebook), filled with fine armour and displays of Slakan history, great wooden furniture and elegant bedsteads. 'Here the Bishop likes to have his pray,' says Mari Lubijova, looking round a large, ornate, plastered bedroom, 'I think he liked to have every girl in the city. You see how God works for some.' He goes to the Wicwok shop, to look at Scotch tweeds and tartans, and to the heimat shop, to look at, and buy, fine hand-made embroidery, wood-carving, a small pot or two. He goes to parks where old people sit, and children play in groups under the regard of fat nannies in big, deep skirts. He goes to the great department store, MUG, where the people go to inspect the prospect of shopping, and manages to buy there, with some of his remaining vloskan, a big glass decanter, finely made. He makes a visit to the puppet house; he goes to the museum of old pianos. On some trips, Marisja Lubijova comes with him; sometimes, busy with her own unknown life in Slaka, she does not. He learns how to use the trams, buying tickets from the stalls marked UTTU; he begins to make in his mind a rough map of the city, though it must be admitted that, when there is no guide to describe it, no voice to tell its story, Slaka does not seem very different from any city anywhere else. The pink trams clatter, the men go by in khaki, the women in headscarves; the crowds stand outside the cinema in a bleak line, waiting to see something called *Yups*. And if there are troubles, vague drummings of disturbance, then life seems normal. From time to time, using the greasy telephones in the stand-up cafeterias where he catches a snack lunch, he tries to find out more, attempting to reach Mr Steadiman, at the Embassy, at home; but for some reason the telephone links seem to be severed. And once in a while, with great caution, he tries the number that has been given him by Katya Princip; but the telephone rings and rings in what, even down the imperfect apparatus, seems to be an empty room.

But on the third day, when he rises, and goes down to the lobby, to collect on his way to breakfast, the red-masted newspaper, he senses that something has changed. Then, over the slow breakfast, he sees what the change is, a perfectly small one: *P'rtyuu Populatuuu* has become *P'rtyii Populatiii* again. The fresh breakfast menu has gone from the table, to be replaced by a very old one, food-stained but in the words he had begun to learn when he arrived; the food is the same; and when he goes back upstairs to his room, to get ready for the events of this national day, men are lowering down from the opposite building the big neon sign that says SCH'VEPPUU. Over the square, the flags wave, for today's day of National Culture; Marisja Lubijova, when she arrives in the lobby, wears a red carnation in her lapel, and seems full of excitement. 'Well, it is your last day, and our day of happy rejoicering,' she says, 'It will be a good day, are you ready? Do you excite about our parade? I expect they will find a fine place for you.' They leave the hotel to go out into packed and busy streets: 'Oh, such a crowd on our special day,' says Marisja Lubijova, 'I hope I don't lose you again. But I think you know the way now to Plazsci P'rtyii.' 'Wasn't it once called Plazscu P'rtyuu?' asks Petworth. 'Oh, was it really?' asks Marisja Lubijova, 'I don't remember. Of course our language is a little bit difficult.' 'Well, perhaps there was just a little confusion,' says Petworth. But they come to the great square, whatever its name, and it has turned into a solid mass of people, standing, pressing, moving, eddying. The armed men who are everywhere are everywhere: 'Push, push,' says Marisja, excitedly, 'We have a special seat, of course. And now do you see how well we love our writers and our teachers?' And evidently they do, for it is clear that the people have come in their thousands: the soldiers and the waiters, the city-dwellers and the peasants from the countryside, the old men and women and the schoolchildren, the tourists from the first world, and the second, and the third, and however many more there are – they have all come and are standing together in the square.

A soldier blocks the way, in a beret, with a gun and a radio transmitter; Lubijova shows him a pass, and they climb up wooden steps onto a viewing stand. 'You see we have a good place,' says Lubijova, as they go up high, 'You are an important visitor. From here you will see everything.' Petworth looks across the great masses, a man not used to them. There is a little rain in the air, and some hold up umbrellas, some black, some plastic and transparent, so that they have the effect of a great pebbled beach. But more important than the umbrellas are the flags that are waving from side to side: red flags, blue and green flags, white and brown flags. 'Oh, don't you like the flags?' says Lubijova, 'Please don't think of all the nice shirts they would make. We like them very much on our special occasions.' And above the flags in the crowd are the great banners flapping on the poles; and above the banners and the bunting are the great photographs, those realistic images of constructed seriousness. 'Do you recognize them?' asks Lubijova, 'Comrade Marx, Comrade Lenin, Comrade Brezhnev, Comrade Grigoric, Comrade Vulcani?' 'What happened to Comrade Wanko?' asks Petworth 'I don't think I remember this Wanko,' says Marisja Lubijova, 'Of course it is hard for you to remember names in another language.' 'And who is Vulcani?' asks Petworth. 'Well, there you see him,' says Marisja Lubijova, 'Look, down the stand. The men of the Party take up their positions.' Petworth looks along the stand, and sees faces he knows: Felix and Budgie Steadiman, she in a great green garden party hat, are waving at him. And there, in the middle, right in the centre of things, is Tankic, grinning in his plastic Homburg hat. 'Oh, Tankic, where does he stand?' asks Marisja, craning to see, 'That is what we come to look for. Oh, that is nice; they must have made him the Minister of Culture! And that is Vulcani beside him, with the Russian minister. Don't you think he is a handsome president? Oh, don't you excite? And now they have come, the parade will begin.'

From round the comer, where the Palace of Culture stands, there comes a noise of martial music; then, through the strip in the centre, which the armed men keep clear, there comes, for some reason, a row of rocket launchers, and a tank or two. Behind the tanks comes a marching procession: 'First the musicians,' says Lubijova. At the front there steps a military band; behind the band are musicians of another kind, carrying violins and French horns and bassoons and cymbals. Then behind them there come, in great quantities, children in leotards, all of them carrying bunches of flowers which they wave, in ceremonial fashion, from side to side in rhythm, first to the left, then to the right. The smallest children are in the front, and then the sizes grade upward, toward the adult. 'They are the lovers of revolutionary culture,' says Marisja Lubijova, 'And now, look, the academicians, our very best scholars.' And now there marches, behind the children through the square, a very solemn body of men, eminent in their grey hair and neat suits. Among them it is possible to see a very familiar figure, Professor Rom Rum, his topcoat loose on his shoulders, a medal on his lapel, a sash across his chest. The barriers to the side break, to let through a bevy of small children, all carrying bouquets of flowers; they hand the flowers to the eminent men, and Professor Rum bends to kiss one on the cheek. 'I hope you treat also so your professors and your writers,' says Marisja

Lubijova, 'It shows how we like to value them. Oh, yes, look please, here come next our professors. I expect you will remember some of them from your travels.'

The professors, it must be admitted, march somewhat raggedly, like a poor conscript army following on from the élite troops the academy has managed to muster. Their armaments, too, seem less: a few have sashes, and one or two have medals, but others attempt to define their rôle by holding up, like winners of a world cup, their trophies, which are in the form of books. Among them it is indeed possible to recognize a number of familiar faces, like a reprise of the recent past. For Mrs Goko from Slaka is there, marching sturdily, and beside her the little assistants Miss Bancic and Miss Mamorian, as well as the big Mr Picnic, who still wears his sunshades and carries his camera. Professor Vlic from Glit has somehow, despite the troubled air-routes, managed to be there, transporting himself somehow from one side of the country to the other; and there too are all the short stout lady professors from the Restaurant Nada, holding up great big bunches of flowers. 'And which are the people I didn't meet?' asks Petworth, 'The ones from Nogod and Provd?' 'Oh, I don't think I see them,' says Marisja Lubijova, 'I expect there has been just a little confusion. But see, look, there is your good old friend, I think? Of course he has to be there.' Petworth looks around, and then sees, a little to the side, as if he has a procession of his own to march in, none other than Dr Plitplov. He steps out in his suit and his white sportshirt, with a blazon on the pocket, and holds rather low down over his head a big black umbrella; conspicuous in his chosen inconspicuousness, he slinks by the saluting stand, where Vulcani salutes his intellectual troops.

'And now the writers!' cries Lubijova, as another large company emerges from the corner beside the Palace of Culture. 'Such a lot of them,' says Petworth, staring at the large massed company. 'Of course,' says Lubijova, 'You know we are literate country. Of course some are journalists and some make only translations, but here too are many poets and novelists.

Do you impress?' The writers, men and women, step out; the children run out from the crowd to give them flowers; there is applause from the crowd. 'Oh, and there walks your little princess,' says Marisja Lubijova, 'So she is in Slaka.' And there, indeed, toward the back, walks Katya Princip, looking very well. Despite the rain that is falling increasingly, she still wears her sunglasses, pushed back into her blonde hair, and is clad in the familiar batik dress. Her expression, as Petworth tries to stare into it, is clear. Around her the writers walk; and, though not generally known for their skill with flags, they all carry little flags, and wave them from side to side, now to the left, now to the right, with a regulated efficiency. Above them blow the bigger flags, the banners on the poles, red, blue and green, white and brown. And higher still, over the whole display, unbelievably big against the tiny faces of the marchers down below (at whom, or rather at one of whom, Petworth is looking), are the greater faces, some goatee-ed and some pince-nez-ed, some moustached and some bearded, some stern and clean-shaven, of Marx and Lenin, Engels and Grigoric, Brezhnev and Vulcani, those writers of history without whom the present occasion would not have been possible. The writers go off toward the lower end of the square, past Grigoric's tomb; the batik dress disappears into the mass; 'Oh, look, now here the painters,' cries Lubijova, tugging at Petworth's arm.

II

It is Petworth's last day in Slaka, and tomorrow he flies; so, as the crowds disintegrate, carrying their flags, and they all leave Plazsci P'rtyii, it makes sense to tell Marisja Lubijova that he would like to take the afternoon to himself. He takes his lunch in a stand-up cafeteria, looking out into the hotel square where men are putting up a new sign that says SCH'VEPPII; the word is changing in Slaka. Then he goes to the greasy telephone, finds a number written on a small slip of paper, and carefully dials it. 'Da?' says a voice at the other end. 'Katya Princip?' he asks. There is a pause; then the voice says, 'Oh, really, is it you?' 'Yes, it's me,' says Petworth. 'And you have made a good tour?' says the voice, 'You go to many places in my country? But now you are back, someone told me.' 'Yes,' says Petworth. 'And did you learn anything, I hope so, you were not here for fun,' says the voice. 'I don't know,' says Petworth. 'And do you wear still that stone?' asks the voice, 'Perhaps you have lost it.' 'No, I still have it,' says Petworth, 'It's here.' There is another pause, and then the voice says: 'And now do you want to know the end of the story of Stupid?' 'I do,' says Petworth. 'Wait, I think,' says the voice, 'You know we cannot go back there to that place, the one with the lift. Things are not very easy now, I told you how it might be. You are all right?' 'Yes,' says Petworth. 'You know I like to see you very much,' says the voice. 'And I you,' says Petworth. 'Of course, we are in the same story,' says the voice, 'Listen, there is a place, if you can find it. Do you know where is the Cathedral, to Saint Valdopin?' 'Down by the power station?' asks Petworth. 'Near to the river Niyt?' says the voice, 'Well, can you go there, we say at three o'clock. You have your watch? Go inside there, be somewhere near the altar, wait for me. You can find it, you won't be lost?' 'I can find it,' says Petworth. 'I waited here,' says Katya Princip, 'I knowed you would telephone to me. Of course I am a witch.' 'Yes,' says Petworth. 'And I will witch you again,' says Katya, 'So, go there, wait for me.'

Petworth goes out into the square, buys a ticket from the stall that is marked LITTI, and gets on board a pink tram that is marked VIPNU. It is crowded in the tram, filled with children carrying flags and flowers from the morning celebrations. Gradually the tram empties, as it takes its route out over the Bridge Anniversary May 15, and rattles down the boulevards toward the new workers' apartments; Petworth is almost the only one left when it reaches the end of the line, to turn in a circle in the marshy land near to the power station and the river Niyt. At first sight, the cathedral close to is not impressive, but he walks up the steps toward its massed blackened brick. He is very early, so he walks to the side, and finds the entrance to the crypt; paying his vloska, he goes down into the deep stone rooms where the gallery of ikons hangs. He looks for a long time at the dark strained faces, staring out from the paint, the tempera, the gilding, uttering the pain, the faith, the love behind their sacred stories. It is nearly three, time to look for the person he wants so much to meet again; he goes outside, and walks to the great curved porch, scattered with confetti from a recent wedding. He steps inside, into the great solemn darkness, everywhere lit by spluttering beeswax candles, which scent the air. From the central dome comes more light, falling over painted canopies and the plaster, silver and gold of the great long altar; the altar is set far forward in the nave, as if to protect deeper mysteries within. The cathedral is almost empty; a few, a very few, old ladies in shawls kneel in the side chapels under lit candles; a small number of tourists wander about in the half-dark, with cameras slung round their necks; somewhere in the darkness, a priest is intoning.

Petworth walks toward the altar, looking for the person he has not at all forgotten, the person who makes all other faces somehow look like hers. There are alcoves near the altar, one of them holding a glinting silver tomb; in the half-dark someone comes out of one, toward him. 'Oh, are you here, my good old friend?' says a familiar voice; Petworth stares at Dr Plitplov, with his sharp black eyes, his natty shirt, his elegant little handbag, 'And you have turned back to Slaka safely, I am very glad. You have made your tour in some awkward days, but I hope it did not spoil it at all.' 'Not at all,' says Petworth. 'And now you look at our cathedral,' says Plitplov, 'Do you like it? I do not much, myself. Always I remember how the priests took from the peasants all their money, in those past times. Of course sometimes they have made something very fine of it. I hope you notice this tomb, Saint Valdopin, he was a very famous saint of us.' 'Saint of ours,' says Petworth. 'Of course,' says Plitplov, 'Always I get so excited when I see my good old friend. Do you like to walk? Or perhaps you are meeting someone?' 'Well, no,' says Petworth. 'No, you don't?' asks Plitplov, 'And your lady-guide is not with you? That is very unusual.' 'Yes,' says Petworth. 'But there are certain businesses we must always do on our own,' says Plitplov, 'You are sure you don't meet someone? Perhaps a lady? Always you are lucky with the ladies.' 'No,' says Petworth. 'Of course you are right to be very cautious,' says Plitplov, 'I told you this: in my country always one must be an artist of relations. Well, at last you seem to learn quite well your lesson. But I am your good old friend, I know your wife, you know that you can trust me, I think. I know you mean to meet here a certain lady writer.'

'Really, do you?' says Petworth, walking away. 'My dear friend, please, I do not mean to make you embarrassment,' says Plitplov, coming after him, 'Understand me, please, I also know that lady. You know what is go-between, she sends me with a message. She cannot come now, there is a difficulty, a small confusion. Her life is not so easy now as before, I think you know why, I believe you had a finger in that pie?' 'You've seen her,' says Petworth. 'You rang on the telephone,' says Plitplov, 'That was to my apartment. Sometimes she is there. She asks me to tell that she is very sorry and that she likes to see you, very much. She regrets that you do not meet again before you leave Slaka, it is tomorrow, I think?' 'Yes,' says Petworth. 'But she likes to send you a present,' says Plitplov, 'Do you like to walk outside, on that terrace? Perhaps it is the smoke of all these candles, but I feel again a little headache.' They go out of the porch and onto a paved terrace; side by side, mosquitoes buzzing by their ears, they stare down into the marshy waters of the river below them. 'A present?' asks Petworth. 'A very nice present,' says Plitplov, 'Her new book. And she tells that if you read it you will find the end of the story of Stupid.' Petworth stares down at the turgid waters below; 'But I can't read it,' he says after a moment, 'I haven't learned the language.' 'I think you will read it,' says Plitplov, 'I think you read French.' 'It's in French?' asks Petworth. 'No, it is not yet in French,' says Plitplov, 'But there is someone in Paris, a good old friend. He likes to translate that book, and publish it there. You understand that since certain difficulties, I think you know them, you had a finger in that pie, she cannot publish that book here. Of course it is not so easy to get it out of the country.'

'I see,' says Petworth, 'You want me to take this typescript out of the country.' 'I believe you have a book by this writer before,' says Plitplov, 'Well, it is just another. No one will stop you, you carry papers all the time, you are a lecturer. And the next weekend you can take it to that person in Paris.' 'I'm not going to Paris next weekend,' says Petworth. 'Well, I think so,' says Plitplov, 'I have telephoned your wife, your Lottie. She asks why you do not call, and sends you her love. We have made some arrangements and she likes to be in Paris. Of course she thinks I will be there also but that will not be possible. There is a café, the Rotonde, that person will meet you there. I hope you don't mind, you know how I like to make plans for you. Already I begin to arrange your tour next year in my country.' 'My tour?' asks Petworth. 'Of course,' says Plitplov, 'You still have those lectures to make at Nogod and Provd. Everyone likes you to come because you make such good talks. And you know I have a string or so I can pull.' 'I don't think I want to make another tour here,' says Petworth. 'My dear good friend,' says Plitplov, 'Do you know how you get a good apartment here, I will tell you. You must make some bribes in hard currency. Otherwise you wait for five years.' 'What has that to do with it?' asks Petworth. 'Of course,' says Plitplov, 'By this time there will be many francs in Paris, of the book. You change those francs into dollar, bring here all those dollar when you make your next tour, and there is a very nice apartment.' 'And who is this very nice apartment for?' asks Petworth. 'That lady writer, who sends you her present, and cares for you so much,' says Plitplov, 'And also perhaps her very good friend.'

Petworth stares down at the stagnant water below him; he

says, after a moment, 'And you are that very good friend?' Plitplov stares down at the water too; he says, after a moment, 'Perhaps we all have a secret. Sometimes it is a sausage, sometimes it is more.' 'And you've been that good friend for quite a long time?' asks Petworth. 'Of course in my country, people need a friend,' says Plitplov, 'I have made some books, I write in the newspaper, my criticisms are well respected, even on Hemingway. It is not so easy to survive here if people do not help each other. I am sorry you did not meet my wife. She is a very dull person. She does not even make a very good dinner. I think you would understand it, but perhaps you do. You know very well these things yourself. Really I think we know each other very well, now. I am very glad you came, and I enjoy well your lectures. Sometimes your theories are not correct, but you make up for it with good examples. Well, of course, I will say farewell to you at the airport. The package will be small and it will go well into your briefcase. If they ask you at the *donay'ii*, tell them you must have picked it up by accident in a confusion at a conference. And I think it is always a pleasure to go to Paris, perhaps like a little honeymoon.' 'And why should I do this?' asks Petworth. 'Of course there are ways of embarrassing everyone,' says Plitplov, 'You have not been so discreet on your tour. Really it would not be hard to make some difficulties for you. Perhaps you would have to stay here a long time in our country, not in the best conditions. But I do not make those reasons to you, because you know there is another.' 'Do I?' asks Petworth. 'Oh, that lady writer, she likes me a little, and I am useful. Soon Professor Rum will not be doing so well, there is a new regime, so it is good to have a friend who is all right, with Tankic and some others. These are our necessities, you know it. But for you there is a different feeling, I don't know why, of course I am jealous. She tells she has to see you again: that is why she sends her book, it is the book of you both together. You will see she dedicates to you. She says: here you will see, you are in one story. Also she asks me to say to you one more thing: I mean to give you a better sense of existence. Do you think you know what that means?'

'Yes,' says Petworth, turning away from the parapet. 'And so I find you at the airport?' asks Plitplov, 'I must know you really mean it. You know you will do something very good.' 'Yes,' says Petworth. 'Well, perhaps I will be a bit elusive there, you may not see me,' says Plitplov, 'Now, how our exchange is done, what you must do. Take in there your bags, put them down by the stall that is marked Cosmoplot. It is in the centre, you do not miss. Do not lock please your briefcase. Leave it there, ask to go for a cup of coffee, there is a place. Wait a few minute, then remember you have left it, and go back. That is all, and you do it?' 'Yes,'says Petworth. 'I am so pleased to see you again, my good old friend,' says Plitplov, shaking his hand, 'And you have made very good visit. I do not ashame I pulled those string for you. Well, my friend, I think perhaps here is our farewell. I don't think I will talk to you tomorrow, though I wish your flight well. I hope you will remember always your visit very nicely, I hope you think once more about the work of Hemingway, I hope you give to your nice Lottie my love and wishes to meet again. Most, I cannot tell you how much I wait your next visit here. And not I only, you know that other one waits longingly for you.' 'Yes,' says Petworth. 'So, do you go back now to your hotel?' asks Plitplov briskly, 'It is the tram marked Wang'liki over there, but first you must buy ticket at the Litti.' 'I know,' says Petworth. As he gets on the tram, Petworth looks across to the Cathedral of Saint Valdopin; Plitplov, with his bright, bird-like look, is standing on the steps. But when, a moment later, he looks through the glass, he has gone, quite suddenly, as he once did before.

That night, in the hotel, Petworth eats a solitary meal in the great dining-room, where the sad singer sings again, songs of love, songs of betrayal; he sits and thinks of obscure processes, strange machinations, stories perhaps of love, perhaps of betrayal, in which he has some unexpected part. He does not know whether these stories started before he arrived, or because he arrived. The singer tosses her hair, the gipsies fiddle, in the city of flowers and song, chaos and confession; Petworth goes down into the cellar bar, where the silvery whores laugh, and look at him. Late that night, he wakes up; he is sweating, and in a state of high anxiety. He exists, he does not. Darkness fills the room he is in; he is not quite sure what room it is, where he is. A tram clatters somewhere; he is in the dark, and under the dialectic. The duvet has come off him and his naked legs are out in cold air. The duvet is piled beside him, tugged over someone who lies there, her back against him, warm. His hand is evidently trapped under her shoulders, the circulation fading, pain in his fingers; his heart beats furiously. Troubled, curious, he senses the shape of the flesh beside him: the skin in its long planes, hollowed here, puffed there, the outward spill of the breasts, the pucker of the nipples, the inward tug of the navel, the fuzz at the groin, the intricate vaginal crease. He is afraid he has done wrong, he feels guilt. And someone watches the wrong, requires a confession and an expiation. He switches on the great brass bedside lamp; the duvet is crumpled beside him; there is no one there. Light flashes on the ceiling, with its romping cupids, its great crack; he puts off the lamp, covers himself, struggles for sleep.

III

And now it is morning again, and Petworth sits for the last time in a red plastic chair in the lobby of the Hotel Slaka, his luggage – the blue suitcase, the battered briefcase, but no longer the Heathrow bag – round about his feet. He has taken breakfast, the familiar breakfast that bears no relation to the menu, the old food-stained menu he had seen on his very first day. A weak sun shines across the square outside, with its grinding trams, and looks into the great dusty hallway. In the hallway, his guide, Marisja Lubijova, stands at the desk, talking to the Cosmoplot girl with the splayed lacquered hair, under the photographs showing portraits of Lenin, Grigoric and Vulcani. 'Oh, they are such bureaucrats,' Marisja cries, hurrying over to him, 'They say you have burned a hole in the bedspread at Glit. Of course I have fixed it, I tell them the Min'stratii will pay it. And now do you have everything, all your presents, your souvenirs? You are ready to go?' An orange taxi is already waiting beyond the glass doors; they get into it, and drive out through the busy square. СЛОРТ, says a sign, and РЕСТОРАН; in the little side street, down toward Plazsci P'rtyii, the faces of the men of history hang, with the wind taking them; so that now it is Marx high and Lenin low, now Engels up and Kruschev down, now Grigoric above and Vulcani below, and now it is the opposite. In the corner of the taxi, Lubijova sits, twisting the strap of her shoulder-bag. 'Well, my dear Comrade Petwurt, you know I shall miss you?' she says, 'In my country we have a saying; I am always telling you our sayings. We say, if you come to Slaka once, always you come again. And I think it is a little bit possible, don't you?' 'Yes,' says Petworth, 'I think it is quite possible.'

'Well, that is good, I think it means you liked our country,' says Lubijova, taking out a notebook and scribbling in it, 'And, look, if I give you an address, do you try and see me? Perhaps I will not be there, but you can try. Or perhaps I might even be your guide again, if you make an official tour. I hope you do, next time a proper one. This one was really a little unusual.' 'There were just a few small confusions,' says Petworth. 'Oh, I am sorry about my confusions,' says Lubijova, 'But I hope you think I was always good guide, you know I tried it. And I think you always needed one.' 'I think everyone needs one,' says Petworth, 'You were a very good guide.' 'And do you remember what we nearly did at Glit, and did not?' asks Lubijova, 'I remember it.' 'Yes,' says Petworth. 'And now you go home to your wife, is it Lottie?' asks Lubijova, 'The one who smokes the small cigars, the friend of Plitplov.' 'Yes,' says Petworth. 'Well, that will be nice for you,' says Marisja Lubijova, 'But I don't think you will tell her all that happens to you, not this time.' 'No, I don't think so,' says Petworth. 'No,' says Marisja, 'You will have to make up a story. But then you have learned some things about stories. You still have that book I gave you? You know, written by that one? Do you think now you will try to read it?' 'Perhaps,' says Petworth. 'Really you have not learned much of our language,' says Marisja. 'Well, enough to have an idea,' says Petworth. 'And your diseases have all gone away? Your mouth is all better?' asks Marisja. 'Yes,' says Petworth. The long straight road now stretches ahead toward the airport, with the power station and the cathedral to the right. 'Oh, what a pity, you did not go to the cathedral,' says Marisja Lubijova, 'But is good to keep one thing for another time.' 'Yes, it is,' says Petworth. 'And I think you will come,' says Marisja, 'You know I am a little bit psychic.'

A familiar gilded onion dome appears on the skyline; there are aircraft beacons in the flat wide fields that spread out to the jagged horizon. On the airport concourse stand the blue armed men; one of them comes up to the taxi when it stops in an unpermitted place, but Mari Lubijova, a good guide still, is persuasive. They go into the departure building, wooden, low, a little bigger than the building into which, two weeks ago, he came. The crowds mill, with their luggage; 'Change money, change money,' says someone, clutching his arm a trifle desperately, in the press. There is a stall marked LITTI, another marked TYP'ICHII, another marked COSMOPLOT, in the centre, with a girl in a green uniform writing at it. Long lines wait at the two small, slow check-in desks. 'Do you like to check now?' asks Marisja Lubijova. 'I think there's just time for a cup of coffee,' says Petworth, putting down his luggage by the Cosmoplot desk, and looking for a sight of a crisp white sports shirt, a natty pair of trousers, but there is nothing of that sort to be seen at all. 'Oh, do you like?' says Marisja, 'It is this way, and, yes, you have time.' His luggage left by the Cosmoplot stand, Petworth pushes through the crowd after Marisja. But, suddenly, there is a commotion behind them; one of the blue armed men comes urgently through the crowd, pushing aside priests in robes, old ladies with cardboard boxes, shouting and waving his gun. 'Oh, Petwurt, what do you do now?' asks Marisja, stopping, 'Oh, really, how do you do it, he tells you forget again your luggage. It is not permitted to leave it, you must go back. Really, you are hopeless, don't you say so? Maybe I should come to England with you. I do not know how you can live at all without me.' 'No,' says Petworth.

He walks back to the Cosmoplot stall, where his bags stand, apparently undisturbed; and that is hardly surprising, for another blue armed man stands firmly over them, legs astride. 'You see how our militias like to look after you,' says Marisja, 'Now they like you to check it at once. Our people here do not steal, but they do not like anything to happen to you. You are our important visitor.' So, an important visitor, firmly flanked by two armed men, Petworth is led to the head of the queue at check-in, while the other passengers stand patiently, casting only the smallest and most oblique of glances at the business being conducted. The green Cosmoplot girl takes his ticket and both his bags; slowly and painfully, she writes LHR on two baggage tags, fixes them to the luggage, and puts it behind her. 'That is good,' says Lubijova, 'Now you will not see them again until you must show what you have at the *donay'ii*. That is your boarding pass, put it please in your pocket, one where you will find it, or you will be in Slaka all your life. I don't mind, but perhaps you do. And your passport, you have it? And what about your moneys? You know you must not take any vloskan out of the country?' 'I'd better give it all to you,' says Petworth, reaching in his pocket for the finished money, useless for further exchange. 'Oh, Petwurt, are those your riches?' asks Marisja, laughing, 'Don't you know you have left only five? This is not too much. Perhaps a hundred tram tickets, or thirty loaves of bread. I think you can keep that in case you have some duties on your souvenirs. Our *donay'ii*, very strict. And I hope you don't take any forbidden things. Antiquities, any ikons? They will not like you if you have such things.' 'No, I don't,' says Petworth. 'Well, now if you like, we take our cup of coffee, with no worries,' says Marisja, 'I do not like to say goodbye to you, do you understand?'

Petworth understands, but something is happening to him; under the strange dulling grammar of airports, all feeling except a sense of anxiety begins to go. The announcements come through the loudspeakers, in a confusion of languages; words become part of the endless web of multilingua that runs through the head like a dream. The flight-boards are fluttering, signs turning toward redundancy; the city that two weeks has built in his mind no longer seems close. The coffee cloys and does not taste like coffee; the people already begin to look strange. 'Attenzie, slibob,' says a girl over the loudspeakers, 'The flucht of BA to London now boards after all formalities.' 'My flight,' says Petworth. Facing him at the counter, her features looking paler and more tense than he has ever seen, Marisja Lubijova is looking at him. 'Petwurt, Petwurt,' she says, 'Oh, it is goodbye. And there is no way to say it, really, no words that can be right. Do you know any? I don't. But you remember our custom?' 'Your custom?' asks Petworth; but his words choke, as two warm arms come round his neck, his face goes down, he is tugged forward into two soft breasts that are pressed forward at him, into him. 'Thank you,' says Petworth, 'My very good guide.' 'Cam'radakii,' says Mari, adding a kiss, 'For me you really are. And I hope for you I am a little bit also.' 'You are,' says Petworth; but the crowd is moving, toward the labyrinth of departure, and he must move with them, to get on his flight, and ahead there is an armed man, holding his gun out over a black line across the floor, and beyond there is a row of small curtained stalls, and a sign that says IDENTAY'II. He looks back, and sees that he has already gone through a gate that Marisja Lubijova cannot pass; she stands behind it, waving, shouting 'Goodbye, comrade Petwurt.' He turns and waves and shouts goodbye; the armed man nudges him lightly with the gun, to move him forward.

And then he is again in the familiar labyrinth of the airport, the boxes that follow on from boxes. In the booth marked IDENTAY'II, where four armed men sit, they look at his passport, and one of the men tears away the rest of his visa. In the booth marked GELDAY'II, his unfilled document causes doubt and much inspection; but 'Ned vloskan, turnii off'icayii min'stratam culturam komitetam,' says Petworth; 'Ah, da, va,' says the man, stamping the document and letting him through. Caught in the grammar of airports, already less a subject and more an object, Petworth walks on, into the larger hall beyond, marked DONAY'II. At the end of it, many uniformed men work in supermarket aisles, tipping out luggage, checking pockets and wallets. The tagged flight luggage is stacked on trolleys at the entrance to the hall, to be identified and carried to the inspection. The blue suitcase, the battered briefcase, sit there; and, as Petworth picks them up, anxiety strikes him, an anxiety like the anxiety that has been with him throughout his tour, an anxiety not unlike that which has been with him all his life, but an anxiety incremented, made intense, so that, if one was looking for a word to describe it, as a linguist should, then perhaps the word would be: terror. He puts the bags down in front of one of the uniformed men, who looks at him, and begins to open them: first the blue suitcase, with its jumble of dirtied shirts, discarded underpants and used socks, its torn best suit, split past the crotch, its small scatter of peacemaking presents, its scrap of handmade embroidery, its well-wrapped glass decanter from MUG, the sum of his travelling being. But not quite the full sum, for there is also his briefcase, with his lectures and writings and notes, his mature reflections on the Uvular R, his comprehensive version of English as a medium of international communication. The case falls open, and there are the books, Lyons and Chomsky, Fowler and Princip, *Transformational Grammar and Nodu Hug*; and the crumpled, beaten papers, held together with their rusting paperclips; and, in the middle, a thick bright wad of new paper, shining in its cleanliness, the story of Stupid.

And Petworth now thinks that he knows the end of the story of Stupid, and that it is here, where the uniformed man stands fumbling into the bags, unfolding, unwrapping, unpacking, scattering. For Petworth can see very clearly that not all the people who are lining up in expectation of taking this flight are going onward, into the departure lounge further on; some are being turned back, some being led off into side rooms for further questioning, some being inspected by more senior officers who come from a room at the back. And it is one of these that is being called by the uniformed man now; he walks over, in his blue shirt, and stares into the two jumbled bags. 'Something wrong?' asks Petworth. 'You don't speak our language?' says the man. 'No,' says Petworth, 'Not really.' 'Yes, a thing wrong,' says the man. 'What is it?' asks Petworth. 'You don't know?' says the man, 'You make an offence.' 'What offence?' asks Petworth. 'This,' says the man, reaching into the luggage, and picking up the glass decanter that Petworth has bought in MUG, 'Not for export.' 'No?' says Petworth. 'No,' says the man, holding the decanter up high, as if to examine the texture of the glass; it slips, as if by mistake, though it does not seem to be a mistake, from his fingers, and smashes to the floor. On the tiles, glinting, lie the broken pieces of the elegant, crafted construction; Petworth stares at them. 'You don't know it is not permitted?' asks the man. 'No,' says Petworth, 'I'm sorry.' 'You will know when you come again,' says the man, going back into his office.

And Petworth walks on, into the small departure lounge, where a strained and clearly depleted band of passengers stands, wiping their heads with handkerchieves and waiting for the London flight. There are some hard chairs and even a small duty-free shop, selling vodka and rot'vitti, hand embroidery and glass decanters, curiously like the one that has just been shattered in DONAY'II. But this does not detain Petworth, for the room has mesh-covered windows, and beyond them is the tarmac, where there stand the blue buses, the tank carriers, the rows of lined-up planes. One of the planes is in British Airways livery; it is an ancient Trident, the union flag flaking rather on its tail; that does not matter, for Petworth would like to be on it. But there is a wait, a long wait, as passengers filter through into the tiny lounge. Then, suddenly, a green stewardess comes through and goes to the locked door; she picks up a microphone. 'Attention, slibob, here is flugzig informato,' she says, 'Soon the flight to London of BA boards at a certain gate. For security, all baggages, including hand ones, shall be identified and placed on the cart before is boarded the bus. To take baggages into the plane is not permitted.' She unlocks the door; Petworth steps outside, puts the old, heavy burden of his luggage onto the trolley, and gets inside the blue bus. Soon it is juddering him across the concrete to the stand where the Trident waits. He goes up the steps, into the round cabin where a concealed tape plays, for some reason, 'Way Down Upon the Swanee River.' 'Hello sir,' says an affable stewardess in a familiar uniform; 'This way, please,' says another, with gloves on, leading him down the cabin to seat 21D.

'Thank you,' says Petworth, sitting down, 'Thank you very much.' Fastening his lap-strap, he leans across the passenger between him and the window, in 21E, and looks out through the globed glass. Beyond it, no distance at all away really, is the tarmac, with on it a few flight-handlers working at their familiar tasks, and a crowd of armed men, with long flared topcoats and boots up to the knee in cavalry fashion. Beyond them are the lined-up planes on their stands; beyond them one can see, white in the sunlight, the wooden terminal buildings, with their tightly closed doors, the signs above them saying OTVAT. On the roof of the building is an area where people stand and wave; they are, most of them, dressed in a certain formality, the women in bulky cotton dresses, the men in Sunday suits, though it is in fact Saturday. The plane windows are curdled from flight, so that it is not easy to project distances, or identify anyone exactly. But it does seem that, among the waving wavers, one of them, tall and dressed in grey, could well be Marisja Lubijova, her hand in the air. There are more men than women, and they look indistinguishable; but there is one, much further along, right at the end of the row, in natty sports shirt and trousers, who might possibly be Dr Plitplov, though this could well be an optical illusion. But, however hard one looks, there is no one there at all resembling the brilliant, batik-clad magical realist novelist Katya Princip. Beyond are the trees that line the airport perimeter, and poking up into the sky amongst them a golden onion, the spire-dome of a church; and beyond that is, as is well-known, the city, with its hotels and bars, its museums and cathedrals.

And inside is the cabin. On the forward bulkhead are lighted signs, saying FASTEN SEAT BELTS and NO SMOKING. It smells faintly of cleaning fluid, though no one has cleaned out the seat-pockets or the ashtrays. Petworth is old, old enough to remember the days when all British air captains had names like Hardy, and Frobisher, and Savage, just as all stewardesses seemed to come from county families and served, as it were, from the sideboard. But things change; it is not quite so on today's flight BA231. The gloved stewardess who is now checking his lapstrap has acne. 'Well, ladies and gentlemen, this is your Captain, Captain Smith,' says a voice over the intercom, 'We've got what they call a gatehold here, that means something or other's got to be sorted out. We'd serve you a drink, but local regulations don't allow it. I'd like to introduce your steward today, Mr Maggs, and your delightful stewardesses Babs and Shirlene. Let's hope the delay won't be long, and we'll soon be pushing off.' 'Isn't that typical Slaka?' says the passenger who sits between Petworth and the window, in 21E. It seems to Petworth that the man, who wears a suit and striped tie, and has a smell of rot'vitti strongly on his breath, is familiar; that indeed he closely resembles the man who was led off by the khaki soldiers on the day of Petworth's arrival, two remote weeks ago. 'They let you all on so they can take you off again,' says the man, 'Just to create a false sense of security. I've seen it, I've seen it. Fifty get on, only forty fly. I'm here often, I sell scalpels.' 'Do you really?' asks Petworth. 'Oh, yes,' says the man, 'One of those fields in which they respect our British know-how.' 'Do they?' asks Petworth. 'It's an interesting job,' says the man, 'I like travel. The only problem is, they have no idea how to do business. For instance, you can never find anybody there who's actually empowered to buy anything. You have a very nice time, sitting in cafés talking over coffee and brandy; then you find you're with completely the wrong chap. They're a little bit elusive, if you know what I mean.' 'Yes, I do,' says Petworth. 'Oh, look,' says the man, tapping the window, 'This is what all the fuss is about.'

Petworth cranes to look out; two figures, one carrying a suitpack, and both surrounded by a bevy of armed men, are coming toward the plane, disappearing under the wing. The steps are put back against the plane's side; there is a thudding of footsteps, and of people entering at the back of the cabin. Petworth turns to look, to see coming down the aisle a man in a fine suit, carrying an umbrella, and a woman bright in a green party hat. 'Oh, look, how marvellous,' says the lady, looking down at him, 'It's darling Angus. Do you mind if I sit next to you?' 'Well, ladies and gentlemen, we have our start clearance, so we'll push off now,' says Captain Smith over the intercom, 'We're flying to Heathrow with a stopover at Frankfurt, a short stop, so we'd like all ongoing passengers to remain in their seats. I can't give you a flight-time because there's still a bit of a problem at Heathrow, and we may be diverted. But I'll let you know more about that nearer the time.' The engines roar; slowly at first, then with growing rapidity, the plane begins to move. 'Thank God,' says the man who sells scalpels, in 21E. 'Take hold of my hand and hold it very tight,' says Budgie Steadiman in 21C, 'I've never understood why these things should suddenly rise up into the air, when the perfectly natural thing is for them to continue straight along the ground.' But rise, rise, rise into the air it does, over the polythene crop covers and the onion dome. 'They seem to have given you very special treatment,' says Petworth, 'Is this diplomatic privilege?' 'Yes, I suppose so,' says Budgie, continuing to squeeze Petworth's hand very tightly, 'We were being bundled out of the country. I thought they did it very well.'

The wheels come up, the casings lock; below, in a haze, is the city, the apartment blocks, the strange web of streets, the moving pink trams, the great central square, Plazsci P'rtyii, the castle of Vlam up on its rock. The bulkhead signs go out; Petworth, one-handed, lights a cigarette, thinking of the brief-case in the hold, the story of Stupid, the troubled world he flies above. 'Bundled out?' he says, 'God, I hope it had nothing to do with—' 'Of course,' says Budgie, 'Everyone's bound to think it was I. Being so famous for my indiscretion. No, that was absolutely nothing to do with it. I come out white as driven snow.' Below, cloud is drifting over, but one can just see the orange pollution of a power station, the bulk of a cathedral that seems to have had its top knocked off, a river spilling everywhere beyond its banks, a jagged cup of mountains. 'Then what was it?' asks Petworth. 'It was Felix,' says Budgie, still holding his hand, 'He did something to a peasant.' 'Ra ra ran over him, actually,' says Felix Steadiman, leaning across the aisle in his blood-speckled shirt. 'He stepped out in front when Felix was driving along, absolutely perfectly properly actually,' says Budgie, 'Then he lay in the road and said he was dead.' 'Yes, we were in a pa pa part of the country we shouldn't have been. That rather counted against us,' says Steadiman. 'The ambassador moved awfully fast, though, I must say,' says Budgie, 'For one of his years.' 'Probably turn out to be a bi bi bit of luck,' says Steadiman, 'You know they expect the Vulcani regime to announce martial law this evening. Oh, froliki, some thirsty people here. Could we have a gin and tonic?' 'Yes, sir, as soon as we leave their airspace,' says the stewardess, smiling down at him, 'Sma sma smashing girl,' says Steadiman.

Below, the cloud has covered, and there is nothing to be seen. There is something in the air, perhaps to do with the ears, that changes the world obscurely; one can scarcely dispute Marx's proposition that changes in condition produce changes in thought. Consciousness shifts; words and concepts change in weight; reality is not eternal, but a collective construct. Yet things elsewhere matter, history is universal: 'Martial law?' asks Petworth. 'Yes, end of lib lib liberalization,' says Steadiman, 'Vulcani's an old soldier. I expect things will be rather sticky for some of those people you met. You're well out. I tried to call you at the ho ho hotel actually, but the telephones were cut. You had no trouble leaving?' 'No, not really,' says Petworth. 'Well, jolly good,' says Steadiman, 'Ah, my dear, I take it we're all gin and tonics? Yes, three, please, with ice and lemon, and could you bring some nice nuts?' 'It's the quarrelling I'm looking forward to,' says Budgie, 'We can do it all the time.' 'You realize this is probably the end of my dip dip diplomatic career?' says Steadiman. 'Don't be gloomy, Felix,' says Budgie, 'Better than twenty years with your lorry drivers. And there's still always Bangladesh. I do hope Angus, you'll come and visit us on your next tour. You do do this kind of thing a lot, don't you? One would not want an acquaintance like ours to lapse.' 'Here you are, drinkies,' says Felix Steadiman, 'Did you actually get to Provd?' 'No,' says Petworth, 'There was a small confusion and they dropped out that bit.' 'Pity, really,' says Steadiman, 'That might have been interesting. That's where they were shoe shoe shooting people. You didn't see anything of that anywhere?' 'No,' says Petworth, 'I suppose I'm just not a character in the world historical sense.' 'Well, anyway,' says Steadiman, 'Ch ch ch ch cheers.' 'Yes, cheers,' says Petworth.

There is a brief stopover in a very rainy Frankfurt, where a few of the passengers get off; the rest remain strapped in their seats, unable even to go and visit Dr Müller's Sex Shop, for that intimate small present that might please her so much. There is a glimpse of autobahn, packed, as the flight resumes, and then soon they are circling and recircling a strikebound Heathrow, while Budgie grasps Petworth's hand in a desperate grip: 'These people always think they've got more petrol than they really have,' she says. But the signs come on, and soon there is a glimpse of a red bus and they are running along the runway. They go through the long half-empty endless corridors and through the United Kingdom channel in immigration; beyond is the luggage hall where the carousels turn. Petworth collects a cart and goes to the turning machine with a sign marked SLAKA, where luggage vomits into view and is collected. The businessman in scalpels, from 21E, waves and walks off; 'Are you coming?' asks Budgie, holding his hand again. 'No, my briefcase hasn't turned up, they seem to be leaving it till last,' says Petworth. 'Well, Felix has to go straight to a debriefing at the FO,' says Budgie, 'So it looks like au revoir, though not, I trust, goodbye.' There is another kiss, and then, in their fine clothes, the Steadimen walk out. Petworth waits for a while longer, and then goes to a desk. A clerk in a white shirt makes some telephone calls, and then says: 'I'm afraid they offloaded your briefcase at Frankfurt by mistake.' 'Oh, no,' says Petworth, 'When will I get it?' 'I'm afraid you won't,' says the clerk, 'When they found the passenger wasn't scheduled through the airport, their security people blew it up.' 'I see,' says Petworth, 'You'll take more care of me.' 'Well, these days one has to be very cautious,' says the clerk, 'You're entitled to make a claim, of course. Was there anything in it of great value?' 'I suppose not,' says Stupid. He walks away, following the signs, the words, the arrows, that lead him out, through the green channel that means nothing to declare, into the Heathrow concourse; where, at the barrier, he sees, waving at him, his dark wife.

WHY COME TO SLAKA?

WHY COME TO SLAKA?

A Guidebook and a Phrasebook

TRANSLATED INTO ENGLISH BY DR F. PLITPLOV

(Dozent Extraordinarius, Universitet Dvarfim Borism)

INTRODUCTION BY DR A. PETWORTH

ISSUED BY THE MIN'STRATII KULTURI KOMIT'ETIII
(MUN'STRATUU KULTURU KOMUT'ETUUU)

PUBLISHED BY THE STATE PUBLISHING HOUSE 'V. I. LENINIM'
(PRAV'DI V. I. LENINSKI/PRAV'DU V. U. LENUNSKU)

PEOPLE'S REPUBLIC OF SLAKA
(STATII PRO'LETANIII SLAKAM/STATUU PRO'LETANUUU SLAKAM)

CONTENTI

*Information on Weighs, Measures, Healths etc. etc. are dissipated
through this book: somewhere there are maps and typical photographies.*

WHY GO TO SLAKA?

Slaka!!!

Where is the heart that does not high upleap at the very merest name of your immemorable city! Slaka!!! city of flours and gipsy musick, of great buildungs and fine arts, we toast you in your own brandy-spiritus!! Slaka!!! great city at the international crossroads, where for centuries people of the most various parts have liked to come together for congress. Slaka!!! bustling metropole of traders and entrepreners, where one time a year exhibitionists of worldwide fame foregather in your great halls of conference in most festivating mood for the justly renowned 'Once-A-Year Commercial Travellers' World Fair'. Slaka!!! sweet city of musicality and song, trios and filharmonias, where each summer the most prodigious musicians of all lands come to perform in amazing fashions at the honoured 'Z. Leblat Musicology Festivi', the highest point of everyone's musical dairy. Slaka!!! cosmopolite capital and shop-walker's paradise!!! where in your noble bulevars pricey shops offer at bargainous prices the very best of everythings. Slaka!!! duel of the crown of of our favoured country, where the best heritages of old times and the the contemporary charms of socialistical cooperation meld to composite a lifestyle both antiquated and progressive. Slaka!!! city of all-sorts, where in wondrous and orgiastic mixtures the rationalistic clarities of the North meet the boisterous intemperances of the South, the techniks of the West meet the relaxing lethergies of the East, and everyone is delighted! Slaka!!! capital of chic, so when nights descend and the motor-cars swatch on our brightly lightered boulevards, only a short stroll in this fine old town will convince you at a start there is much to be had.

Slaka!!! with your fine sepulchres and your rectorates of baroque accretion, who cannot smell everywhere your history? Slaka!!! with your laughing boys and your imping girls, who cannot want to delight in your happy people's? Slaka!!! with your exotic plates and your nightlife of the chicest kind, who can deny your pleasurabilities? Slaka!!! city which has captivated the soul and bodies of so many of all the ages, who can ever oblivate you?

Slaka!!! Oh, why do I not go there pronto?

How to Utilitate this Book

This book contains everything you need to survive in Slaka.
It is:
***Guidebook: with pictures of cities; maps of streets!!!
***Phrasebook: in probable situations and familiar usages, we show you how to master us linguistically. One look and you will see how simplified our language really is!!!
***Dictionary: how we list all our major nouns, verbs and other participles. Remember: we use both Cyrillies and Romanesque alfabetz, but for you we are Romanesque only?!!

MESSAGE FROM THE SLAKAN
HEAD OF STATE,
COMRADE-GENERAL I. VULCANI

Comrade Tourists!!!

In Slaka, when we drink, we like always to make toast. Our favourite toast is 'to dialogi!' With 'dialogi', we mean many things. 'Dialogi' is the friendship of all pease-loving fraternal peoples. 'Dialogi' is the great spirit of amity and concorde. 'Dialogi' means the desire for true intercurse – an intercurse where each parter is an equal and no one is on top! Now, in the mood of 'dialogi', I like to wellcome all turstiis, from here and there, from wherever and who knows, to the ambiant airs of our romantikal country. We wellcome you indisiscrimatly, from the friendly socialistical republics and from the imperialistic-fascist western powers, gladly recieving all nations and taking all currences! You will find our people warm to host you! See their arms, stretched out to greet you!! See their faces, smiling to meet you!! See their loins, girded to the task of giving you pleasure!! Know our motto: please come to us, and we promise, one day we will come to you!!

The land you wellcome to is a nation proud of its socialistik emulations. You will find our peoples marching bravely forward with their eyes ficked on the horizon of the future, their hands meanwhile baldly undertaking the works needed to achieve it. Everywhere you will find great and startling projets. We do not mind to make a criticism. In the past mistakes have been made, but we do not mention them. Certain errors have been committed, but now we correct them. In Slaka today, not all is perfet, but allmost. You will find here a land of noble achievements and fantastikal promises. And remember, for us even your vacancy is a contribution! Last year a toto of 400,000 turstiis visited Slaka. This year our heroic travel-workers have pledged a new target: 500,000 plus turstii!! We know you like to help them brake their records!!

We summons you to come, asking only you observe our customs, as we like always to observe yours. We ask that you do not come with long hairs, if a man, or short, if a woman; this offends the modesse of our people and we cannot admit you. We ask also that you do not make a drunkness in public, except on our many state holidays, listed later on in this book. Obey please our kind laws and you will truly say, having wunderful time! Comrade turstiis, in Slaka we belief in travel, as a true striving for knowledge. If you come here, remember you do not take only holidays: you advance the brotherhood of nations and the cause of history. Of course you will also find some very nice beeches, and take home an excellent needleworks!!

By way of contusion, I extend my comradely embrace to those whose hard labors bore forth this book. I mention our great Min'stratii Kulturi Komit'etiii, who concieved this great projet under the wise new dirigation of our notable Culture-Minister F. Tankic; our National Academy of Arts and Sciences, whose excellent historical advisements were directed by Hero-Academician Dr Professor Rom Rum; our national-hero publishers and printers of the state press-house 'V. I. Leninim', whose redactive achievements are everywhere manfusted here; our culture-hero translator Dr F. Plitplov, whose prodigious interpretational facilitations made passable this Englisch-language edition; and our many fine travel-workers who exist only to turn your turstii dream into harsh reality.

Vulani

Comrade-General I. Vulcani

INTRODUCTION

By Doktor Angus Petworthim
(Lektor in Linguistics, Bradford, England)

Not long ago, in the course of my professional duties (I lecture on the English language as a medium of international communication), I was invited to visit the fascinating Eastern country of Slaka. I am an experienced traveller who has lectured extensively for the British Council and can claim to have had diarrhoea for that excellent organization in most parts of the globe. It had however long been a matter of regret that I had never visited Eastern Europe, a place of fascination for me as for most Westerners. As for Slaka, I have to confess that I had never heard of it, thought it was somewhere quite different, and had never identified it on the map. This, perhaps, is not surprising, since it has frequently not been on it, having been often occupied by one or other of its nearer or further neighbours. Happily this ignorance was soon to be dispelled.

For, by great good fortune, I received an official letter from the Min'stratii Kulturi Komit'etiii of the People's Republic asking me to undertake a lecture tour in their land. The Min'stratii – the state cultural organization, for which the term 'Arts Council' would be a profoundly inadequate translation – would be my hosts and arrange my journey. Naturally I accepted at once. The visit that followed was, to say the least, unusual, and I regard it as one of the more amazing and indelible experiences of my life. To the Min'stratii I remain grateful for the spirited hospitality they afforded me – all the more generous since, owing to some small bureaucratic confusion, they were expecting a quite different Dr Petworth to come and lecture on a quite different topic. For three weeks I travelled in the country, not simply visiting universities, but going everywhere I liked (except of course in the restricted areas), seeing everything I cared to (apart, naturally, from materials of strategic importance) and meeting everyone I wanted (except, inevitably, in their own homes). To this day I recall the heavy savour of Slakan life, and the piquant texture of its political existence. I can truly say that a surprise awaited me round every corner, and I found myself captivated wherever I went.

What made this trip a journey I am never likely to forget? From the moment I stepped out of the flashy modern impermanence of Heathrow Airport into the COMFLUG plane (COMFLUG is of course the Slakan state airline) I felt my tour would be different. They tell us that mass travel has made the whole world much the same; if so, Slaka was clearly to be an exception. Where Western airlines obscure the discomforts and aggressions of travel with plastic food, bad films, strong drinks and fixed smiles from swollen-ankled stewardesses, COMFLUG with its wooden seating offered an immediate feeling of getting back to life's basics. That impact of the hard, sturdy roots of experience was to last throughout my tour, as I walked through Slaka's fine people's parks, inspected its great highrise developments of workers' apartments, toured its modern steelworks and its collective state farms, and saw the determined spirit of progress proclaimed on its banners everywhere. Despite the somewhat complicated currency rules (foreigners must change so much a day, to allow them to take advantage of the excellent export products, like the notable bottled beetroot and the incomparable brown shoes), and the difficulties of the language, even for an expert like myself, I feel I came to know the country, and it came to know me.

I also, I think, came to know its delightful people. It can surely be said that in no country is the Western visitor better watched over, and nowhere are there so many people who seem solely concerned for his or her interests and needs. Slaka is a land where no one need feel lonely or neglected, and those who think attentive hospitality is a lost art would be well advised to visit it. In the public buildings, the parks, the cafés, I made innumerable new friends, who pursued me wherever I went. Some courteously asked about the people I had met or intended meeting, offering all the help they could in identifying them. Others affectionately tried to help any transaction I might desire to undertake, generously asking if I cared to sell them my clothes, meet their female relatives, or engage in the various tradings and exchanges that are a kind of sport in this bantering and bartering land. With typical Slakan good nature they constantly asked for my autograph, took my address, and loaded me with introductions and messages for their relatives in other countries. So warm-hearted were they that there were times when I thought they would never let me go. The feeling of their affectionate attention still persists, and indeed explains why I am privileged to introduce this delightful book, so effectively rendered into his typically brilliant English by my old and demanding friend Dr F. Plitplov, presently Dozent Extraordinarius of Glit's renowned Boris the Small University, a leading Slakan translator, and a most vigorous international correspondent.

What shall I say about this fine volume? Like any regular traveller I have always felt dependent on having first-rate guides – ideally ones that are well organized, truly informative, neatly shaped, easily handled, not difficult to open or use, and instinctively ready to satisfy all one's most urgent needs. Indeed on my visit to Slaka, I was fortunate to have two of these. One, provided by the Min'stratii, was a most pleasant young lady, who acted as my interpreter, travelled everywhere with me, did all she could to display to me the mysterious face of her country, and even saved my life on a couple of occasions. I remain deeply in her debt. The other, equally helpful in its own more inanimate way, was this very book – or rather, not quite this very book, since it did not have a preface by me, for at that time I had not been there, and could not have been prevailed upon to write one, but an earlier edition, now, since it contains a good many outdated facts and figures (one of them the previous head of state, ~~Professor Vlad'mir Wanko~~), quite out-of-print. Thanks to various small changes that have lately taken place in the country (many of them occurring, as it happens, during my visit), a new edition, purging all previous errors, has proved necessary. This work, undertaken by the great state publishing house V. I. Leninim, now brings only totally accurate information, and I am delighted to participate in this, to use the Slakan phrase, great and startling project.

In these pages you will find everything needed to facilitate your journey to and in Slaka, and even out again. Like my own more human guide it will assist you linguistically and in every other way through every situation you are likely to encounter. Unlike her, it slips easily into the pocket. It has many uses, as tourist guide, detailed phrasebook and, in the waterproof edition, as a bathplug. It affords valuable information on almost everything: the problems of obtaining a visa, finding a hotel room, mastering the intricacies of the complex Slakan railway system, shopping, getting out of the various small confusions that arise on any holiday or business trip, and displaying the fascinating life and landsape of a country infinitely rich in this and not at all lacking in that. I am particularly pleased to see included an account of the Z. Leblat's great opera *Vedontakal Vrop*, having been fortunate enough to attend that work's modern revival, after it had been lost for 200 years. I recall with pleasure the evening I sat through that famous five-hour performance in Slakan, and can honestly say that its tale of comic confusions, mistaken identities and sexual chaos is one of the great expressions of the depth and interest of Slakan culture.

If you do intend to visit Slaka, this guide can be warmly recommended as quite incomparable (indeed, it is the only one). It can be recommended quite as warmly if you are *not* going to Slaka. In my book *The English Language As a Medium of International Communication* (University of Watermouth Press, 1981; reissued with corrections, 1986), I have occasion to remark that the world is structured like a language, and language is structured like a world. And – like those American menus so mouthwateringly descriptive of the meal to come that they can almost be eaten instead of it, and are frequently rather better done – this book similarly could be said to be a verbal visit to Slaka in itself. Thus if you should not be able to make an actual visit to Slaka – and flights there are, it is true, not frequent, visas sometimes hard to obtain, travel arrangements, despite the efficient facilities of the state tourist board COSMOPLOT, sometimes complicated, and the language difficult, so that despite my own professional expertise I was unable to master it, even subsequently – this book could be an effective substitute. Indeed these delightfully produced pages may be said to contain almost everything about Slaka that can possibly be known.

But do not let reading this book deter you from making a visit. Slaka, as the guidebook says, is not to be missed. If the journey is hard, the compensations are many. The welcome is indeed warm, the atmosphere contemporary, and you can be truly promised a different kind of holiday. The food is pleasant, the drink excellent (especially the famous peach brandy, *rot'vitti*, which is definitely not to be missed!), the girls are pretty, especially after the drink, and so, it is said, are the men, especially after the girls. The artistic achievements are considerable, if sometimes baffling. Many fine buildings survive from ancient times, though I do not recommend the Cathedral, which is a long way out of town, inconveniently down by the River Nyit, and appears to be used as a place of unfortunate assignations. However, the tomb of the great liberator Grigoric affords a far more modern and comfortable place of pilgrimage. The state glass-blowing industry is well worth a visit, as are the fine museums of socialist achievement. Slaka is a great commercial capital, and you will find its great streets always lined with shoppers, keenly awaiting the arrival of some splendid new commodity. For any adventurous holidaymaker, Slaka offers a truly different and more up-to-date kind of holiday, and despite its extraordinary attractions it remains relatively uncrowded with fellow travellers. Velki in Slaka, the Slakans like to say, and, if you are like me, you will find yourself velki indeed. Vy'aggii boyo, da!!!

GEOGRAPHY AND HISTORY

By Professor-Academician Rom Rum
(Slakan Academy of Arts and Sciences)

SLAKA: WHERE IS?

Imagine please a beatiful small country from a fairytale, where
on each high cragtop stands an ancient castello and in fine rustic
residences the traditionally dressed pheasants of folklore plie
away at their rural trades and practice their ancient customs,
and dances by pheasants in regional costumes are regularly
performed. Then please imagine also a paradisial workers' state,
where the best principles of socialistic emulation guide advance
into the future and agro-industry progresses appace with the
willing cooperation of all. Now please put together one with
the other these two fine imaginings, both pittoresque and progressive. What do you have? Perhaps you think, an unattainable
paradise? Ignoramus!!!, it is not so! What you have is fact not a
dream. Of course, it is the People's Republic of Slaka (Statii
Pro'letanayii Slakam), which you should not neglect to visit.

Set by the generous hand of prodigious Mother Nature in a
warm and wooded declivity between the delightful Vronopian
mountains, truly we have in the city of Slaka just the kind of
place where everyone likes to come. With the great Storkian
plain to the east and the rolled hills of Pritprip to the west,
fecundly watered by the great river Nyit which floods its
proudish way throughout our verdant country, our famous city
may fairly be called, in Dante's own evocative word, a 'parad-
iso'. Beyond spreads natural wonders and our great small cities,
ancient and modern, blessed each in their own ways. Consider
our wethers, neither Northern neither Southern. Here in benefi-
cent circumstances the warm zephyrs of the Mediterranean

meet the fine mistrals of Siberia to produce our famous laughing climat, sweetly warming in summers and bracingly colding in winters. Little wonder that at every season tourists in many numbers come to enjoy us, and of course we like to enjoy them.

And truly has so smiling been Nature's lavish hand that Slaka may claim all the geophysological advantages. Favoured by gaps in the great bandchain of mountainous ridges of Mittle Europe, offering all the vantage of river crossing from East and West or even vice verse, our land is the historical fountainhead of all the great trading routs. Equidistantly placed between the Baltic and the Adriatic, the Danube and the Blub, Slaka itself may still properly claim its ancient title as the central city of the universe. Stretched out as they are between norther plain and Alpine mont, alluvial plantain to sea-girt salted coast, our peoples may think themselves truely favoured. To them belongs a heritage of variousness. A land of infinite variables and unpredicted contrastables, the Slakan People's Republic may claim to be the melting pot of all human life. Here the oriental caravanseri of the great Silk Roads with their accompanies of Tartar hoards made their way to the westward, to encounter the Crusader armies of the West. In consequences, here was war and trade. Here scimitar struck blunderbum, and spice and silk traded for manufactured tricket and mechanistic geegaw. Known as 'the cultured crossroads', and also 'the bloody battle-field (tol'sto'ii incard'ninu) of Middle Europe', Slaka may count itself fortunate, not to say lucky, for what has been done it.

Such heritage still mirks Slaka today. As if the spirit of the Hunnish Atilla has met the romantic sole of middle Europe, the genii of Kublai Khan met with the essence of Martin Luther to create a rare people, fraught with the best weight of innumberable traditions. Truly our culture is a *pot pourri*, our heritage a salad. Over time our borders have been wide, small, and often not there at all. Today it is often said that our country is in a place quite differing from the place it started. Our faiths and loyalties have in the past been mixed, our languages many. Can such variety be made as one country, united in one progressive cause?

The answer is, yes!!, or, as we have it, da da!! Today under the secure guidance of the Praesidium of the People's Republic, and with the wise wings of the USSR ever cast watchfully over us, Slaka shows everywhere its metal. Our peoples are united as one. Our borders of 1,200 vlodim are guaranteed to us, except in emergence. Our natural resources of beetroot and tin (how well one goes in the other!) are secondary to none. Home to the stork and the barbary goose, our terrains produce envious surplices. Industry does not neglect: our steel-production leaps by bounds.

SLAKA: HOW WAS?

Over generations historians and scholars have chittered and raged over Slakan history, but accurate facks are scarce and perplexiculities abound. Born far ago in the darkest ians of time, nurtured in the soul of that primeval forest which cradled all human life and kultur, to this day, history in Slaka is a mistery! No good recordings exist before Century X. The chronicle of Nostrum, famous monk of Kiev, believes our people were born first in the Bosphorus, but even such is dispute. Everywhere in Slaka we find human deposits which indicates our people have primitive origins. Our hero-archeologists find constant troves of primeval character, indicating the presents of hunter-wanderers. But who they were and what they were up for, which they hunted and why they wandered still is not evident. We know the incursive wondering tribes of the steppelands (the notorious Mogul hoards) came here, and there is not doubt that our Slakan salad has been flavoured by a Tartar source. Yet other tribes of the rape and pillage kind can also lay claim to the privilege of discovering the wonderful lands of Slaka. Medes and Swedes, Asians and Thracians, Tartars and Cassocks, Mortars and Turds clearly settled our terrain of lake and forest. All have left their imprint, their customs, and their jeans. This

Peasant youth with famous plums

shows clearly in the physical character of our peoples, who, you will find, are fair in the upper part and dark in the lower. And this explains too why in our natures you will find always a little bit of the Caucasian and a little bit of the Arrabesque!!

Today diggers of all kinds keep on upearthing bits of our pluralistic heritage. What is clear is that our paganistic times were interrupted – in Century IX, or possibly IIX, or X – by the comings-and-goings of Christianity. Legends tell that this was brought to Slaka by the former Comrade Patron-Saint of the country, Valdopin (??3–??8) but even these datums are oscure! Story tells that Valdopin came from either Byzantium or Constantinople to convert our tribals to the Christian heresy, and for a time succeeded. In consequences our land was recognized by the Holly Sea and became first a nation, beginning her great advance forward into the future of history. Alas not so Valdopin! He went on to convertate the paganistical tribals to the north, or the west, or maybe the south or just possibly the east, though this is particularly strongly disputed. By them he was tortued, massaced, and minced by swords into very fine pieces. Our Slakan fourbears liked to give him a marter's burial, and requested the fine-chopped corse. A famous legend tells that a bargain was made in the Slakan fashion. The pieces of corse were set on one scale, measurated against an equal weigh of gold in the other. But all the gold of the Slakan treasor was piled and still that scale did not like to tipple!! Then came an old woman and set down her lively savings, a tiny coin!! Now did the scales tipple, and Valdopin's corse came to Slaka. The Domo of Saint Valdopin, now triumphantly restorated after bombings by our progressive architects, remains still by the waters of the River Nyit, but the sight is inassessible. Many church propagandas were made of this legend, and in past times when our people were deluded by religious values pilgrims came there often to repair their sights or throw away their cruches. Today the interpretations of socialistick materialist science explain the correct meaning of the story. Now it is recognize as a major folkish legend displaying that power belongs never to those rich and spoiled princies but to always to the people. Today our modern pilgrims preferate to visit the tombo of our great warrior-liberator of Marxist-Leninism, V. Grigoric. Yet we do not deny our Valdopin-legend. Certain it is that from that data forward, our Slakan peoples have always had a great love of exchange!!

So was our nation founded, but alas in following saecula history was not always so very kind to us. In the later millenaria constant sackings, pillage-and-rapings, invasions and external oppressions ocured: the dark-age of the history of the Slakan people. False prancelings and margraves dominated the land, nominated by our compressors. A succession of Transylvanian princes, Ottoman mamelukes, Teutonic nights and bishops-kratokrator swayed over us. In one reign only, under the bastard king Kermit the Indeterminate, our country was occupied no less than eighteen times by different foreign oppressors, while Kermit sat on his trone looking this way and that. No wonders then that over these times our morals declined. Our oppressors brought many faiths, and made our people swear. Our churches fell into neglect and wolves made their houses there. Our people leaders were cut down without ruth. Our learning halted and our langue fell to decline. No wonders then that few records of our dark age exist. Only one traveller of these times left an impression. The famed British tourer, Sir Fyffe Ffiennes, did reach in 1608 to Slaka, and recorded of his travellings: 'Wondrouf it if, that peoplef fhould have fettled here, there being here no wellf, no fuelf, no building ftuff of any kind to be efpied, and little for any to do fave confume their domeftick animalf. No artf of any kind are cultivated fave a form of dominoef, and mufik if alone the baggepyppef.'

Yet it if faid that the refourcy fluidneff of the Slakan character was forged by such evenements, so not all was bad. Famous oppressors emerged, as Boris the Short, who married Marie-Theresa the Fat, successored by his yet worse son, Quasimodo the Square. He liked to take our women to his castle and put our men to death down wells, unlike his son, Ladslav the Pretty, whose preference was opposite. Not until century XVIII did come a great cultural revival under Bishop 'Wencher' Vlam, whose castello still stands on top of Slaka today, and whose baroque tendencies are everywhere apparent in the city architectonics and the depravities of his court-life. Nudish masques were danced before the alters, and eunuchs performed in the streets. Today we may forgive some of these depravities because of Vlam's love of the arts. He nominated many musicians to haunt his courtings, including Z. Leblat, our great composer, who united the songing of folk and court, and is awarded if posthumously the title of First People's Artist for his unexcelling achievements.

Not however till the national arisering of century XVIX, led by Prince Bohumil the Shy, did our people seek a relief from oppression. In 1848 when all peoples of the region defiantly raised the banner of national liberations, the Slakans were not absent. Their gallant army of 350 men arose to throw off the yoke of the Turks, the Greeks, the Slovaks, the Prussians, the Swedes, the Piedmontese, the Serbs and the Gipsies. This united all nations against them, and in a heroical fight of twenty minutes they were bravely defeated. This great evenement was celebrated by our national poet-hero V. Hrovdat, killed on his horse as he very quickly receipted in battel his great 7,000-line epic poem *Rambo Flambo*. Since that time, our nation continued to alleagure with countries and protective alliances of all kinds, but always in the interests of our decadent burgois gentry and never in favour of the workers.

But as modern times rose it was clear that great evenements were on the iffing. Founded in 1910, the Slakan Workers' Party brought the vanguards of socialistikal thinkings to our country. Our great leader Grigoric, top-scoring student of Moscova in the 1920s, whose tombo we venerate in Plaz'scii P'rtyii, raleighed all enlightened souls under the slogo, 'Struvo vitam novam' (Strife for a new life). The scared-to-death landlording classes did not however budge, and a World War was required to release the promises of the great Comitern. During the war our peoples fought heroically on several sides, and numberous marble plaques dedicated to those who fell in national struggle remind us of those heroic days. In 1944 as the war concluded

Senathus of Hrovdat Universitet

Grigoric began a great workers' purge and liberated us to the fraternal Soviet army, and Slaka was proclaimed 'a people's republic'. Veritably here was a new day of dawning, and the peasants willingly gave up their lands and the house-owners their properties in their lust to become tools of hsitory. Truly Slaka today has proved by its creative application of the principals of Marxism-Leninism that all can contribute to concreate historical reality.

ACHIEVEMENTS AND POLITICAL SYSTEM

By Min'strat I. Tankic
(Minister of Culture)

SLAKA: WHO RUNS?

Today Slaka is a People's Republic belonging proudly to the fraternal brotherhood of socialistical societies and dedicated to the advance of history everywhere. Member of Warsava Pact and Comecon, loyal peas-loving 'brother in arms' of the URSS, it is a socialistic state of the working people of the country, run by the outstanding representatives of the proletariat class. Modern Slaka proudly boasts three political parties – the Slaka People's Communist Party (SPCP), the People's Slakan Communist Party (PSCP), and the Communist Slakan People's Party (CSPP). All have no difficulty to agree on the same progressive policies. If necessary, elections are frequently held, their victors often afforded the opportunity of entering government offices. Nowhere does proletarian democracy better flourish, or the will of the people more resolutely express itself. This can be seen in the fact that very often one popular candidate, deeply desired by the people, may stand for all three parties. This compares very famously with so-called democratical conditions in the West.

Today Slaka truly contributes to the great treasure-store of experience accumulated in the construction of socialism. The governmenting body, representing the sovereign will of the worker-people, is the *National Assemblage of the Fatherland*, responsible for policies of revolutionary socialistic emulation, and the advancement of the progress of history. So clear is the will of the people in Slaka that it needs to meet but four days a year. Following always the mott, 'Prolo Solido' ('Solidarity with

Slakan shepherd urges into the future his flock

the Workers'), this Assemblage holds representatives of all groups: the committee for State Security, the counsel of Ministers, our military leaders, and even elected representatives. These give their advises to the *Supreme Counsel* ('Politburo') which decides on executions. The Members of the National Assemblage appoint the Politburo, which appoints the President, who appoints the members of the National Assemblage. This insures coherent polices.

Nor does our democracy stop here. In every district and throughout every workerplace or rural collective are the representative devisions of the communistical and anti-fascist parties, and even the young can enjoy by being admitted if their critical thinking is correct to the Young Communistical League. Other associations are the Slakan Hikers' Union and the Union of Slakan Motorists. This structure produces ultimate democratization, and the hopeful sensations so typical of our progressive people's republic.

SLAKA: HOW NOW?

Modern Slaka is a society in the front van of progress. Since the heroic liberation of 1944, about 2 million dwellings of the workers have been constructed, and the average space permitted our livers is 10^2 meters. Notable cities of workers have been built by miracles of prefabrication in Hiririsi'stat and Engel'stat, constituting a tortuous complex of 60,000 pops. The trade unions direct socialistic emulation and are responsible for the sucess of the 'rationalization' movement. Under our fourth Five Year Plan petro-chemical growths nearly doubled almost, and our shoe production multiplied five-folds, producing more than 750,000 units, or three shoes for each of our citizens. Agriculture has more than matched our industrializing development. Over 300 state cooperatives of 1000 ha flourish, and our sour milk and yoghurt production is the envy of the wide world. The advanced watercress industry is a miracle of aggro-organization. Our nuclear technology is proud of its piles, and our RMBK Kiev-type reactor, with its spectacular emissions, offers the means of electrifying our entire people. We wish one day to export these enervating facilities worldwide.

In social welfare and education large expanses have been made. Now our women are gladly paid a wage to make children, and free teachings in Marxist-Leninist arts and sciences are availed from kindergarden to universitet. Our literacies advance by leap and bound, and our sporting achievements are spectacular. Our Olympical synchro-swimmers take many golds, and our hero ballroom-dancers triumph universally in competitional events. Slaka is famous also for its pretty stamps, beloved of filatelists everywhere. In times when in the west economical decline is profuse and unemployment widespreads, Slaka boasts its achievement of total employment for all, along with technical progress. Who cannot envy it? Can you truly say your society is better?? Truly we say modern Slaka is a young nation proudly on the march, its eyes firmly fixed not on the day after yesterday but the day before tomorrow!!!

THE LANGUAGES OF SLAKA

by Katya Princip
(People's Novelist)

For me, as a good writer, what an unusual honour it is to be asked to write in this official state guidebook about the language of my country. Naturally it is an invitation one cannot refuse. So I try to explain you if I can.

Slaka is not a very famous country, and we speak a little language not many understand, not even us. Sometimes it is said that this is because of all the Eastern Europe tongs ours is hardest to learn. It is the purport of this excellent little book – which is fine phrasebook and vocabulary book as well as guidebook – to learn you at once this is not true. Really, I can tell you: to learn our official Slakan language is a matter of simplicity itself. In our country there is a saying (ours is a country full of sayings, and, as we say, 'With so many sayings who needs any doings?'). It tells: 'Of course our language is easy! See, even our babies can learn it!' And of course it is clear that if babies can learn it, so can you. It also helps if you have some Finnish and perhaps a little Hittite. Of course our grammas are different; but if you think our grammas a little odd, think how your English grammas appear to us! All you must remember is that, like Turkish and some others, our language *agglutinates*. This means we make up our cases by adding some more syllabubs. That is not so hard, is it? Really, I think after a few days in Slaka, you will soon be agglutinating too!

Some people like to say that to learn Slaka is a wasting of time, because it is not a world-langauage. About this we also have a saying: 'We are not yet, but we will be.' What I like to tell you is that for your small efforts there come very great rewards. After a week or so of praxis, think, you may be able to read many more official books, just like this one! A bit more endevors, and you will be able to listen to and try to understand the great speechs of our leaders! A little more work yet, and all the great tresors of Slakan literatur will ope to you! You will be able to delight in the great works of all my collegues in the Writers' Union of Slaka, where we all agree that their novels, depicting with such a profound insight the lifes of tractor-drivers as desperately they seek to outdo all previous records of production, are quite definitely major contributions to world-literature! Please, we are not just a little flyshit on the map of the world! So do not think there is a better way to spend your time!

All that makes our language seem difficult to learn is that it is not just one language, but several – and we keep changing them all the time! So in our country no two people speech quite the same, but this is quite natural. It displays you our liberalism, and the historical confusons of our people, who are so mixed up in heritags and so mingled in roots they do not know at all where they stand. Naturally, each region likes to speech in its own way, and every district likes to keep its own dialetics. As a result we have perhaps three main languages, and fiften dialetics, and so of course we do not understand ourselves very well. But do not dismay. With socialistik rationalizations this great 'Tower of Babble' problema has been triumphantly undercome. With characteristikal brilliancy, our wise leaders and party-cadres in their fine offices have given us a new language, Official Slakan, called 'Tom'Slakam', which means, of course, Book-Slakan. They have employed only the best and more perfect fetures of all our languages, and no bad ingredients are used. Thank to this intervention, we are all able to talk to ourselves. Today it is forbidden to write any state pronciament or publish any book in other than 'Tom'Slakam'. Only one problema remains – nobody ever speaks it, so nobody understands it. But then we remember our great saying: 'You cannot build socialism in a day, or produce a baby in a

370

week!' How fortunate we are in Slaka, to have such brave officials who determine to try!

You are confused? Please do not be. Strange to say, an excellent explication of our language is to be found (of all places!!) in a novellum written by a British liberal-burgerish writer M. Bradburyim, called *Rates of Exchange* (in the Slakan translation it is called *Cursi'Cursii*, but this is really quite hard to get). This account of certain so-called going-ons in our country misrepresents from the standpoint of some ignoramus British language-expert the historical realities of Slakan life. However, the reported intervention of national-hero-translator Comrade M. Lubijova puts clearly to this man of strange linguistic pratfalls the basical simplitude of our Slakan tongues:

> It is not so complicate. All you must know is the nouns end in 'i', or sometimes two or three, but with many exceptions. We have one spoken language and one book language. Really there are only three cases, but sometimes seven. Mostly it is inflected, but sometimes not. It is different from country to town, also from region to region, because of our confused history. Vocabulary is a little bit Latin, a little bit German, a little bit Finn. So really it is quite simple. I think you will speak it very well, soon.

This description makes clear that the task is straightforward, though we do not to this day know whether that British visitor succeeded it.

However apart from such passages the novellum of Bradburyim is not to be commended. It is not a useful story, and alludes to events that did not happen, particularly a language revolution, the so-called 'Revolution of the UUU's', when liberal elements sought to change the language. And though nothing that book did describe did ever take place, we are proud to say that these events which did not occur afford decisive proof that free and frank discussion, dissent and criticism are always permitted in my country.

Why, if these events did not occur, is it necessary (or even wise) to mention it? Here you must know another of our sayings: 'It is best not to forget the past entirely; you will probably need it again in the future.' We also like to say: 'A good Slakan knows two languages, this for now, the other for later.' The fact that this or that has not happened in the past does not deny that it may happen in the future. Here, in a very fraternist spirit, I like to offer a small word of advise. If you come to my country, and you wish to open your mouth, be just a little cautious. If you arrive in a time of linguistic uphevals – and I think you will know this by the sound of gunfire in the streets, for we take our languages quite seriously – take a care: keep down the head, and mind also your 'i's' and 'u's'. In these days it is best to speak only 'Nova'Slakam'. In other days it is not. As we like to say: 'History is a fickle mother, and sometimes she is bad father as well.' Really, it is best to get this right unless you like to stay in my country a very long time, and perhaps you do not.

But such confusions should not muddle you so much. Our country is delightful, and you will find that quite a lot of young people here speak some Englisch, especially the words of Punk Floyd songs. This phrasebook you hold will do all that is necessary, and presents you all familiar useages and probable situations. This will help you to find the Cathedral, or the lavatory, to make friends in street or in the sleazed ambiance of some gipsy art-strip club, and communicate well with our friendly police and national security force if you are detained

---

Interpretational Facilitations

Interpretors of the most expert kind are always availed in Slaka, for, congresses, diplomatical purports, commercialistic enterprises, etc. Apply only to the Burosk Dolmetschim, Min'stratii Kulturi Komit'etiii, and your incomprehensible problems will be over!!!

for currency or other severe offenses against the state. Therefore we advise you to carry this book with you at all times. Perhaps it is also a guidebook to your own country. Here we have another saying: 'Always read a book twice, once on the pages, once between the pages.' A good book has many uses, so carry it carefully, read it often, look in it everywhere. And, whatever you do, this time do not lose it!!

GETTING AROUND IN SLAKA:
A HANDY PHRASEBOOK AND GUIDE

CONTENTI

MAKING A TOUR IN SLAKA

SLAKA: WHY TO COME?

So much for our backgrounds, but let nothing detter your visit to this beautiful place. Truly Slaka is a country not to be missed. Large woods invite sportsmen, and 'vacations in saddel' delight horse-riding fans. Especially lovely is the month of May, when the magnolias bloomb. But other excellent seasons include autum, spring, summer, and winter. However you like to come in Slaka, we oblige. And if our transports or hotels are some-times not quite perfect (we do not mind to make a criticicm), we recall a wise saying of our Russian brothers: 'A little rigour makes a holiday better!'

Slaka has always been famous to travelers, a land for all of curious tastes. Our own great traveller, Vrop Personip, who stems from Gilt, a town famous for its humours, was asked once 'Why come to Slaka?' He thought for many minutes, then retarted: 'Everywhere you go in Slaka there is something, and then a lot more!' If asked what more there was, he thought for minutes, then repiled: 'I do not know, but you will find it!' His wise saw is long-remembered with us. Truly in Slaka travellers have found always that 'lot more'!

So we invite you!!! attend to our cities and townlets, our congress and our festivis!!! We invite you!!! come, rest at our spars and drink the water in our baths!!! We invite you!!! dance at our gipsy nightspots, or sip our hot meads and salt almons in our tavernas, or sit under a bird-filled tree and enjoy a village wed!!! We invite you!!! join please our gourmandizings, enjoy-ing our famous speciality 'sarkii banati' (folded pate on a bun) or the great delicatesse of the Pritprip region 'tortosa bakum' (tortoise baked in its shells). We invite you!!! drink with us in our vinous regions, and remember in their native sets even the strangest potions acquire a delirious taste! We invite you!!! to our prehistorical deposits, our centres of balneation, our busting marketplaces!!! We invite you! Do you come?

You will not regret. For holiday-making there are fine modern hotels, where your room will often have balcony with WC. For the sun-loafer, there are our fine beeches. For the glutton, Slaka is a lasting festival of oat cuisine. The dionysian disciple cannot fail to become delirious with our fine local vintages. The hiker will delight in our famous long marches, and the mountain-climer will not forget our faces. Folklore lovers will delight in our yogurt competitions, where dances by pheasants in their long skirts are frequently performed, accompanied by their women on the bagpipes. The archeological digger will enjoy many a poke in our ruins. Theater-lovers will delight in the products of our great 'Gorky-Ensemble' Theatre Company, and do not forget the Puppet Theatre, next to the Russian Embassy, which gives great delight to small audiences. The music-buffer will make by instinct for the great 'Z. Leblat Musiology Festivi', and leave with our filharmonias still ringing in his ears. If of operatic bent, you will undoubtedly seek out our great 'Oper Z. Leblatim' oper-hus, where you may see a major operatic repertoire with the world's leading singers mounted by our great operturge Leo Fenycx (geb. Praha, 1958).

Truely, in Slaka there is something for all!!!

SLAKA: WHEN TO COME?

Always famed for its wethers, Slaka offers you delight at all seasons of the year. Springs in Slaka, celebrate in song and story, are a balmy time, when warm zephyrs of the mediterranean meet wafts of the North to create a climat always melba and never extreme. Summer delights us, and when our fine sun brills it is the Slakan way to retire to our lakesidings and make one endless sportfest. Autumn when the sun is gentile is our fruitiest time, when we suck mouthwatered appels and collect the grapes and olives from which we make our exceptionalist wines. Winter with its snows and fogs is ski-time, when we like to slip on our slopes and then all foregather to make our famous hot baths in the woodshed. Neither hot neither cod, Slaka is through the year long a place of unstinting resort. Come when you like, you find wether to please. When to come in Slaka? Any time!!!

For seasonal coutume we offer this advise. Almost never does it rain in Slaka, but raincloths are desirable in some season, mostly spring, summer and autumn. For traditional reasons many of our people carry umbrellas in the streets, so take good care of them!!! In summer bring sporting gears, from the whites of tennis to the latexes of skindivering. In winter we recommend a furpiece and perhaps it is wise to wear a rubber on your foot.

SLAKA: HOW TO COME?

By Airs

The state airline, Comflug, tries to fly to all countries with which Slaka has friendly relations. In a mere 4 hours from London (usually longer from New York), their weekly flight will wisk you to a new vacation wonderland. The airport at Slaka, 'Flyt'dromo Z. Leblatim', is but 5km/8mi from the city. Busses to the central Comflug office, Wodji'mutu 217 (no chekkin facilities), depart by the hour. Tickets must be bought in avance at the airport tobacco stall (Littii) and are not available in board. Only the orange-coloured taxis should be used.

By Seas

You cannot come by seas to Slaka.

By Rails

No direct train-routes like to come from the West of Europe to Slaka. Yet indirect trains from such centres as Riga or Bucharest

378

bring many travellers. Such trains stop at many places, and sometimes at stations, in our country. Train service inside Slaka is of two kinds: quite fast (es'pressii) and quite not so fast (rapidii). There are two classes (III and IV) and IIIrd class is commended to travellers who like their comforts and prefer to be seated. Some *es'pressi* bear on occasion a dining car, though often reserved for party officials. (Attenzie: photygrafing of trains and transportation systems is a state crime, suspected to severe penalties.)

By Roads

No main autoroutes pass through our country, because we like to keep it nice, but British travellers will be accustomed to this. But Slaka lies not remotely from the route Berlin-Calcutta and Moscova-Sevilla. Slakan roads are often asphlat and many are free of boulders. Foreign drivers are permitted an entry at 3 frontiers, Pilaf, Splat and Vitosk. Insurances and permits of travel may be purchased (75 vloskan) from the boarder. There are more than 15 stations of petrol (bin'zinii) in the country, and tourists may buy with western currency at special high prices. Types of petrol: regular (regli), 15 octane, and extra (ex'trii), 18 octane. We practise our driving on the right, but pass only on the inside. Traffic regulations are a little distinctive: e.g. forbidden is to overtake haycart. Also forbidden is to drive at night, drunk, and in a restricted area, especially at once. Speed limit: town, five vlods an hour, countries, eight vlods an hour. Everywhere there are special police patrols to help you and tow you somewhere. Parts of western cars are not availed,

---

Distances in Slaka

The main unities of long measurement in Slaka are the nippii and the vlod (73½ nippin = 1 vlod). For convenience, one vlod = 10 kilometers or 2 miles (approximative).

but our mechanicals are very resourceful. However you do well to travel with screwdriver and string. Penalties for accident are severe, and our peasants know this and sometimes like to have them. And remember!!! in our country we like to drive with a little excitement, so expect always on the road some surprises!!!

Getting Around in Slakan: A Phrase Book

Often Slakan is considered one of the more difficult European languages. Here we show you it is not true!! This small phrasebook is designated to help, presenting probable situations and familiar usages. Remember, we like to write our language with both the Cyrillic and Roman alfabets, but most of our semiotics are in both.

Also included is a list of vocabulary. One look and you will see how very simple our language is!!!

AT THE AIRPORT

[Remember!!! Our Slakan state airline, Comflug, likes to fly to most capitals with which our country has a friendly relation!!!]

This is the airport	Hic fo flyt'dromo
There is the entrance/exit	Hac fo invat/otvat
Go to arrivals/departures	Invo in'venii/ot'venii
Have a wonderful trip!!	Bone vy'aggii!!
Please check your baggage	Chekkii'chekkii, da?
What is your destination?	Quo toc destino?
You want to leave our country?	Toc volo parto no statiim?
The plane is full	Flytbom fo pleto
There is another in three days	Ultro in trezim diazim
But that is full too	Ma hoc fo pleto als
Do not be dejected	Nei winj'o
We have found you a place	No trovo plaz'scim

Someone has been taken off the plane	No grabo oi dan flytbomum
The passengers are boarding	Vy'aggii fendo inburdi
Follow the signs	Suvo semioticii
Slakan Nationals/Foreign Nationals	In'diginii/ot'diginii
Passengers/Groundstaff	Vy'agii/Terri'towii
Flightcrew/Cabincrew	Flugsi'mannnii/flugsi'frolikii
Identity check/Currency check	Ident'ayii/Geld'ayii
X-ray check/Body-search	Skelli'makii/Bot'proddii
Be so good as to undress	Nakiii!
Kindly bend over	Bend'ii!
This is forbidden	Hic fo prohibito
That is indecent	Hac fo porno
Those cannot be exported	Ho nei poso ex'porto
Have a good flight!!	Bone flugso!

ON THE PLANE

Welcome aboard	Velki in'burdu
Fasten your seat-belts	Lupi lupi
No smoking	Noki roki
Do not take photographs	Noki fyto'gryfi
Pay attention	Attenzie
Read your leaflets	Voyo sifti'pimflitim
Lifebelts are under the seats	Flatt'in umper stuli
Oxygen masks will appear	Maskaya ick'sgeni flipifloppa
Here are the emergency exits	Poddo immerg'nicina
The crew have parachutes	Flugsimanni ho puffi'packim
The stewardesses do not serve drinks	Flugsi'froliki nei ho buvam
The toilets are closed	Evak'ebo fermo
Small delays may occur	Flyto di'verto
We have found a good place	No trovvo plazscii possibli
You will like it here	Toc amico
Now we are landing	Standaki noc
Stay in your seats	Resti in stuli

The police will inspect you	Mulit'zayuu toc voyo
The soldiers will protect you	Soldati toc tecto
Do not move	Noki moti
Do not speak	Noki sondo
The bus will take you	Auto toc fendo
Push to the back	Shuvo bakom
It is only four hours	Solo versi ora
Welcome to Slaka!	Velki in Slakam!!

Clocks

Slakan time is 2½ hours in front Greenwitch Meal Time, except in provincial cities and the countryside, where local custom prevails.

SLAKA: AT THE FRONTIERS

Visa

All visitor require a passport with visa, obtenu at the 'Consolii dan Popliim Prol'etaniim Stattim Slakam' in most Western capitals. Seventeen copies of photographs are require. On arrive, visitors must registrate with the local Militia each night and change residences only with permissions. Passipotti are normally returned in a few hours, unless there is a little confusion.

Customs

Our customs like to be very friendly, but certain rules are strict. Is forbidden to bring to Slaka: a) fusils and boms, b) benzines and acids, c) drugs and hihis, d) books and papers, c) pornos and vidi'nasties. Dutyfree is foods, drinks and tabacs needed in holiday, but all personals must be delared and listed on entry. Gifts of a value of 100 vloskan may be taken at depart, but only if on our 'exportable list', and not on our new 'unexportable list' which arrests the exports of our national tresors.

Currence (Geld'ayii)

Is forbidden to enter or leave Slaka with Slakan monies. Also restricted is the money brought into the country. Each traveller makes a declaration emptying the pockets and undertaking to change so much a day. Change may be performed only at the offices of the state bank (Burs'ii Prole'tanii) or at the change-desk (camb'ayii) of your Cosmoplot hotel. All currencies must be accounted at departure, so keep always your recipes.

The units of currence are the vloska and the bitti (one

hundred bittiin to the vloska). As a rough guide, one bitti purchase matchbox, five a postcard. With one vloska you may take twenty times the tram, or buy 2 kilo tomates, or 1 kilo dry sausage. With fifty vloskan, maybe you like a nice trouser, or a beautiful lady. There are four rates of exchange: diplomatic rate, congress rate, business rate and tourist rate. All rates fluctate according to the decline of the western economy. (Attenzie: illegal transactions are sometimes offer. Remember, we say in friendly way!!! Currence offences are severe crimes against the state, and attract the most severe penaltos!!!)

MEETING, GREETING, ETC.

This is a meeting	Hic fo receptii
Here is a greeting	Hac fo grussi
How are you?	Com'fo, da?
Very well	Bone, da
I am delighted to be here	Mi boyo fendo in Slakam
We are delighted to have you	No fo boyo als
I bring greetings from our comrades	Mi grusso dan cam'radakam
I bring love from our government	Mi grusso dan burosk'nikki
Are you my interpreter?	Toc fo mi dolmetschi?
Do you speak Slakan?	Toc ho lingam Slakam?
I am a foreigner	Mi fo estrangi
I have not been here before	Nei fo vanti in Slakam
I do not speak the language	Nei parlo lingam Slakam
I cannot understand you	Nei capisco
Don't you speak English?	Nei parlo lingam Anglistikam?
We speak it a little	No ho poco
But not much	Ma na mamoro
You speak too quickly	Toc lungo malto volto
Please talk more slowly	Lungo lenti
More slowly still	Lenti ma
Write it down	Scripto, da?

We can't read it	No nei terpo
This is very difficult	Hac fo malto stupido
Please don't leave me	Nei lasco
Help, help	Sosso!! Sosso!!

FINDING DIRECTIONS

Can someone help me?	Poso sosso?
I am a friend	Mi fo amicato
Pleased to meet you	Favi grusso
How can I assist you?	Com'sisto?
Where is the tramstop?	Quo trovo halti'truggiim?
Or else the bus-stop?	Als halti'autobussom?
I wish to go to the city	Volo fendo in stattim
I have much baggage	Malto baggii
There is no problem	Nei problema
What are you doing?	Qua fo?
Where are you going?	Qui fendo?
He has taken my baggage	Ig tako mim baggim
Make way	Accesso, pardi
Sorry, excuse me	Pardi
Follow that man	Suvo hac frollin
He has disappeared	Ig parito
This is an emergency	Hac fo immerg'nicina
Do not worry	Nei frenzo
Here we do not steal	Nei grabo hac
It is a crime against the state	Multo penalto
There is a policeman	Voyo, jend'armi
He takes you to the policehouse	Toc fendo in jend'arm'nosk
You must make a statement	Toc fo splicaro
And stay there three days	Oc resto trezi diazi
I do not want my baggage	Nei volo mim baggiim
It was very old	Malto antish'ki
Thanks for your help	Malto slibob po sosso
I hope to see you again	Spiro nac toc voyo
I hope you see me again	Spiro nac mi voyo
You have helped me very much	Toc fo malto soso

I don't know what I would have done without you	Nei capisco quo fo sin toc

TRAVELLING TO THE CITY

Can I get a taxi here?	Mi grabo tacksi, hic?
I have waited an hour	Mi stando una ora
Is this an official taxi?	Tacksi officiale?
Take me to the city centre	Tako mi in centrim, da?
You drive very fast	To chargo masti, da?
Please drive more slowly	Lenti, lenti, nei?
More slowly still	Malto lenti, da
He was only a peasant	Agrico solo
His friends will assist him	Amici sisto
Please turn down the music	Devolvo musika, da?
Much as I admire military bands	Toc concerto milut'aristiku fu superbo
What a lovely view!	Qua voyo dur'agayo!!
The countryside is splendid	Rurim fo splendido!
And what a fine city!	Qua stattii boyo!!
Here are the workers' apartments	Voyo, hi'risi proletan'ayii
They are a miracle of construction	Miraculo structi, da?
This is an industrial district	Hic fo plaz'scii meckanistici
See the records of production	Voyo semiotica product'im
Our workers work long hours	Proli labore oram mamoram
They do not get tired	Nei fo flaggo
That is why we are successful	Hac tecto no fama
Work is good	Laboro fo bone
But everything is closed on Saturday	Fermi samzi, naturo
What is this fine place?	Quac fo hac structi grandi?
This is your hotel	Voyo, toc otelli
I have enjoyed our trip	Bone tui, slibob
What is the fare!	Koliko po vy'aggiim?
For you, a special rate	Po toc, cursi specialistiki

Better than the clock	Melio quan tictok
Please pay in dollars	Dollari, nei?
Alas, I have no change	Nemi camb'ayii, pardi
Thanks, guv	Malto slibob, cam'radaki
I hope you can manage	Toc fendo okay, okay?
I have a bad back	Vertibri fibli

Telephones and Posts

Slaka has telefonic communications with many parts of the world. To make an international call you must book one day in advance with your hotel telefonist or the police. To keep tidy streets, telefon booths do not litter our cities, but post offices have faculties for interior calls. Telephone numbers may be obtained from the Ministry of State Security or the communications officer in your hotel. If you here strange noises in the line, remember!!! our system is different!

Letters and postcards may be sent abroad by delivering them personally to the People's Post Office.

TRAVELLING IN SLAKA

COSMOPLOT WELCOMES YOU!!!

The word of welcome in Slakan is 'velki', except sometimes 'grussi', and always we like to say 'velki in Slakam'. Tourism in Slaka is a well-practised art, with every convenience. For under the wise dirigation of our Ministry of Tourism all tourist enterprises have been designated to the state tourist board, 'Cosmoplot'. Famous for their organizations and working beneath their proud slogo 'We have ways of making you tour!', Cosmoplot operates all tourists hotels and trippings, plans your congress and overseas your vacance from starts to finishes. Their desks are in the airporto and the lobbys of all hotels, and their fine hostesses in distinctive blue uniforms delight in instructing and telling you to have a very good holiday!!

Today most travellers like to go inside packages, and 'Cosmoplot' affords tours of every kind from the historical to the mercenary. But even if you do not fit in a package, you may still avail of 'Cosmoplot's' incomparable services. Trained personal will put you in a room, make sure you trip when you want to, and in general ensure your pleasurable experiences. They will provide you with girl guides, and try to interpret you in any way. Only ask – it is their work and they love to service you. In fact really it is impossible to tour in Slaka without their facilitations!!!

YOU LIKE AN HOTEL???

For the benefit of tourists who like a place to stay, Cosmoplot provides hotels in many of our cities and countrysides. Here to

Prospect of artisan dwellings with twin towers of HOGPo

highest standards are availed all the facilities of western comforts. Do you like a room that has bad-wc? It is available for all-in prices. Free services include the transport of baggages inside the chamber, cloth's brushes, footwipers, information of the temperature of the air. Only small charges are made for a wash and an iron. All foreign guests must stay in these places. This is to avail them of further advantages, for all have automatically insurance against death, loss of power to work due to accident, and disappearance of baggages. Lobbies often contain a tobacco shop, a perukist, and a Wicwok foreign currency shop for the delight of the turstii. Here with your fingertips you may buy magazines and sweets, postcards and matches, some decorated, vestments of leather and carpet, folkloric tissues, our fine party newspaper, *P'rtyii Popu'latiii*, the English *Morning Star*, and the best Slakan novels and poems in fine British translattions. Here, if you do not have it, you may buy this very book!!! Also conveniently place is a desk for exchange. Remember to use it!!! Foreign visitors must change so much a day. We make this rule

389

only to facilitate your opportunities of shopping, enabling you to purchase our excellent export products (the notable bottled beetroot!! the incomparable brown shoes!!) and enjoy the privileged arrangements in hotel, restaurant and art-strip club.

Every major town affords these magnificent hotel-palaces. In Slaka leading hotels are «Hotel Cosmoplot-Slaka»*** «Hotel Cosmoplot-Orbis»**, «Hotel Cosmoplot-Volga»**, and «Hotel Cosmoplot-Yalta»†. All afford complet services of eating, drinking and sleeping. For example, in «Hotel Slaka», do not neglect to visit: ***RESTAURANT SLAKA: offered are such delicacies as, Kyrbi Churba (mutton soap), Cotelette de l'Amateur (chop-lovers' chops), Sarkii Banatu (folded pate) and the notable Boyard Plate, animated with folkloric singeres and typical orchester:***NIGHTCLUBZIPZIP: the personal are clothed as peasants from mountains and national fame artists give remarkable performances of, jiggling, songing, art-strip, etc.: ***BARR'II TZIGANA: the personal are in coutumes Romany, and both spiritual and non-alcoolical drinks are availed.

Further afield, in the interior, at mountain or balneological resorts, hotels both traditional and modern welcome your sojourn. At «Hotel Cosmoplot-Kosmos»**, in Glit, a waterwheel perpetually roules, and the ristorant, perched high on rocks, offers a superb vertigo, while sheep are roasted as you watch. A bar in the arabesque style proposes romanticism, and the nearby verdure provides you with a place of quiet resort. At «Hotel Cosmoplot-Siberia»††, in Nogod, a beach is afforded with comfortable bathchair and we invite yo to spend many plesant hours in the lake.

Whatever your taste, from luxury to primitivism, we are happy to provide. Our lakeside resorts offer cabins and right on the spot you may hire a tent or field-kitchen for a camp experience.

No doubt about it, all will be sattisfied by their sojourn in this beautiful land. And know again our other slogo, 'Cosmoplot, tota po toc servic'im ('Cosmoplot is always at your service'). Yes, truly we can say 'Velki in Slakam!!'

REGISTERING AT THE HOTEL

[Hotels in Slaka are run by the state tourist board, Cosmoplot. Their comforts are outstanding and all western currencies are taken.]

Welcome to your Cosmoplot hotel	Velki in toc otellim Cosmoplottim
It has a newspaper stall	Habo litti
A hairdresser, a tourist shop	Py'ruki, Wicwok
A desk to change your money	Camb'ayii
A restaurant, a nightclub	Ristor'anti, Club Zip-Zip
There is a nice bar downstairs	Bone barriii umper
With many lovely ladies	Malto froliki amici
They are forbidden	Stricto prohibito
But we like visitors to be happy	Ma no volo boyo no vy'aggim
First you must register	Primo, fo reg'ystrayo
Here is the registration desk	Hac reg'ystrayii
Just past the man in the big hat	Passo frollin dan krapam mamoram
I want a room	Volo rom
There is no room	Nema rom
Oh, you have Slakan currency	Ah, vloskan!
Perhaps one small room	Solo poco rom
I'll take it	Tako, slibob
Fill the registration form	Scripto permi, da?
Your name, address	Nami, husi
Street, Town, City, Country	Stratti, Osk, Statti, Dig'ini
Name of Father, name of Mother	Nami papi, nami mami
Passport number	Nombo passi'potti
Identity card number	Nombo ident'ayii
Date of birth	Dati nati
Where from? Where to?	Fendo vanti? Fendo nac?
What for? Why here?	Purporti? Rat'yonali?
This is your doorkey	Locki, da?

Your hotel identity card	Identay'ii, da?
No card, no breakfast	Nei hac, nei for'tost
Please carry my bags	Porto baggi, slibob
They are too heavy	Fo mamoro
Is there a porter?	Hac fo baggi'manni?
He is at a meeting	Noki baggi'manni
Where is the maid?	Quo fo sklaf'rom'rub'froliki?
The maid is on holiday	Sklaf'rom'rub'froliki fo festo
Go to the lift, elevator	Fendo in up'zippim
Alas, it does not work	Noki fendo
There is the staircase	Hac fo up'ploddi
Yours is the seventh floor	Toc ho plino septi
Enjoy the facilities of your Cosmoplot hotel!!	Resti bone po otellim Cosmoplottim!!

FINDING YOUR ROOM

Which is the number of my room?	Qua schlaff'roma?
It is down the corridor	Fendo pa kafkam
I will show you	Mi proddo
I am the floor maid	Mi fo du'enna
I sit here always	Mi suto simper
I watch over you all the time	Mi toc toto surveio
This is your bedroom	Hei, toc sklaf'rom
I will unlock it	Mi oppo
Look, a bathroom!	Voyo, badi!
There is no toilet paper	Nema bad'i'papuri
You should bring your own	Obligato porto bad'i'papuri
I like this room very much	Amico malto sklaf'rom
It has been cleaned very well	Netto splendido, ha!
We like to work hard	Amico laboro
We do not accept tips	Noki retro'mannii
We work for the state	Laboro po stattim
But my mother is ill	Ma mati in'bone
My uncle is dying	Nunco fo morti
My child is incurable	Mi petto vasto
Thank you very much	Multo slibob

STAYING IN YOUR HOTEL ROOM

Have a nice stay	Bone resti!!
We are not responsible	Noi pendo on no
Lock your door at all times	Noppo portim simper
Vacate room by nine o'clock	Ora parto, 9:00
Breakfast is available	For'tost, 5:00–7:30
Lunch is regularly served	Mi'tost, 11:20–12:00
There is an excellent dinner service	Bak'tost, 5:00–6:30
Ring for our laundry maids	Sono lavo'frolikim
They love to wash you	Amico toc lavo
For a small fee	Mamoro grato
List your customery	Listo habitom
Declare your underwearings	Scripto umper'habitom
Pants and knickers	Wy'frontii, combii
Vests and braziers	Bodici, floppa'chekki
Shirts and blouses	Blusii, blusi'frolikii
Jackets and trousers	Vesti, pantii
Do not make iron in your room	Nei ferro
Do not fume in your bed	Prohibito!! Noki roki in sklaf'burdim
Take fire precautions	Attenzie!!! Combusto!!!
Listen always for the bell	Attendo clappa'clappa
Immediately leave your belongings	Lasco bagiim pronti
Do not use the lift	Noi fendo up'zippim
Climb out of the window	Parto po fen'strum
We are not responsible	Noi pendo on no
Have a nice stay	Bone resti!!

Electrical faculties

The voltage is 110 AC/DC (20 cycles, 8 watts). Wall-fitments are of the usual five-pin type. Electrical shaving in hotels is an offence against the state, attracting severe penalties.

LEAVING YOUR HOTEL

I had a nice stay	Mi fo bonem restim
The service was splendid	Servico splendido
The food was out of this world	Mamo'tost incred'ibili
Everywhere I was looked after	Mi surveyo tota
Where do I pay my bill?	Qui fo tottii?
There is the cash-desk	Kassa do, da?
Run by the State Bank	Po Burs'ii Prol'anii
Here is your account	Voyo tottii
This is a lot	Hei, mamora!
Your rate of exchange is bad	Cursii mali, da?
The vloska is rising	Vloska levo
The pound and dollar are sinking	Punti oc dollari lapso
Due to the degeneration of the West	Ecun'moco chil'ial
We have a good economy	Ecun'moco splendido
Founded on socialist principles	Princ'ipo socialistikum
It is far too much	Totti malto malto
I cannot pay it	Nei capo pagayo
You have to pay it	Obligo pagayo
You must have a credit-card	Toc ho kartam'umperi'plastikum?
You are a westerner	Toc fo occidento
We always can fix things	Experto rematiko
We have been traders for centuries	No fixo po millen'ariim
Just sign here	Scripto, da?
Oh, your telephone call to Japan	Hei, telefono in Nippom
And you burned the eiderdown	Als singo duvetim
That is very serious	Maximo penalto
I forgot to include them	Oblivo, oblivo
But your bank will settle	Bursii solvo
Please come again	Reveni, da?
Cosmoplot is always at your service	Cosmoplot, tota po toc servic'im

YOU LIKE TO MAKE A SHOP???

In our country we have a saying (always a saying!): 'Put a Slakan on an island and he starts a shop!' This alludes to the tradition of trade which has always been so much a piece of the Slakan caracter. Because of its place at the international cross-road, the goods and chatells of all lands have usually found their ways to Slaka. In our gay street markets peedlers like to peedle vegetables of infinite strangeness, and shops of distinction carry imitations of major branded goods. If you like to buy a 'Pirker' pen, a 'Guchi' shoe, or a 'Famous Mouse' scotch, you will probably find that somewherre in Slaka.

Where to go? Walk first to the great shopping bulevar 'Stalingradsi'mutu', where specialty and delicacy shops of each kind abound. Do you like to filatalize? Do you want a glass boot? In elegant windowdress you will doubtless find. Go to the bespoke men's shop and suit yourself!! Go to the elegant woman's boutique and try the lingueries!! And then there are the distinctive Slakan comodes: glasswear, fine brod-eries, carved wooden things of the foret. Our peasants when they do not labour at their field love to take up the knife at home, while, perhaps, the wife of the house cardles and spinds.

Eminent on Stalingradsi'mutu is our great state department story, MUG, so famous that many visit it not to shop. Here is a true world-emporium at last, a tresor-trove of goodies, leder and pelt, woovens and spuns, nitware, bottied beetroot, and 'national cotume' dollies!! Rations of goods come in frequently, and then what a fight to by!!! Trickets and knackknicks of all kinds make fine presence to take home to someone you love or your wife. Only remember!!! certain goods of the 'national tresor' class may not be exported, and can be taken back from you at our friendly customs!!! But this is the luck of the drawer.

Also notice the special foreign currency shop, Wicwok, where are availed: scitches and gins, jeannies 'Levi-Strass' and 'Gloriana Vanderbuilt', barbers 'Filishave', and the likes, at laughable prices. Truly we may remember another Slakan proverb: 'No one leaves Slaka with an empty hand or a full purse!!'

FINDING THE SHOPS

Good morning, today I want to shop	Grussi, mi volo apporto hodi
Fine idea, here our shops are excellent	Bone, no mag'osk fo superbo
Are they expensive?	Fo ex'torto, hei?
No, they are very cheap	Nei, fo in'torto
What are the best things to buy?	Qua apporto bone?
Here everything is superb	Hic tota fo marveloso
We have the best goods from all lands	No habo tingo superbo dan tota mundo
Our people were always traders	No pupli simper fo fixi'fixii
Allow me to show you	Permetto mi proddo
We go to the best shopping street	No fendo po chamsi'lissii
I know you will be tempted	Cognosco toc fo tempto
But don't you need to do something first?	Ma nei habo obligo primo?
I think you like to go to the bank	Flecto toc fendo in bursliim, da?

GOING TO THE BANK

Welcome to the state bank	Grussi in Bursiim Prolet'anim
How can we help you?	Como sisto, cam'radakii?
May I change a little money?	Volo curso geld'ayiim
I should like to go shopping	Mi volo porto
That is our very function	Hac fo exactom purportim
What currency do you have?	Qua geld'ayii?
My money is English pounds	Mi porto puntam Anglistikam
What a pity, the rate is bad	Ah, morti, curso fo male

Owing to Japanese competition	Falta Nippon
Kindly tell me the rate of exchange	Dico, qua cursi'cursii?
There are many rates of exchange	Malto cursi'cursii
The diplomatic rate	Cursii diplomatiki
The business rate	Cursii commerkii
The congress rate	Cursii congressii
The tourist rate	Cursii turstii
Yours is the worst	Toc ho malto male
I will just change five pounds	Chango solo funvism puntim
Alas, you must change more	Morte, obligo chango malto
This is our rule	Hac fo no principii
This is to allow you the pleasure of our shops	Po permetto toc apporto malto
I will change you fifty	Mi chango michenti
Then you can have a nice shop	Toc habo porto splendido

THE FOREIGNERS' SHOP

Here is a good place	Hac plazscii boni
Look how full of things it is	Voyo, malto proditti
All the things you are used to	Tota famil'ali
Scotch whisky, London gin	Scitch'viski, Beefeatim
Jeans, videos, stereos	Levii, vivi'nastii, Sonii
All of outstanding quality	Mako excillintii!
Truly it is a cave of Aladdin	Vero cavi Ala'dinii
Of course you must pay in dollars	Solo dollari, da?
This is our famous shop WICWOK	Hac WICWOK
It is for foreigners only	Po strangim, solo
Oh, mind the man in the big hat	Ah, gardo frollin dan krapam mamorem
Try not to offend him	Nei fendo, hei?
It is also for the party officials	Als po parti'cheffii da?

397

THE DEPARTMENT STORE

We will do better in here	No fo ma bone hac
You know this famous place?	Cognosco hic plazsciim notabiliim?
See how big it is?	Voyo qua mamoro
How beautiful it looks?	Qua dur'agayii?
It must be the great department store, MUG	Vero, MUG
You are right	Correcto
How enormous it is!	Malto mamoro!
A true palace of commerce	Pil'azzi commerciii
And filled with such rare things!!	Proditto excillenti!
Glassware, leatherware	Glassii, ledii
Kitchenware, Tupperware	Utin'slii, plastikii
Radios and televisions	Radii, ti'vii
Corkscrews and tin-openers	Pullii, cuttii
All made by state enterprise	Macho priso stattiim!
Do you like to buy a present for your lovely lady?	Volo porto dono po toc frolikin
Perhaps one for your wife as well?	Als po toc femmo?
I see you like underwear	Voyo toc amico umper'habitom
This one, for the deep winter?	Ha, po hiberna
This one, for the hot summer?	Ha, po sveltro
Yes, you have chosen well	Da, toc selecto bone
Now I take you somewhere else	Noc, fendo als

AT THE GROCER/GREENGROCER

What is this fine shop?	Qua fo hac mag'osk raro?
It is our state supermarket PLUC	No super'mag'osk PLUC
Do you see a queue?	Voyo filo?
Only many happy people	Solo malto puplii boyo
Your Western press misleads you	Press imperial'istiki decepto

How much they have to sell!!	Qui produtto mamoro!!
Do you see a shortage?	Voyo minso?
Never have I seen such good things!	Nei voyo si bonem prodittim!
Give me a banana, a carrot	Porto nani, fallii
A beetroot, a melon, a pumpkin	Burschti, lambo, nurdu
What good sugar, give me some	Sugo superbo, mi dono
A thousand grams, two thousand	Milo grambo, duzi milo
There is plenty for everyone	Malto po totam
You have mastered the principles of production	Toc macho principi productim
I will tell all at home	Mi dico mi in'diginim
Everything can be had in Slaka!	Toto trovo in Slakam!!
Try my banana	Tasto nannim, nei?

AT THE CLOTHES SHOP

Now there is a clothes shop	Noc, vesti'mentii
A men's shop, a women's shop	Picca'dillii, froli'kosk
Do you want to look?	Volo voyo?
Yes, they are so fashionable	Da, malto chico
What a nice suit!	Vesto superbo
What is it made of?	Qua pendo?
Good, nylon is my favourite	Bone, amico gluc
And brown is my favourite colour	Oc amico bruno
But do you have my size?	Ma mi shapii?
All sizes are in stock	Tota shapii
May I try it on?	Permetto porto?
What an excellent fit	Shapii exactii!
Is it also a hat-shop?	Krapa'husi als?
A hat to go with this incredible suit	Krapa po vestim superbim
I love this plastic cap	Amico krapam plastikum

I'll take three	Volo trezi
You will not regret it	Nei hitznazo
It all suits you very well	Aha, qua bone, qua bone
Look please at these shoes	Voyo sulii
We make them in Slaka	Makina in Slakam
There are three sizes	Trezi shapii
All will fit you	Tota exacto

OTHER SHOPS

Are you tired now?	Toc lapso, da?
You have some problem with your feet?	Toc ploddi, ig pango?
No, I want more excellent shops	Na, ancora mag'osk superbo
The butcher, the baker	Besti, baki!
The chemist, the perfumery!	Apoteko, par'fumi!
The book shop, the cake shop!	Toma'husi, pattii!!
The smart shop, the art shop!	Gal'erri, ort'iski!!!
The furniture shop	Noc in fern'ii
I want a cake, a steak	Volo gattii, cuttii
I want a table, a chair, a settee	Volo tablo, toolo, ottomanii
The taste is incredible	Tasti incredibli!
Please help me carry it	Favi, porto, da!
Up a bit your end	Alto, da?
Stop, look, a craft shop	Hei, heimat'nosk
What extraordinary objects	Ojetti strangii!
They are made by hand in the country	Fato po mano in rurim
Our peasants do not like to be idle	Agrico despico fo inoccupato
They work long hours for the state	Laboro oram mamorem po stattiim
This is beautiful	Qui bellii
I have always wanted a well-pole	Desiro longa plumbi'pullim
You have bought very wisely	Toc apporto sago

You look like a king	Semblo mon'archo
You take home excellent things	Apporto prodittim excillintim
I hope the customs do not stop you	Aspiro don'ayii nei halto

Weighs and Mesures

In Slaka the conventional metrical cystern is used, except only
that one kilo = 50 grams.

HOW DO SLAKANS LIVE?

SOCIAL HABITS AND CUSTOMS

All countries of the world have their own custom, and Slaka does not make an exception. Naturally we like you to respect our habits and way of doing things, and perhaps then we all understand each other, no?

Various of our ways confuse some western visitors. In the street it is very polite to follow people, and it is a great mark of respect when people comment on your clothes, sometimes offering to buy them, though this is a crime against the state. Our men when walking like often to hold hands, and this has misled some foreign visitors to their intention, sometimes to a comical result. Also remember please, in Slaka we shake the heads for 'yes' and nod the heads for 'no'. Laughable confusions can result of this. At the toilet, the sign for man is someone in a skirts, and for a woman someone in a trousers. This also can produce a ludicral consequence. Notice also that the familiar western word 'hallo' does not mean the same for us. In our language it is the worst obscenity, and if spoken to a stranger will undoubtedly led to fightings.

Consider also that while conscious of their proud socialistikal heritage our people like to go with a certin formalism. We like to shake hands at you on all occasions, and when we make a business we like a tie at the neck and a hat at the hairs. Our people are hospitalistic, and like much to entertain, usually in a public convenience. When conducting an official affair it is polite always to offer a brandy (rot'vittii) and, remember!!!, when we drink we always like to make toast. Naturally we have

Vronopian pipers with bags

abolisted the burgish forms of address, as 'Mr', and it is always polite to address a man or woman as 'cam'radakii!' (comrade). Though we have no old title of rank, the titles of socialistic service are used (so 'Hero-Worker-Scientist Academikian Professor Dr Rom Rum').

Our formalities often make a surprise for western visitors, who amaze when at, e.g., the first night of the oper, they first discover our stylish glitter and dash. Indeed Hollywood starlings do not exceed our firstnighters in fineries, parfumeries and wonders of dècollage. Amazing indeed when these glittering cognoscentis prove no other than our music-loving workers and peasants, who have cast off the rank sweats of labour for a festive night!!!

So, when you come to Slaka, if a lady, carry a cocktail. If you like to be a man, bear a formal suiting of the better kind. And remember!! in Slaka the cloths of jog are worn but for the jog itself, and we do not port them at social functions!!! Another small advise: in case our climats are variable, we keep our buildings warm, on the inside. In restaurant, nightclub or government bureau you should at once divest, and leave cloths (coats, hats, etc.) at the doorway for a ticket. If you hold to this ticket, such clothings are normally turned back to you when leaving.

At our resorts, watershore chics prevail and good beach apparells are proudly worn. But here one more word of advice!!! Please be topless only if a man, and nude never. Decadent western practises are not admired, and always we like to keep in Slaka a certain decence.

Healths

In Slaka no diseases are truly endemical, but we advise a vaccine for smallpocks, choler, and typoon. The waters of our cities are potable usually, but in the country always fry your waters before tippling. Our medical service is free of charge. When necessary, tourists are taken to hospital. Medical cares are advanced and if you have diseases you will find Slaka a paradice. Please remember!!! if you like to extend your stay with illness, advice the nearest post of the people's Militia, unless you like the interference of our controlling organs!!!

YOU LIKE TO EAT AND DRINK???

Slaka is a well-known dreamland to all lovers of the culinary art, and your stay will be delighted by access to our fine gastronomes. Whether you like a tosthouse or a snackbarr, a sausage palace or a folkloric restaurant, a Paris repas or an Oriental kebab, you are like to be satisfied. In many a pleasing ambience, often animated by a typical chanteuse or a band of brigandish tziganes, you may find plates of almost every kind. Perhaps you like a small dark place with dancing and a short sharp show? Or a typical Slakan set-up where Olde Shoppe customes are demonstrated? Do you wish a gulasch, or a tripe soup? Do you relish bull's testicle, or perhap a special grass from under goats on a mountain? Our delightful restorants offer amazing menus, and when ingredients are availed they will serve you to the best of their disabilities.

Also our country is a festival of fine drinks. Famous specialities are our spiritual brandies, especially rot'vittii, made of the mush of a peach, kicrak, made of the squish of a pear, and lub'duss, made of the glub of a plum. Notable wines come of our state vineyards, and beware please of their remarkable potence. In better places the finest western drinks are availed, as ginni'tonikii and scitch'viskii.

Slaka is also famous for its compulsive nightlife. Famous name acts perform in our state art-strip clubs, and police and military choirs sing our rousing national songs. If you have a taste for dancing, sate it here, with a stately mazurk or a dervish wirl, perhaps in the companies of one of the dark-eyed beauties for which we are famous. (In Slaka we do not like our foreign friends, often missing their wives, to be lonely!!!) And beyond the city of Slaka itself is a wonderland of typical and untypical pleasures, of eating, drinking and nighting, enough for a lifetime of holidays!!!

Do not say we do not know how to live in Slaka!!!

FINDING A RESTAURANT

Today I shall try some Slakan delicacies	Noc mi boyo finim Slakam
Your gastronomic tradition is famous	Tok kukki fo notabili
Please give me your advice	Aviso, da?
You are very wise	Toc fo bone
You have many choices here	Mamoro selectii
Everything is available	Toc trova tota
What is your desire?	Qua loco??
A snackbar or a coffee shop?	Tosti, kaf'iffi'tosti??
A café or a restaurant?	Cave, rist'oranti??
Western style or Eastern style?	Kukki occidentii, kukkii orientalii??
No, I think you like something typical	Nei, volo kukki typico!!
Slaka is a gourmet's paradise	Slaka, paradiso po gurmandim
Every region has its speciality	Toc pitsat ho finam
Many are quite unusual	Mamoro rarii
Do you like to eat a brain?	Volo branim?
The veal of a sheep?	Lakuku kamissim?
The milk chords of a goat?	Yurti bletiim?
Our boiled tortoise is world famous	Tortosi grillii fo fama in globam
I will try anything once	Mi risko
Then I recommend the Restaurant Nada	Aviso Rist'oranti Nada

GETTING A TABLE

Good evening, maître	Bone starrii, maestro
May I have a table for two?	Mi volo tablo po duzim
I do not have a reservation	Ni reservo
But there is no one else here	Ma nemi smako
Perhaps this will help find one	Vloskan, da?
Near to the band, please	Proximo bandi, slibob
Nearer, and indoors	Matto proximo, in husam
I love the moaning of gypsies	Amico whingo tziganim

This table will do very well	Hac fo bone
May we have a cloth on it?	Possi tablo coverto?
Is there a chair?	Volo toolo
One with a cushion on?	Toolo paddito?
May we have a knife and a fork?	Volo nuga, firka
A spoon and a glass?	Zupa, vitri
Please light the candle	Flamo chandlim, da?
Evidently this place is very typical	Claro, hac fo typico, da?

ORDERING YOUR MEAL

Please bring me the bill of fare	Listii, da
Do you have it in English	Listii angliski, da?
Then you must explain it to me	Splico, slibob
Here are our splendid offerings	Voyo no smako splendido
Milk, honey, yoghurt	Piim, mesi, yurt
Soup, fish, game	Sopa, svimmi, flug'ti
Cold meat, warm meat, wild meat	Vurstii, besti, vildi
Vegetables and fruit	Rutti, frutti
Ox, lamb, veal	Harg, kammasi, laakuki
Duck, goose, turkey	Crak'aki, boo'si, gobbli
Bread, cake, pudding	Baki, gati, mushi
Here are three native kinds of soup	Trezi sopa ethnico
Soup with a rabbit	Kupush'nic
Soup with red cabbages	Bursht
Soup with feet in	Kurbi churba
Here are five kinds of fish	Funvsi s'vimmi typico
Fish with a sword	Ruspi
Fish with two pencils in its nose	Dentex
Fish with red hands	Canceri
Fish with a bad face	Dogna
Fish with no face at all	Dovri'sol

407

Here are three regional meat dishes	Trezi besti nativii
Folded pate on a bun	Sarkii banatu
Thighs of wild boar	Lads'latu
Testicles of bull in best vinegar	Natupashu
This is a flaming dessert	Hac vish'nou
We have found the ideal place	No trovo plazsciim exactim
Alas, none of these are available	Morti, nei possi
I bring you the goulasch	Porti gooli

ORDERING A DRINK

The waiter has taken your order?	Toc ho commando?
A drink with your meal?	Buvi, da?
Water, milk, orange juice?	Voday, piim, pumpi?
Beer, wine, spirits?	Olli, pfin, sp'riti?
Peach brandy, pear brandy, plum brandy?	Rot' vitti, kicrak, lub'duss?
Vodka, Scotch whisky?	Vid'ki, Blackii'whitii?
Gin and tonic?	Ginni'toniki?
Brandy and soda?	Bran'sodi?
A bottle of local wine	Flas'ci pfinim ethnicim
Here is an excellent vintage	Hac vinti excillinti
Made by the state vineyard	Mackino po vintom pro'letaniim
Once it belonged to the monks	Forfram kloster
Now it belongs to the people	Noc teno po poplim
It is far too good to export	Nei ex'porto hac
Our people love it too much	Popli amico malto
It has plenty of body	Malto forcii, hei?
That is why the cork flies out	Pardi, toc pango
Your trousers will soon dry	Pantii seco
Afterwards I recommend the peach brandy	Tardo, aviso rot'vitti
It is definitely not to be missed	Vero, toc nei lasco

PAYING THE BILL

Bring me the bill, please	Porto totti, da?
How much?	Koliko?
Really this much?	Vero?
You have eaten a lot	Malto tosti, da?
You have drunk enormously	Malto buvi als
The cloth is extra	Coverto als
The cushion is supplementary	Paddito als
Peach brandy is not cheap	Rot'vitti fo chero
You smiled at the gipsy	Tzig'anna fo malto chero
She played the violin for you	Ig stringo strad'variim
She sat on your knee	Ig sisto in lappim
American Express?	Hei, Ameksi?
That will do very nicely	Hac fo bone!!

YOU MAKE A SIGHTSEE???

Where Italian peoples like to say 'See Niples and Die', we Slakans like to say 'See Slaka and Live!!' Little doubt that sightseering is one of the plesures of vacation, and 'Cosmoplot' attends to this too. Guides with enormous busses delight to take you to our Slaka view-spots: the Storkian Mountains, the advanced glassblowing factory, the collective state farm.

Or do you like to walk by foot? Here is a brief tour you can make in Slaka. Go from your Cosmoplot hotel to 'Plaz'scii P'rtyii', our central square of finest proportions where the people of Slaka like to make their great parades. Here is the 'Tombo I. Grigoric', Grigoric's Tomb, where in a line you may make your respects. See how all our children love him! Exiting hence, you see facing, with red star, Party Headquarters, and next the Ministry of Strange Affairs and the Ministry of State Security, headquarters of our police of state security, HOGPo.

Pass now to the left down a dark narrow street, and you come to a fine Romanesque building, the People's Palace of Culture, where have offices our Writers' Union, our Journalists' Union, our Painters' Union, our Publishers' Union, our

Bohumil the Shy ignites his monumental gun (detail)

Thespians' Union, and of course our Translattors' Union. Next
is the publishing house 'V. I. Leninim', publishers of finely
printed books (you hold now one!!!). Next the Young People's
Palace, formerly the Theological Seminary. Next the People's
Artist Z. Leblat House, which contains a musee of old pianos.

Now greenery delights the eye, for here is the Park of Slakan-Soviet Friendship, where pensioners enjoy their well-deserved repose, carefree children play, and enamored couples dream of the hopeful future. Here notice the Monument of the Liberators, carved by our great socialist-realist art-hero sculptor-painter Lev Pric. Enought for a day!!! Please, you have hardly started, but perhaps you are very tired . . .!!!

MAKING A TOUR OF SLAKA

I am a tourist	Mi fo turst'ii
I want to take a walk	Mi volo prom'nado
I wish to enjoy your fine city	Volo boyo statiim dur'agayiim
Here is an excellent route	Voyo, hac ruti fo splendido
Go along Lenin Boulevard	Fendo po Leninski'cursii
Down Stalingrad Street	Po Stalingradsi'mutu
Through the park of friendship with the Russian people	Po Jardini Camradakii Ivanovskii
Past the Karl Marx Institute of Economics	Po Instit'tutii Ecun'moco Karliim Marxim
Is it easy to find?	Facilo, da?
Ah, this lady will take you	Hac froliki toc tako
She is an experienced interpreter	Dolmetschi officiali
She happens to go in that direction	Fortuno, ig fendo po da
She does not cost you a penny	Nei pagayo una bittim!!
What wonderful streets!	Mutu marv'osa!!
What wonderful buildings!	Qua structi nob'lii!!
How well they are restored	Bone restoro
What is this splendid place?	Que, hac structii superbo?
The Ministry of Culture	Min'stratii Kulturi Komit'etii
The Museum of Old Pianos	Musi tinki'tinki antiski
The Russian Embassy	Embassadi Ivanovski
The State Puppet Theatre	Dram'hus puppetii Prolet'anii
The Z. Leblat House	Husi Z. Leblatim
Here in Z. Leblat Street	Hac Z. Leblatsi'mutu

Just off Z. Leblat Square	Po Plazscii Z. Leblatsim
We are proud of Z. Leblat	No miro Z. Leblat
He invented our folkish musicology	Trovo no tradiim musik'im poplim
We give him many prizes	Po ho, malto presco
Alas he is two hundred years dead	Ma ig morto duzicentim anum
Don't you love our city?	Amico no stattim?
I have never seen anywhere better	Nei voyo statiim maltom superbim
Now I show you something special	Hei, toc voyo tankim espec'm

VISITING A STATE MOMUMENT

Just go down this dark passage	Fendo pa kafkam grisim
Stop by the soldiers	Halto po militar'iim
You recognize this man?	Hac frollii, toc cognosci?
I have never seen him before in my life, honestly	Nei voyo forfram, suro
He is Grigoric, our great liberator	Grigoric, no mamoro liberato
He freed us to the Russians	No libero dan Ivanovskiim
That is why we love him	Suro no amico malto
He looks alive but he is dead	Semblo vivo, ma fo morto
That is why we embalmed him	Hac qui no mummo
This is his famous tomb	Hac ig tombo famoso
See how all the children come	Voyo, totti veni
And all our peasants from the country	Als agricii dan fermii collectivii
They bring their flowers	Porto flureskim
Do you do this for your great men?	Toc fo po frollinim mamoremim?
Perhaps you do not love them so much	Poso toc nei amico si immalto
Now we go somewhere else	Na fendo als
Or perhaps you are very tired	Toc lapso, nei?

IN THE PEOPLE'S PARK

This is a park of the people	Jardini prolet'anii, hei?
Future citizens come to play	Totsi jumpo
Pensioners enjoy well-earned repose	Gerat'rici sunno
Our soldiers take a deserved rest	Militarii glaro
How pretty the flowers are	Malto flureski, da?
How well behaved everyone is!	Malto sereno, als!!
Does that man follow you?	Hac frollin toc suvo?
What does he say to you?	Qua dico?
He asks to buy your trousers	Volo apporto toc leggim
Do not listen	Ma nei attendo
That is a crime against the state	Malto penalto
Probably he is a stool pigeon	Suro, provoc'tato
He has gone behind a tree	Disparo po pulim
That is not good	Nei bone, da?
They are very nice trousers	Leggim superbo, nei?
How much do you want for them?	Quanto totto?

VISITING A PUBLIC PLACE

This is our great square	Voyo, Plazscii'P'rtyii!!
Here we have our great demonstrations	Hic fo no man'fustii
Over there the National Assembly	Hac fo Prasidium
Once it was the royal palace	Bakom, pal'itzo monarchico
Now our People's Government meets here	Noc semblo no Apparat'i Prolet'anii
Next door Party Headquarters	Voyo, Burosk P'rtyiim Prolet'aniim
Where work our Party-Chiefs	Qui laboro no P'rti'cheffii
The Ministry of Strange Affairs	Min'stratii Uffufii Estrangiim
The Berlin Wall Café and Pastry Shop	Cave'patii Berlinim

The Slakan Hikers' Union	Co'opo Vandistiim Slakam
There are the civil servants	Malto burosk'nik, da?
See their nice official cars	Voyo Volgam!!
With the lace curtains on the windows	Blindi el'ganti po fenestrim
How well they look after us!	Iggi no gardo malto!!
The Ministry of State Security	Min'stratii Stifufii Stattiim
They inspect all our activities	Ig specto tota no fo'do
To make sure we are happy	Po suro no fendo boyo
Do not go in there!	Prohibito fendo!!
I stopped you just in time!	Mi toc halto bonem tempem!!

AT THE ART GALLERY

This is the gallery of People's Art	Hic fo Galeri'ortiski Proletanii
Our Worker-Artists exhibit here	Hac man'fusto no malorim ort'hero'im
See the pictures of tractors	Voyo, pittori tract'imim
Really you can almost smell them!	Vero, toc poso skento!!
Our artists love socialist realism	No malori amico realismusim social'iskim
No decadent tendencies have taken root	Prohibito declinim imperial'istim
The work of the great Lev Pric!	Voyo, pittori Levim Pricim!!
How well he can draw a tank!	Vero, bombom superbim!!
Look, a sculpture to our liberators!	Voyo, plintho po libero!!
You must be getting tired	Volo sklaffo, da?

OTHER THINGS TO SEE

I think we have had a very nice tour	Bone turistiki, nei?
But this is enough for today	Suffico, da?
I will come in the morning	Mi veno meanzi
What would you like to see?	Qua volo voyo?

The Museum of Slakan-Soviet Amity?	Musi Amicatim Slako-Russom?
The Diorama of War Heroes?	Dia'rama Militario'hero'im?
Or do you like to see something else?	Toco volo als?
You have not been well advised	Aviso stupido
I cannot recommend the Cathedral	Nei commendo domom
We are a secular materialist country	No sono mater'alistiko seculumi
The architecture is deplorable	Structii pilloki
The archbishop is senile	Ark'episkopii dikrepii
They do not like visitors	Nei amico tur'stii
Also there are many mosquitoes	Als malto mesquitii
You should see the steelworks	Toc voyo bessemim
The great watercress factory	Oc mack'im kressim
The fine workers' apartments	Hi'risii prolet'anii
But do not bring your camera	Noki fity'gryphi
I will be here at seven	Mi veno setti oram
I think you are very tired	Toc delapso, da?

Filatelical Delights!!!

Slaka is famed for its filatelical delights, and the beauty of its stamps is loved everywhere. Stamp-keepers love to mount our special issues, featuring, this year: (a) Kinds of Bear; (b) Feminist Heroes; (c) Historical Pianos.

DO YOU LIKE ARTS AND CULTURES???
But do not think Slakan national culture is no more than its eatings and its drinkings! The many musees in our capital and our other cities attest that our artistic achievings go all the way

back to antiquity and before. Throughout time those who wield the brush and the chisel have always found much in our land to inspire them. Only inspect the paints on the walls of our ancient klosters, now art-museums, or the fine galleria of our People's Gallery of State Art (Gal'erii Prole'tanayiii). These abundant works of all periods and phases manifest that all world thought-waves of the highest kind have passed through the nation. At the same time no decadent tendencies have taken route among our patriotic worker artists and writers. The work of the expressionist artist-hero Lev Pric, on display in the murales of the National Assemblage and the People's Gallery of State Art, represents at best the popular sentimentals that have always animated our finest painters.

Slakans too are great book-lovers, and the long lines you see outside shops in our streets are our famous readers, waiting the publication of the newest novel. Under oppression our talents were stinted, but we celebrate still our great national poet-hero V. Hrovdat, whose statue stands before the universitet, and whose great national epic *Rambo Flambo* (The Rising Flame) depicts the miserable lots of our people and their great spirit from primal times until his own death in a bottle in 1848. All our literary arts since continue his tradition of critical realismus and progressive national sentiments. Since the liberation the first has been unnecessary, but our great Writers' Union has encouraged the proud tradition of socialist realism; remember, we like our books to be a little useful and serve a good cause!!! Today Slaka boasts of its world-famous writers and contemporary masters, as, poet-hero N. Nan, author of *Poemii Grigoricim* (Poem to Grigoric), P. Botic, author of the great novel *Bessemim* (The Steelworks), the socialist-realist L. Tarnac, and Katya Princip, who after the not-so-correct *Nodi Hug* returned to the mainstream with *Suvo Tractiim* (Follow the Tractors).

Of our great musics, the fine musicological historian N. Vlin put it best when he writes: 'Slakan music can rightly claim always to have kept one foot among the folk-people, while with the other becoming the father of the great musical arts of

Civil Reserve marksmen training with butts

Europe.' In Z. Leblat's great oper *Vedontakal Vrop*, once lost
but recovered since the liberation and now triumphantly restorated, missing only the last act, this mixture of the folkloristic
and the classical may be seen at best. With all the funnery of
the folk tradition, and all the magnification of the courtly arts,
it is now in the repertory of the Oper Prolet'anyiim Slakam, and
a fragment of the liber is somewhere in this book. Today our
musicals maintain the tradition Z. Leblat, as may be seen at the
'Z. Leblat Musicology Festivi', held each year on a mountain
near Glit, where our national prodigies mingle with the flower
of world-wide performers in acknowledgement of our globe-
class arts. Truly Slakan art still has a lesson to teach everywhere,
summed up for us perhaps in another of our Slakan proverbs:
'It is best always to walk forward, but try please not to lose
your behind!'

Our pride in the arts may be seen on the Slakan Day of
National Rejoicering for Art and Culture (September 24–38),
worthy of a visit. On this notable day our worker-tespians,
writers, journalists, art-officials, professors and academicians
proudly parade the streets, and children give them flowers.
We ask only: do you also do this for your great artists and
writers??? Perhaps you do not love them so much!!!

417

LOOKING FOR AN AMUSE

Today I want to enjoy myself	Noc mi volo boyo
My trip has been hard and long	Mi vy'agii fo duro
I know you have superb entertainments	Cognosco amusii fo superbo
And Slaka is at the cultural crossroads	Oc Slaka fo centrum kulturim
What ought I to see?	Quo voyo?
Our evening delights are manifold	No amusii stariim fo malto
Our nightlife is of the choicest kind	Norti'viva malto selecto
What do you like best?	Qui prifero
Our cinema, our theatre, our opera?	Kino, dram, oper?
Our fine musicians in concert and chamber	No superbi musika, concetto oc chambrii
Our leading classical worker-dancers	No balleti'heroi
Our national fame jiggling artists	No jongli'statii
Our great performers of art-strip	No art'strippii
Our singers are wonderful	No tosca fo superbo
Our actors are world-famous	No thespi fo globo'nosk
Dances by peasants in regional costumes are regularly performed	My'zurki po rurim typicim fo per'fendo totam tempim
How can I advise you?	Com aviso?
Quite, I will try all of it	Mi visito tota
I do not come to Slaka very often	Nei simper in Slakam

VISITING THE OPERA

Here is our great opera house	Voyo no oper'husi
Built in classic style by our enemies	Structii classico, ma po burgim

Yet our people love music	Ma no popli amico musikaz
They do not destroy it	Nei troyano
They make it a place for the folk	Fato plazsciim po pro'letanim
See all the workers in their best clothes	Voyo proli in picca'dillim
They like to dress well for the night	Volo gran'habito po nortim
See the decolletee and the jewels	Voyo decollettom, gemmiim
These are the workers and the peasants?	Hac proli, ruri?
I see you impress	Voyo toc presso
A few are party officials	Nadri fo burosk'nikiim
Some are their mistresses	Als curt'sanim
Or perhaps tomorrow	Oc als man'yani
Now see our radical programme	Voyo no re'perto
Next week *Madame Butterfly*	Semini man'yani, *Frollin Schmutterlinki*
An epic of colonial exploitations	Epico contra imperial'istikum
With finest costume	Habilito splendido
Also the felines of Webberim	Als *Kattii*, po A. L. Webberim
About the exploitation of animals	Epico grun'pacim
But this week you are very lucky	Hac semini, qua fortuno
A work of Z. Leblat	Oper po Z. Leblatim
Remember, he was our great art-hero	Nei oblivo, no ort'hero
He founded modern oper	Ig fondo operam modernam
Mozart learned all from him	Ig structo Mozartim
Rossini could not exist without him	Nei Rossini sin Z. Leblatim
And here, his greatest work of music	Oc primo musika Z. Leblatim

It is called *Vedontakal Vrop*	Nomo, *Vedontakal Vrop*
That means . . . oh, too difficult	Signo . . . ah, duro, duro!
I think you have heard of it?	Toc cognosco?
Perhaps you are not so well informed	Ignorantii!!
It is opera bouffe from century XXVIII	Oper buffo dan centi ichti oc oi
Once it was lost but now is found	Nac lasco, noc trovo
Missing only the last act	Solo acta trezi nei performo
Truly we are very lucky	Felici, da?
I think we go in	No fendo?
But I wish you had a better suit	Ma toc vestii, tza tza!!

VEDONTAKAL VROP

('The Secret Unmasked')

Vedontakal Vrop is one of the highest treasures of the great Slakan musical tradition, an oper bouffe created from authentical folk sources by national writer-hero Z. Leblat. Performed first before the ears of many listening bishops at the Cast'ullu Vlam in 1770, for two hundred years score and liber were unhappily lost. Yet in modern times fortune laughed and the work was rediscovered with revolutionary enterprise in 1970, missing only Acta 3. Triumphantly restorated, in 1984 the work was reperformed for the first time since 1770 at the Oper Prole'tannuu Slakam, in a repertoire with *Frollin Schmutterlunki* (Frollin Schmutterlunki po Panhilda Pic, Upratti Linkerton po Peti Lavo), *Katya Kabana* dan Janocekim, *Katti* dan A. L. Webberim, *Sondo Musikam* dan J. Andrewsim, and *I Placebo* dan L. Spirin, beneath the expert dirigation of Leo Fenycx (geb. Praha, 1958), our leading operturge.

What constructs the undoubted greatfulness of *Vedontakal Vrop*? Many have asked this question. Yet, primitive and sophistical all at once, this tale of disguises and mistook identities offered new futures to operatic history. At the one hand a simple folk-oper, at the other it is the origin of oper in the modern world of today. Criticals everywhere have rightly seen it as the true prefigure of all other great oper works, and it is clear that Mozart himself could not have been conceived without the assistance of Leblat. Thus the Mozartian *Figaro Weds* and *The Hareem-Slaves*, and *The Seville Haircutting Man* of Rossini, owe everything to this oper, for so long sadly losted and mislooked.

The plot of *Vedontakal Vrop* is so laughable that no one can fail to take a delight in its immense confusions. When ups the curtain, unfolds a brilliant scene. We are at a clear in the midst of a forest where the apothetic magician Zenu keeps his cave, where he likes to close himself with his pretty fun-servant Yukka and make strange experimentations. Smokings arise in the air to manufest his strange activities. Then in the glade appears a young student imitting an old man with a grey beard. A bear has near wolfed him, and only for food are some throstles. His woe are many. His crude father no more loves him, and tells him he must not marriage but make travel to the big city and take his examen to become famous bureaucrat. But because he likes to stay near to his loved one he does not travel and puts on beard instead. Heartily he tells how he loves that girl, the daughter of the apothetic magician who despicates them both. Yet no sooner has he sung his woe than who does appear in the forest but no als than his beloved love, disguised as a soldier with an arm. She likes to go to the city to find her lover, but is lost in her ways. Yet so good do they make their maskings that these fond lovers do not recognize, and she thinks he is old and he believe her of a very strange sex. But now appears in sedan a great king from Turk. He sings us that he is really the uncle of the girl who love the mutter of the boy and comes in an impressive disguise to woodle her and make his wedding. Of course this is not so possible because she is married still the apothetic magico. With him als is his servant Boco, who has annoyed the magico in the forest and is turned to a bear. When he encounts the pretty servant Yucca, naturalistically he falls als in love with the soldier boy who is a girl. So does a famous cavalry officer and many more. Of course soon appears in the centrum of the forest the father and the mutter of the boy, the mutter of the girl, the apothetic magician, the servants of the shah, and many villagers who like to celebrate a natural festival with a cake, some policemans, some sailors and a big host.

Herewith, in only Acta first, are the beginning of many

confusions which can but delight and amuse. Good drink is available at the interspersum, and our oper house is one of the architectonic glories of Europe. Join then our music-loving workers in this great revivification of the oper to end all opers . . .

Quoted from the English programme notes by Dr F. Plitplov, now out of print.

AT THE PERFORMANCE

May I have two tickets?	Dono duzim billettim
And the English translation	Oc dol'metschu anglistikim
Alas, it is out of print	Morte, verlagi finito
There is a Chinese translation	Dol'metschu chino
But that may not help you	Ma hac nei sisto, da?
Our seats are splendid	No stuli, splendido
They are very near the orchestra	Concerto boomo, nei?
But now we can see our worker-musicians	No voyo no proli'musika bone, da?
They work hard for the state	Voiko duro po stattiim
So hard there is no time to rehearse	Si duro, nei herso
This produces small confusions	Hac fo petti'pillokim
But oper is about confusions, no?	Ma oper, tota petti'pilloki, ne?
Oh, see, the head of state	Voyo, no primati
He sits in the box	Sisto in logim
Let us stand and salute him	Resto oc saluto
It is only polite	Polito, da?
Now I will translate the programme	Noc mi dol'metschu
The man is a woman	Frolli fo frol'ikim
The uncle is her mother	Nunki fo mamim
The servant is a bear	Servo fo his'patchom
The scene is a river	Sceno, rica

Slaka's classic worker film *Bridge on the River Ny'it* (still)

It sings for five hours
Without an interval
We love our music so much
We do not like it to stop!
It is in the original Slakan, of
    course
But I will translate you
If I understand it
Or do you prefer the cinema?

AT THE CINEMA
What a long line of people
They like to wait in rain to see
    a film
Our workers love the cinema
It is their relief from their
    labour
This is a Slakan film

Sungo funvsim oram
Sin inter'spersom
Amico malto no musikum
Nei amico halto!
Certo, in linguam Slakam

Ma mi dol'metscho
Si cognisco qua paso
Oc prefero kinom?

Mamoro lino, da?
Amico halto in pluvim po kino

Prolo amico kinom
Levo dan laborom

Cellulo dan Slakam

One of our best	Maximo ex'cillinti
It tells of a power station	Tema, dyn'amistiko
The marvels of its construction	Marvello di structiim
The thrills of its wattage	Boyo di wattiim
Real people star in it	Popli vero starro
Not Hollywood starlets	Nei star'letti Holl'woodii
Their performances are very natural	Performo, malto vero
You cannot tell they are actors	Nei simulo thespim
Are your films all like this?	Toc cellulo als?
We like them very much	No amico malto
We should buy toffee apples	No porto stickii'stickiim
Or do you prefer the strip-club?	Oc prefero art'strippim?

AT THE NIGHTCLUB

This is our finest nightclub	No primo clubbi
It is run by the state	Parto stattim
Only the highest art standards are allowed	Solo maximo formo
See, there is a pop-group	Voyo, poppi-groppii
And the policemen's choir	Oc choro jend'armim!
Some gipsy violinists	Buskii tzig'anii
A stripper with seven veils	Art'strip'froliki dan chemisiin septiim
Isn't it delightful?	Bone, da?
Let us sit down	Suti plac
Bring us a bottle of bubbly	Porto fles gaz'gazzii
Cheers! Up bottoms!	Toçtic!! Versi'versii!!
Your drinks are very good	Bone spiritii, nei?
Why don't we dance?	Volo bongo'bongo?
Music, ho!	Hei, musiki!
Where did you learn the mazurka?	Cognosco mazurk?
Bring another bottle of bubbly	Ancora fles gaz'gazzii
I enjoy your company	Mi boyo toc
I am your friend	Mi fo amicato

I could not manage without you	Nei survivo sin toc
Let us get married	No fo connubo, da?
Here is the stripper	Voyo, art'strip'froliki
She takes off one vest	Lasco chemisim!
Now another vest	Ancora chemisim!
That is three vests	Voyo, trezi chemisi!
That is all that is permitted	Tota permesso
We have very high moral standards	No ho legim malto alto
Please, it is not permitted to assist her	Prohibito sisto!
It is against the rules	Maximo penalto!
No, not another bottle	Nei ancora gaz'gazzii
I think your delights are complete	Boyo completo, da?
We must celebrate our marriage	No tosto no connubio, da?
Which way to the lavatory?	Quo evakebo?

PENAL CODE

Officially in Slaka no crimes are committed, because of the contentment of our people and the ideal form of social organization which is practised. Even so we like to have a good police force to watch over us, and in fact our people not contented with one like to have two. Our controlling organs are the state militia (blue uniforms), known in a friendly way as the MSP (Mulit'zayii Statiim Prole'taniim), and also our home affairs and government police (no uniform), known in an even more friendly way as HOGPo (Harvi oc Gub'ernoski Pul'itayii). These like to concern with national security and the protection of our socialistical heritage, and work very well with our comrades in the Russian KGB.

Our penal code is democratical and very complicate, and foreigners need not concern themselves, except in certain matters applicated to them. Because of our ideal society criticism of the state is unnecessary, and penalties for this are severe.

Though crimes do not exist, our eager citizens are occasionally led into error. In particular, in keenness to contribute to our economical development, some mistakenly engage in private tradings with foreigners (changing money, exchanging female relatives for western goods, etc.). These are severe crimes against the state, and invite enormous penalizations. Also do not embarass our ever-hospitable peoples by soliciting invitations to their homes. This is forbidden, except with special permissions, to prevent overcrowding in our excellent apartment-blocks, and must be always report to the police. Notice also that in some areas of our country we have private parts, and these are forbidden to foreigners. This is designed to protect our landscapes, and long imprisonments may consequence. Also remember that by Slakan law gatherings up of three or more people in the streets (except when making an official parade) are called a riot, and attract horrific penalizations.

Just remember our little rules and we know you will have good holiday!!!

CONCLUDING THE AMUSING EVENING

Pardon my mistake	Pardi mi petti'pilloki
It was not intentional	Nei intendo
The sign looked like a man	Semiotici semblo frollin
Give her my warm apologies	Mi hitsnazo, da?
I had a table somewhere	Quo tablo?
And a lovely companion	Oc froliki durag'ayii
Is this the bill?	Kolico, da?
My friend will pay	Amico pagayo
When she comes back	Quan retorno
I am an official visitor	Vy'aggi officiali
I am well looked after	Mi gardo, da?
She was here before	Ig sisto forfram
Is there a rear exit?	Otvat bakom?
We had better come to some arrangement	Fendo fixi'fixi?

This watch is very good	Ticki'tocki bone, da?
Do you like my jeans?	Amico leviim?
This jacket was expensive	Vestii luxurio
It looks well on you	Perfetto in toc
We will say nothing to anyone	Tota silenzii, da?
Please call me a taxi	Pello tacksi, slibob
To take me to the hotel	Mi retorno in otellim
Alas, I cannot remember the name	Morte, oblivo nami
It is in a big square	In plazsci'im, da?
Perhaps I will know it when I see it	Posi cognosco quan voyo
Thank you for the evening	Bone meanzi
The nightlife of Slaka is truly excellent	Superbo norti'viva, suro

AT THE APOTHECARY

Is this the pharmacy?	Hac apoteko, da?
I know your medical care is excellent	Cognisco medico superbo in Slaka
I have been enjoying Slakan nightlife	Mi boyo norti'vivam Slakam
I shall recommend it everywhere	Mi commendo tota
However there is a pain in my head	Pango in krapam
Perhaps you can ameliorate it	Toc sisto, da?
Your remedies are world-famous	Toc placebo fo glob'noskii
Is this really necessary?	Hac obligado?
I do not like suppositories	Nei amico bumbom
I prefer to put it in my mouth	Prefero mango
The pain is in my head	Pango vero in krapam

WHAT DO YOU DO ELSE???

Let us recall another famous Slakan proverbo: 'You have shown me the nose, but where is the rest of the face?' We confess!!! At the end of an evenement we make always a criticism, and we know it!!, we scratch only the surface of the water of our complex Slakan life. Only know that this book is but a glimmer of the reality. Our musees are in the hundreds. Our sites of tourism cannot be counted. Why do we not mention so many tresors? The great Monument of the Dying Soldiers? The Cathedral of Saint Valdopin (but this is too hard to reach, and mesquites by the river make the experience unpleasant)? And what of the rest of our land? Remember, ours is not one country, but several, brought together in millenary symbiosis. Each region or privliship has its own aroma, please go and find out!!! Our great railway system FLIP (Ferri Ligni Interstatii Prole'tanii) can trip you anywhere, and under strict regulation even a car may be hired. Cross the gentle hillocks of Pritprip, or wanderlust in the great Storkian mountains, where ramble in deep forets the wolf and wild pig. Go too by the boring Vronopian plain and come to Glit, our ancient university city, where there is the nose mummy of a saint in a case at the fine capella, and the food specialty is a soup with feet in it. Go anywhere, respecting only our private parts. You will not regret!!!

Truly you will make a different kind of holiday. And when, laden with your shoppings and the stains of your experiences, you pass away in our customs and make your final depart, taking care only to carry no vloskan out of the country, we know you will not forget us. We will not let you!!

Vy'aggi boyo!!!/Vy'agguu boyu!!! Velki in Slakam!!!/Velku un Slakam!!!

PLANNING YOUR TRIP

I wish to make a tour of the country	Volo turo toc stattim
I understand there is much to see	Capisco malto po voyo
You have made a very wise decision	Bone aviso
Everything the tourist needs is available	Tota hac po turstiim
Slaka is a tourist's paradise	Slaka, paradiso turstiim
Vacations in saddle await horseriding fans	Turstii hippofilii ho vy'aggim equin
Large woods invite sportsmen	Furesti vasti po fuselim
Perhaps you like mountains, lakes, rivers?	Amico magim, jagim, ricim?
Trees, birds, and wild animals?	Puli, lindi, wildii?
Beaches with umbrellas and swimplaces?	Riva dan brollim oc svim'-plazsciim?
All are availed you	Tota accesso

Perhaps you prefer our fine cities?	Posi toc amico no stadim finim?
Glit, with old houses and a castle?	Glit, husa antiski, barbicani
Nogod, with a fine kloster?	Nogod, kloster fini
Provd, with an excellent steelwork?	Provd, bessimer ex'cillinti
Many tours may be taken	Malta vy'aggim
Led by the fine guides of Cosmoplot	Sisto po prod'frolikim Cosmoplotim
Or you can hire a car	Posi als aviso autobom
The garage is over there	Meckanistiki plac

AT THE GARAGE

Please may I hire a car?	Favi, mi avis autobomom, da?
We are delighted to help you	No volo toc sisto
We will hire you an auto for two weeks	No avis autobom duzim semam
Only a vast deposit is needed	Obligo, malto vloskan
This is a Slakan model	Autobom Slakam, da?
The gearchange is under the seat	Klitchi umper stulim, voyo?
This level pulls on the lights	Heavo hac, flarii, da?
To change the wheel turn the car over	Chango, up'tippii, okay?
Many facilities for motorists are available	Malto fix po automskim
Our country has fifteen petrol stations	Funvsi oc oi ben'zinim
Open for an hour each morning	Opperto meanzi, 7:00–8:00
Tourists are allowed three litres	Po turstiim, trezi litri
The roads are good and free of boulders	Bone mutu, sin lumpim
Our traffic rules are very simple	Legi traffici, malto simplicato
It is forbidden to run over peasants	Cursi on rurim, nei permetto

Haycarts may not be overtaken	Nei passo folksi'cartim
City speed, five vlods an hour	Maximo stattim, funvsi vlod po oram
Country speed, eight vlods an hour	Maximo rurim, octi vlod po oram
Register everywhere with the police	Ry'gystrayo in jend'arm'nosk selim
Do not drive at night	Nei conditto po nortim
Do not leave the approved route	Nei parto di mutum permittim
Carry your papers everywhere	Porto papurim passim
Here is a map which shows forbidden areas	Hac plin ho plaz'sciim stricticim
Please be careful not to enter them	Invo hac, finito, da?
Our police patrol everywhere	Milit'zayuu tota
They like everyone to be happy	Volo tota boyo
Do this, and you will have a good holiday	Suvo, bone turstii
Otherwise you have a bad one	Als male turstii

ON THE ROAD

Left, right	Hinger, vanster
Slow, stop	Lintii, stoppii
People crossing	Criss'crossi
Children crossing	Tottii'crossi
Petrol, oil	Bin'zini, glub
Which way to the country?	Quo trovo rusticim?
Curve, priority	Tvistii, priorito
Hill, slope	Uppi, tumbli
Rocks falling	Slippii ricim
Wolves prowling	Vulpi
To Bruni and Breddi	Po Bruni, Breddi
To Eco and Chem	Po Eco, Chem
To Pillif and Prit'pritti	Po Pillif, Prit'pritti
Restricted area, prohibited	Plaszcii strictico, prohibito

Police car, police chase	Mulit'zayuu, Mulit'chazsu
Please get out of the car	Ot, masti!
Kindly show me your papers	Papurii!!
There are very severe penalties	Malto penalto
This is all a ridiculous mistake	Hac fo petti'pilloki
I am just a simple tourist	Turstii solo
I did not know there was a curfew	Nei cognosco vespinim
My windscreen wipers were stolen	Oi prendo mi flippi'floppa
I could not see it was a tank	Nei voyo hac fo bombom
It was his fault	Ig fo crima, nei mi
He was going much too fast	Ig chargo malto illenti
My Embassy will be informed	Embassadi cognosco
If I can just telephone	Si mi telephono
I am sure they will pay for the tank	Suro, iggi pagayo bombom
Now may I continue my holiday?	Noc, mi fo vy'aggii
Can you tow my car to the garage?	Toc pullo mi autobom dan mechan'istiki?

Official Holidays

Slakans are a festive people, and like to make holiday from their labours to celebrate our great events. Special holidays are: Progressive New Year, January 1–3, Day of Anniversity March 17, March 17–23, Labour Day, May 1–5, Birthday Z. Leblat, June 2, Slakan National Holiday, August 10–20, Day of National Rejoicering for Art and Culture, September 24–38, Anniversary of October Revolution, November 8–12.

Government offices and state trading organizations are closed on Saturday and Sunday, as well as on all official holidays.

AT THE RESORT

How delightful it is here!	Ah, bone, hac
I have had an excellent week	Sema ex'cillinti
My cabin has been delightful	Cabina fina
I enjoyed sharing it with so many	Malti popli
The beach has been pleasant	Rica superbo
The facilities have been outstanding	Faculta grandi
The tennis, the golf, the football	Rak'iki, goffi, fut'balsi
The long marches in the morning	Ploddi longi in meanzim
The group athletics in the afternoon	Olympici co'opti in nei'meanzim
The anti-American singsongs in the evening	Singi'songi basso-Janqui in starrim
Now I must return to the city	Noc, mi trovo stattim
Unfortunately my car is incapacitated	Mi autobom frago
The steering wheel will not work	Vici'versii nei macko
The engine is broken	Makino nei turno
Spare parts are coming from Riga	Parti veno dan Rigam
But this will take six months	Ma halto di sexim mensim
Do you think I should take the train?	Flecto mi fendo in vlakam?

AT THE RAILWAY STATION

Is this the railway station?	Hic fo vlak'drom?
I should like a train to the city	Volo vlakam in Slakam
When is the next one due?	Quan veno?
Surely I need not wait three days	Suro, nei resto trezim diazim
Please sell me a ticket	Slibob, billetii

A first-class ticket	Billetii classam unam
In a corner with my back to the engine	Stuli in bendim, visi forfram
Of course I am allowed to travel	Suro, mi permetto vy'aggo
I am a foreign tourist	Mi turstii estrangii
Here are my documents	Diku'menti hic
Send for the station-master	Metto vlak'drom'cheffim
You are the station-master?	Toc fo vlad'drom'cheffim?
I will wait in the buffet till the train comes	Resto in tost'rom po vlakam, da
Surely there is a buffet	Suro tost'rom?
I will lie under this cart then	Resto umper cartam, okay?
Tell me when the train arrives	Dico veno vlakam, da?

ON THE TRAIN

What a delightful steam engine	Chug'chugga splendido!
With its red star on the front	Qui starrii roti nobili!
Is this the train to Slaka?	Vlaka Slaka?
Does anyone know where this train goes?	Qua fendo vlakam, hei?
I hope I do not disturb you	Aspiro mi nei toc turbo
Are my legs in the way?	Mi hitnazo po mi pendim
Do you mind if I smoke?	Permetto roki?
I will go where it is permitted	Mi fendo quo permetto
It is not permitted anywhere?	Noki roki toti?
I shall go to the restaurant car	Mi fendo in cockam ristorantam
Surely there is a restaurant car	Suro cocka ristoranti?
Very well, a buffet car	Okay, cocka buffeti
Perhaps a tap in the lavatory?	Posi tappa in evakebo?
May I open the window?	Apperto fenestrum?
I wish to photograph the landscape	Volo fyt'grapho scenim
Why are you pulling down the blind?	Qua blindo?

435

The door is jammed	Vac nei mobo
Be careful with your umbrella	Attenzi, toc brollii
Ah, we are stopping	Hei, no halto
You are the guard?	Toc fo vlak'cheffii?
Of course I am allowed to travel	Suro mi permetto vy'aggo
Return my camera to me	Dono mi kodakam
It was very expensive	Mi spendo malto
I do not want to get out	Nei volo ot'vato
It is cold here	Hac fo kalto
It is a very lonely spot	Plazscii malto solo
In the middle of the forest	In centrum furetam
I do not like wild animals	Nei amico wildim
Wild boars and bears repel me	Mi frugo lad'slatum, hispatchum
My government shall hear of this	Gubern'ato GeeBee cognosco!
I think you are a typical woodman	Mi flecto toc fo puli'frollinim typicum
I have walked many miles	Mi ploddo malto vlodim
I have slept all night in a bush	Mi schlaffo po norti in shrubbim
Where am I?	Qui fo?
When is the next train to the city?	Quan proximo vlak in stattim?

436

HIGHLIGHTS OF THE VISIT

AT THE STATE PARADE

This is our greatest day	Hic fo no diazi mamori
The Day of Rejoicing for Our National Culture	Diazi Kulturiim Statiim
It is the birthday of Hrovdat	Nativo Hrovdat
Our great national poet	Poeti'heroi statiim
He fell off his horse in battle	Tombo dan hippom in struvom
Reciting his great national epic	Dico poetim mamoram
We celebrate all our great art-heroes	No flambo totam ort'hero'im
Here in our great square	Hac in Plaz'sciim P'rtyiim
See all the flags and banners	Voyo no mamorim signalim
Think how many shirts they would make	Flecto mako blusim!
But we love our great marches	Ma no amico no man'fustum
See the great crowds	Malto popli, da?
The children all cheer	Tottsi viv'vivo
The high officials are on the podium	P'rty'cheffii grando
See, President Vulcani arrives	Voyo, Vulcani
All the Politburo	Tota Polit'burosk'nikim
Or those still in favour	Als iggi favoro
See, the Minister of Culture	Voyo, Min'strat Kulturi
A general who has read a book	Generali qua toma lecto
Here comes the parade!	Hic fo prom'nadii!
First the state journalists	Primo, pressi pro'letanii
From the national newspaper	Dan *P'rtyii Pop'ulatiii*

437

And the Lenin News Agency	Oc Prav'di Leninski
Now the hero writers	Scruptori'heroii
Carrying their carnations	Porto cam'radakiim carnim
The Socialist Realist painters!	Malori socialistick'realismusim
The professors, the academicians	Pri'fessori, Akademiskii
The dancers, the actors, the musicians	Balleti, thespi, musiki
See their banners!	Voyo signalim!
Art for the People	Ort po Poplim
Culture Is Progress	Kulturi fo Progresso
Strive for a Better Life	Struvo vitam novam
Solidarity with the Workers	Prolo Solido
After them the tanks	Bakom, bombom
Do you love culture so much?	Toc amico kulturim si malto?
Perhaps you are not so advanced	Posi nei fo si vanto

AT THE CATHEDRAL

Your tour is almost over	Vy'aggi finito
You have seen many things	Voyo malto
Perhaps you have something left to see?	Posi toc volo voyo als?
They say the cathedral is not to be missed	Dico nei lasco domi
Of course I am not religious	Suro, nei fideli
I am just a tourist	Mi turstii
It is a long tram-ride	Longi truga
The mosquitoes are enormous	Mamori mesquiti
But we will show you this once	Ma toc voyo, malto priviligo
You see it is not attractive	Voyo, in'plessi, da?
Built by Bishop Wocwit the Good	Structo Piski 'Bonim' Wocwitim
Extended by Bishop 'Wencher' Vlam	Ex'tendo Piski 'Vadim' Vlamim

English	Slakan
The tomb of King Basram the Lazy	Tombo Rat 'Lethargim' Basram
The skillet of Prince Boris the Short	Skilleti Rat 'Dwarfim' Borisim
He married Krista the Mad	Connubio Krista 'Nei'wittim'
The sepulchre of Bishop Valdopin	Sepulchro Piskim Valdopinim
He brought faith to our people	Porto fidem
Then our neighbours chopped him in pieces	Vicini minco
His body was exchanged for gold	Corso cursii po geld'ayim
They made him a saint	Fo sanctim
But we do not talk about it	Nei dico
Of course we still like to exchange things	Suro, no amico chango
It is the Slakan temperament	In Slakam, malto fixi'fixi
Who is this man?	Qui frollin?
Why does he give you papers?	Qua papuri?
He says you made an arrangement	Dico toc fixo
You did something to his car	Frago autobomom
Are you sure this is wise?	Toc suro hac fo aviso?

VISITING THE POLICE STATION

English	Slakan
Welcome to the police station!	Velki in jend'arm'nosk!
Please come this way	Veni, masti
Do not be slow	Nei hesito
Our work makes us very tired	No flaggi
This gentleman would like to chat with you	Hac frolli toc tor'tayo
I am a different kind of policeman	Mi fo dan HOGPo
I do not like wearing uniforms	Nei amico porto un'formim
The clothes are so unattractive	Vesti nei eleganti

439

He was rude, but I am polite	Ig impolito, mi malto polito
I like to help you	Volo toc assisto
I protect state security	Mi tecto stifufi statiim
What were you doing?	Qui fendo?
It is wrong to fight our police	Fo crimo, fendo struvom
They only do their best	Solo fo besti
You do not like to make trouble between our countries?	Nei volo mako striko nuclearim
I do not think your government likes it	Flecto toc gub'erno nei amico
Now the state prosecutor wants to see you	Noc procezzi statii volo voyo
He is not so polite	Nei polito com mi
There will be a trial	Suro toc fo procezzo
You will stay here many years	Toc resto longo in Slakam
Perhaps you do not wish that	Posi nei toc volo
This is why I like a chat	Hac qua tor'tayo
I welcome information	Mi velko format'zie
Everything interests us	No so eclectico
Do you like prohotgraph albums?	Amico albumim fyt'graphim?
Here is one about you	Hac albumo turo toc
We could make a film about you	Posi mako cellulo
In fact we have	Suro, no fo
You are like Robert Redford	Toc simulo Robertim Redfordim
But taller	Ma malto grandi
You have been very busy	Toc fo malto
You have visited many places	Fendo in maltam plaz'sciim
Talked to many people	Tor'tayo malto
Tell us about everything and everyone	Tor'tayo dan totam, totam amicam
I have enjoyed our conversation	Bone tor'tayo, da?
Please put on your clothes	Habilo, da?

SAYING FAREWELL TO SLAKA

This is the airport	Hic fo flyt'dromo
There is the check-in	Voyo chekk'ino
You will not need it	Nei quiro
We will put you right on the plane	No toc imburdo
They will check your baggage	Iggi proddito toc baggim
You can keep what you came with	Toc gardo quan porto
You have bought many things	Porto malto, da?
Alas, they cannot be exported	Morte, prohibito ex'porto
Farewell, comrade	Sayo, cam'radakii
Sorry to leave you	Pardi parto
We wish you friendship, amity and concord	Spiro fraterno, amico, concordo
Have a good trip	Bone vy'aggii!
Back to imperialism	In imperial'istikum
You are always welcome	Simper velki in Slakam
Come back any time	Ri'torno quan toc volo
Or else we will invite you	Posi no toc grabo, hei?

Tippings

In Slaka tippings are officially forbidden. However taxidermists, porters, chambermaidens, factotums, valets, bussboys, sommeliers, pyrukists, and hatchekkin girls in particular regard it as a severe insult not to be tipped by the traditional 25%.

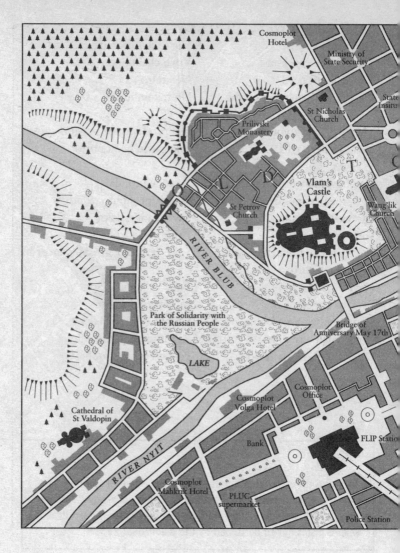

Nestling in the crutch of its rivers, the city of eld melds with modern accretions and facilities, stretching from Century VII (or IX) to Century XX. Routs of public transport are not indicate on this plan, but are sometimes to be met, and often frequent. Here is splayed before you our capitol. Do you explore?

442

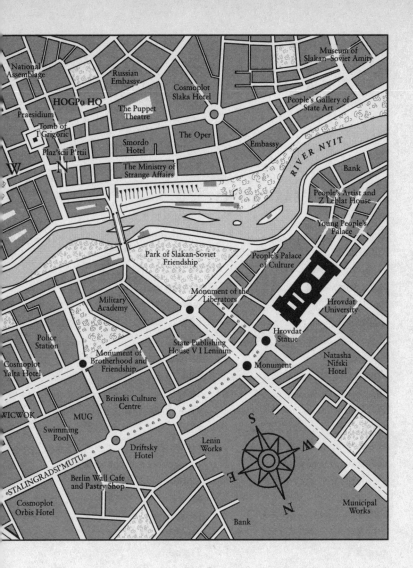

A LIST OF USEFUL WORDS

SOME NECESSARY NOUNS

Accident	Venturi
Airport	Flyt'dromo
American	Janqui
Apartment block	Hi'risi
Art-gallery	Ort'gal'erri
Bank	Bursii
Bar	Barr'ii
Bear	His'patchi
Bedroom	Schlaff'rom
Beer	Olii
Bill	Totti
Bookshop	Toma'hus
Bottle	Fles
Breakfast	For'tost
Capitalist lackey	Lackii Kapitalistikum
Cathedral	Domo
Cashdesk	Kassa
Cell	Host'rom
Child	Totsii
Clock	Tictoc
Cock-up, large confusion	Mamor'pilloki
Comrade	Cam'radakii
Confusion	Pilloki
Corner	Bendi
Country cottage	Dachi

Curfew	Vespini
Curve	Tvisti
Credit card	Karti'umperi'plastiki
Demonstration	Man'fusti
Dollar shop	Wicwok
Drink	Buvi
Duck	Crak'aki
Enemy	Mal'volenti
Father	Horvot
Foot	Plodi
Friendship	Amicato
Greetings	Grussi
Grenade	Gren'adu
Head	Krapa
High official	Up'rat
History	Hist'erici
Horse	Hippo
Imperialism	Umper'alistiki
Imprisonment	Con'valeski
Interpreter	Dolmetschi
Jeans	Levii
Journalist	Pressi
Language, speech	Tat'aki
Lie	In'pravdi
Lift	Up'zippi
Love affair	Senti'menti
Maid	Schlaff'rom'froliki
Man	Frolli
Map	Plin
Milk	Piim
Ministry	Min'stratii
Mistake	Pilloki
Painter	Malori
Parade	Man'fusti
Pen	Feduri

Petrol station	Bin'zini
Pipe	Huba
Plane	Flyt'bom
Police	Jend'armi
Police station	Jend'arm'nosk
Pop group	Poppi'gruppi
Porter	Baggi'manni
Power	Potenzi
President	Cam'radakii Pres'denti
Purpose	Destino
Restricted area	Plaz'scii strictico
Rifle, gun	Fuseli
Scheme	Zschemi
Secret	Vedontakal
Security	Stifufi
Shirt	Blusi
Shower	Sprey'sprey
Stair	Up'ploddi
State Security Police	HOGPo
Steering wheel	Vici'versii
Strip club	Ort'strippi
Subway	Umper'bahn
Tank	Bombom
Taxi	Tacksi
Tear-gas	Cri'gasi
Toilet	Evakebo
Tram	Truga
Trial	Procezzi
Trousers	Panti
Umbrella	Brolli
Waiter	Garsi
Wild boar	Lad'slatu
Windscreen wiper	Flippi'floppi
Witch, wizard	Makku

Woman	Froliki
Woman, married	Frolikuli
Worker	Prolo
Writer	Scriptori

SOME ELEMENTARY ADJECTIVES

Angry	Ragu
Bad	Male
Black	Griso
Capitalistic	Kap'italistiki
Clever	Foxi
Few	Nadri
Imperialistic	Umper'ialistiki
Keen, enthusiastic	Bambuzi
Nasty	In'plessi
Noisy	Im'paci
Red	Roti
Right	Correcto
Rich	Un'indigento
Stupid	Stupido
Very	Malti

SOME VALUABLE VERBS

To apologize, be sorry for	Hitnazo
To arrange for, fix	Rematico
To arrest	Collaro
To be	Fo, fut (*past*), fat (*future*)
To be able	Capo
To be afraid	Frugo
To be in charge of, to order	Commando
To be tired	Flaggo
To borrow	Grabo
To chat	Tor'tayo
To dance	Bongo'bongo
To depose, remove from office	Deposo

To destroy	Troyano
To detain	Hosto
To drive	Chargo
To eat	Smako
To forbid	Prohibito
To forget	Oblivo
To harm	Curso
To have	Habo
To hurt	Blesso
To look for, seek, find	Loco
To lose	Lasco
To lure, tempt	Volito
To make, do, go	Fendo
To need	Quiro
To need help	Sosso
To release, let go	Lasso
To run, flee	Fluco
To shoot	Fuselo
To show	Proddo
To smoke	Roko
To steal	Grabo
To unite, bring together	Congresso
To watch over	Surveio

SOME CONVENIENT CONJUNCTIONS AND CONNECTIVES

And	Oc
But	Ma
Also	Als
If	Ca
When	Quan
What	Qua
Where	Quo
Who	Qui
Why	Quip

SOME PROMINENT PREPOSITIONS

By	Pa
With	Vic
From	Dan
Without	Sin
Sooner	Ante
Later	Tardu
Always	Simper
Never	Nada
Again	Ancoro
Perhaps	Pos'ibli

SOME ESSENTIAL EXPLETIVES

Yes	Da
No, not	Na
No (prohibition)	Noki
Attention	Attenzie
[Interrogatory suffix]	De?
[Negative suffix]	Nei?
Maybe	Hei'ho
Hurry up	Masti
No chance	Negativo
Up with . . .	Uppo . . .
Down with . . .	Basso . . .
Sorry, excuse me	Pardi
Make way	Accesso
Of course	Siv'da

SOME PRIMARY PRONOUNS

I, me	Mi
You	Toc
He, she	Ig
It	Dot
We, us	No
They, them	Iggi

NUMBERS IN SLAKAN

One	Oi
Two	Duzi
Three	Trezi
Four	Versi
Five	Funvsi
Six	Sexi
Seven	Setti
Eight	Ichti
Nine	Nunzi
Ten	Doc
Eleven (etc.)	Doc oc oi (als)
Twenty	Vanti
Thirty	Truc

Brewing mastes of Glit sample *rot'vittii*

Forty	Virti
Fifty	Mi'chenti
One hundred	Chenti

TIME IN SLAKA

Time	Tempi
Clock	Tictoc
Minute	Minuto
Hour	Ora
Day	Diazi
Night	Norti
Morning	Meanzi
Afternoon	Nei'meanzi
Evening	Starri
Week	Semini
Month	Mensi
Year	Jarri
Birthday	Nativo
Holiday	Festi
Curfew	Vespini